PHYSICAL SCIENCE

MAN'S CONQUEST OF MATTER AND SPACE

A GENERAL COURSE IN ASTRONOMY, CHEMISTRY,
HEAT, LIGHT, SOUND, MECHANICS,
ELECTRICITY, WIRELESS AND TELEVISION

CONTRIBUTORS

Professor H. T. S. Britton, D.Sc., D.I.C., F.R.I.C.

F. C. Champion, M.A., Ph.D., F.Inst.P.

Ivor B. N. Evans

R. W. Hallows, M.A. (Cantab), M.I.E.E.

C. L. Johnson, B.Sc.

Sir Harold Spencer Jones, M.A., Sc.D., D.Phil., F.R.S.

B. C. Lee, Ph.D., B.Sc., A.M.I.E.E., A.C.G.I., D.I.C.

Professor H. Levy, M.A., D.Sc.

T. S. Littler, M.Sc., Ph.D., F.Inst.P.

E. T. A. Rapson, M.Sc.(Eng.), A.C.G.I., D.I.C., Wh.Ex., A.M.I.E.E., A.I.R.E., F.P.S., M.Brit.I.R.E.

J. F. Stirling, M.Sc., F.R.I.C.

ODHAMS PRESS LTD · LONG ACRE · LONDON

CONTENTS

4

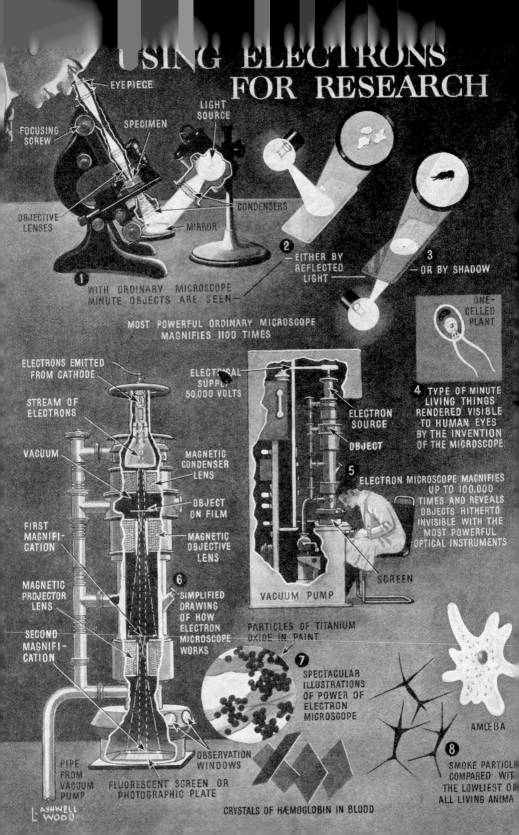

USING ELECTRONS FOR RESEARCH

EYEPIECE

FOCUSING SCREW

SPECIMEN

LIGHT SOURCE

OBJECTIVE LENSES

CONDENSERS

MIRROR

1 WITH ORDINARY MICROSCOPE MINUTE OBJECTS ARE SEEN—

2 —EITHER BY REFLECTED LIGHT—

3 —OR BY SHADOW

MOST POWERFUL ORDINARY MICROSCOPE MAGNIFIES 1100 TIMES

ONE-CELLED PLANT

4 TYPE OF MINUTE LIVING THINGS RENDERED VISIBLE TO HUMAN EYES BY THE INVENTION OF THE MICROSCOPE

ELECTRONS EMITTED FROM CATHODE

ELECTRICAL SUPPLY 50,000 VOLTS

STREAM OF ELECTRONS

ELECTRON SOURCE

OBJECT

VACUUM

MAGNETIC CONDENSER LENS

5 ELECTRON MICROSCOPE MAGNIFIES UP TO 100,000 TIMES AND REVEALS OBJECTS HITHERTO INVISIBLE WITH THE MOST POWERFUL OPTICAL INSTRUMENTS

OBJECT ON FILM

FIRST MAGNIFICATION

MAGNETIC OBJECTIVE LENS

MAGNETIC PROJECTOR LENS

6 SIMPLIFIED DRAWING OF HOW ELECTRON MICROSCOPE WORKS

SECOND MAGNIFICATION

VACUUM PUMP

SCREEN

PARTICLES OF TITANIUM OXIDE IN PAINT

7 SPECTACULAR ILLUSTRATIONS OF POWER OF ELECTRON MICROSCOPE

AMŒBA

PIPE FROM VACUUM PUMP

OBSERVATION WINDOWS

FLUORESCENT SCREEN OR PHOTOGRAPHIC PLATE

8 SMOKE PARTICLE COMPARED WIT THE LOWLIEST O ALL LIVING ANIMA

CRYSTALS OF HÆMOGLOBIN IN BLOOD

ASHWELL WOOD

CHAPTER I

WHAT IS SCIENCE ?

EARLY science came with the dawn and development of intelligence, the expression of a widening experience, and not as a consciously planned and deliberate pursuit. It was severely practical in its content. It was not until late in the history of civilization, with the rise of the Greek states, that theories and theorizing rose to their place in the philosophies of nature. These states excelled in the creation of such philosophies. But they were still not scientific theories in our modern sense. There was no systematic and accepted method to decide whether a theory were true or false. While it was subjected to the most detailed logical examination to make certain that it was consistent in itself, there was no clear appreciation of the need for turning to nature and, indeed, of how to do this, in order to test the truth of any particular theory. Not until the sixteenth and seventeenth centuries did science consciously and deliberately turn to experiment to discover the workings of nature.

Science is Based on Experience

It is important to see the difference between an observational and an experimental science. Astronomy in its early stages was an observational science. Astronomers observed what was taking place in the heavens, catalogued the stars, recorded the times and durations of eclipses, noted the appearance of meteors and meteorites. They did not attempt to arrange or control what was taking place above, but simply observed what nature provided. They did not interfere with nature in order to discover more about it. The planets, stars, and other heavenly bodies moved on their courses independently of the will of man. He looked on.

Geology was in a similar position. The earth and its internal make-up was there, and all one could do was to discover as much as possible from the samples selected. One could not do experiments with the earth. One could not change the earth's structure, certainly not on a geological scale.

The same was true of meteorology. Weather had to be studied as it was found. Even today we have to take the weather as it comes. The earliest science was largely observational—useful as it was in spite of that.

Experimental science, which developed in Western Europe with great rapidity from the seventeenth century onwards, went a stage further. The scientist tried to control the circumstances in which he was going to observe. Behind any experimental plan lies some sort of expectation of what is likely to be found, some kind of theory of what is happening.

Experiments cannot be conducted in a mental blank—the results are already half-expected before the experiment is carried through, and that expectation rests on some theory that in such and such circumstances a certain regularity will be found. The experiment, in fact, is designed to sharpen or accentuate this by arranging the circumstances in a suitable manner. It tests the truth of the theory at the same time as it establishes the facts on which the theory rests, but in order to do so it interferes with nature. By the seventeenth century man was already deliberately interfering with nature by experiment in order to make regularities show themselves sharply and clearly. Let us look at some of these in order to understand the kind of regularities that were being sought.

Simple Natural Laws

(1) A pendulum swings to and fro in such a manner that the time of swing is always the same if the length is unchanged. For the time of swing to be doubled, the length would be required to be increased four-fold; for the time to be trebled, the length would require to be increased nine-fold. . . . In mathematical form, this would be stated as:

Science behind the production of STAINLESS STEEL KNIFE

1700 DEG. C.

ELECTRODES

MOLTEN STEEL BEING POURED

IRON AND—

·3 PER CENT CARBON

13 PER CENT CHROME

① ELECTRIC TILTING FURNACE

② CAST BILLET OF 3-13 STAINLESS STEEL

TEMPERATURE SETTING

CONTACTS

BOURDON TUBE

CONTACTS

PYROMETER TEMPERATURE CONTROL

⑤ GOFFING OR DRAWING

GAS CONTROL VALVE

MERCURY TUBE

⑥ PLATING OR SHAPING

⑦ TEMPERING

DIAMOND

SPECIMEN

HOT-PLATE

GAS JETS

⑧ HARDNESS-TESTING MACHINE

ASHWELL WOOD

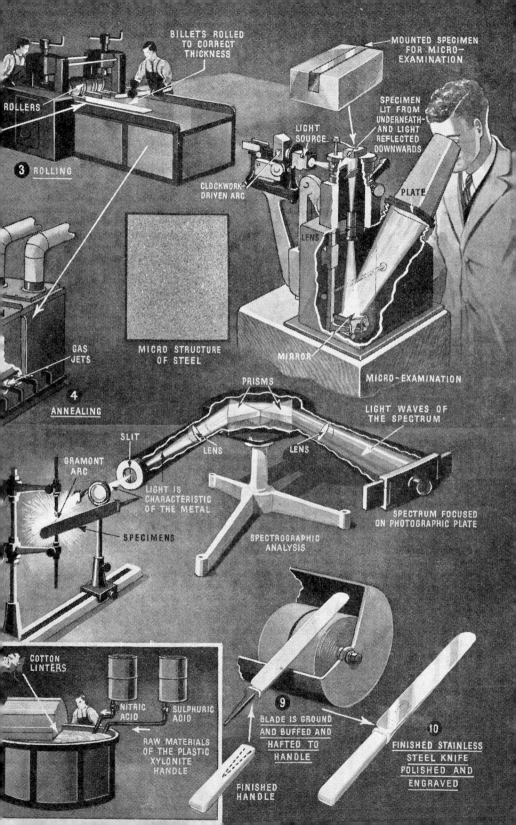

BILLETS ROLLED TO CORRECT THICKNESS

ROLLERS

3 ROLLING

MOUNTED SPECIMEN FOR MICRO-EXAMINATION

SPECIMEN LIT FROM UNDERNEATH—AND LIGHT REFLECTED DOWNWARDS

LIGHT SOURCE

CLOCKWORK-DRIVEN ARC

PLATE

LENS

GAS JETS

MICRO STRUCTURE OF STEEL

MIRROR

MICRO-EXAMINATION

4 ANNEALING

PRISMS

LIGHT WAVES OF THE SPECTRUM

SLIT

LENS

LENS

GRAMONT ARC

LIGHT IS CHARACTERISTIC OF THE METAL

SPECTRUM FOCUSED ON PHOTOGRAPHIC PLATE

SPECIMENS

SPECTROGRAPHIC ANALYSIS

COTTON LINTERS

NITRIC ACID

SULPHURIC ACID

RAW MATERIALS OF THE PLASTIC XYLONITE HANDLE

9 BLADE IS GROUND AND BUFFED AND HAFTED TO HANDLE

FINISHED HANDLE

10 FINISHED STAINLESS STEEL KNIFE POLISHED AND ENGRAVED

"The length of the pendulum is proportional to the square of the time of swing."

(2) If an elastic body such as a strip of rubber or a straight metal wire be pulled lengthwise, the stretch is proportional to the strength of the pull.

(3) If a length of wire be heated, then it increases by an unvarying proportion of its original length for every degree rise in temperature.

(4) A volume of gas is compressed in a cylinder. If the pressure be doubled, the volume will be reduced to half; if the pressure be trebled, the volume will be reduced to one-third, and so on, the temperature remaining unchanged.

(5) If any object be dropped in a space from which the air has been removed, then at the end of each second of fall its speed of fall will have increased by equal amounts; the amount being 32 ft. per second.

Characteristic Regularities

These represent five simple and typical regularities in nature. They provide the groundwork, the bricks and the mortar of the more elaborate theories and laws that scientists have discovered to deal with more complicated situations. Now it is important to notice certain simple features of each of these regularities.

In the *first* place, each states a regularity in quality. It says, for example, that to each length of pendulum there is a definite time of swing. If a piece of metal is heated it expands, if a gas is put under pressure it contracts.

In the *second* place, each states a regularity in quantity or amount. It tells exactly how the time of swing varies with the length, by how much a metal wire extends when its temperature rises by a given amount. It is in this respect that the question of measurement enters. In scientific work, a prediction regarding what may happen may be either qualitative or quantitative. Usually it is both. It is for this reason that it is frequently asserted that the essence of science is measurement, but it must also be stressed that the recognition of qualities and of qualitative change is also a very important feature of science.

There is a *third* point to which attention has to be directed. There is no scientific law that is true without restriction.

When Laws are not Applicable

It is only for small swings—or small amplitudes, as it is called—that the time of swing of a pendulum is related to the length in the simple way indicated. For other than small oscillations, the time of swing will depend also on the angle through which it swings.

It is only for a certain limited range of stretch that a metal wire or a rubber band extends in proportion to the force applied. If the stretch is large enough to rupture the material, the simple law will no longer apply.

If a wire be heated, the simple law of extension will apply only to a range of temperature well below the melting point.

The law concerning gas pressure is invalid if the temperature rises, as in a bicycle pump.

When a gas is compressed, the simple law is no longer true if the temperature of the gas is sufficiently low to bring the gas, under pressure, near to the point at which it becomes a liquid. A liquid is hardly compressed at all by moderate pressures.

Law is no Longer True

The increase in speed of a falling body will not be regular and unchanging if the body falls to earth from a very great height —from any height, in fact, comparable with the diameter of the earth itself. These were the five cases that have been taken to illustrate the occurrence of a regularity in nature.

From this, therefore, it will be clear that in science one seeks: (*a*) the conditions under which a regularity in nature may be found, and that regularity may be either of a qualitative or of a quantitative kind. Precision in science seeks for a quantitative statement of the regularity; (*b*) the limits to the occurrence of the regularity, the conditions under which the regularity no longer persists. To find these limits opens the way to further development, for it suggests that if a search is made beyond the range within which the regularity occurred

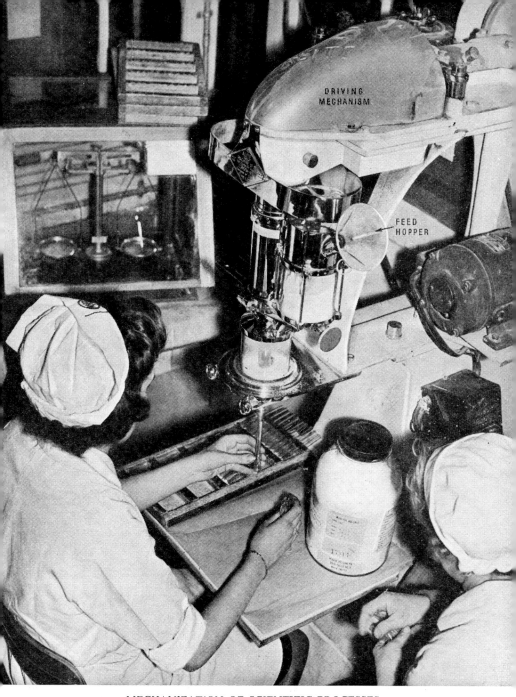

MECHANIZATION OF SCIENTIFIC PROCESSES

The most delicate processes are today carried out with precision by machines. The photo above shows such a machine being used in the preparation of the wonder drug M and B. This machine delivers extremely accurately weighed quantities, each highly consistent in quality. This is simply one instance of how the scientist and engineer act together.

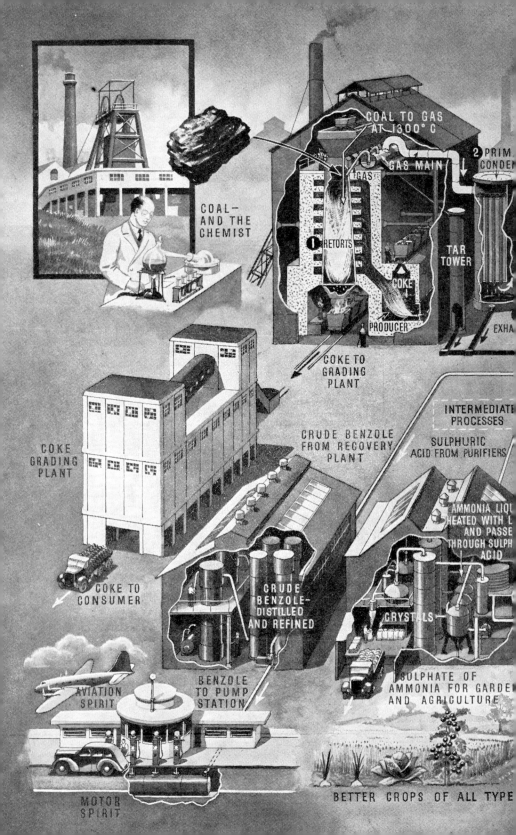

COAL TO GAS AT 1300° C

GAS MAIN

2 PRIM CONDEN

COAL– AND THE CHEMIST

GAS

1 RETORTS

COKE

TAR TOWER

PRODUCER

EXHA

COKE TO GRADING PLANT

COKE GRADING PLANT

CRUDE BENZOLE FROM RECOVERY PLANT

INTERMEDIATE PROCESSES

SULPHURIC ACID FROM PURIFIERS

AMMONIA LIQU HEATED WITH L AND PASSE THROUGH SULPH ACID

COKE TO CONSUMER

CRUDE BENZOLE– DISTILLED AND REFINED

CRYSTALS

AVIATION SPIRIT

BENZOLE TO PUMP STATION

SULPHATE OF AMMONIA FOR GARDE AND AGRICULTURE

MOTOR SPIRIT

BETTER CROPS OF ALL TYPE

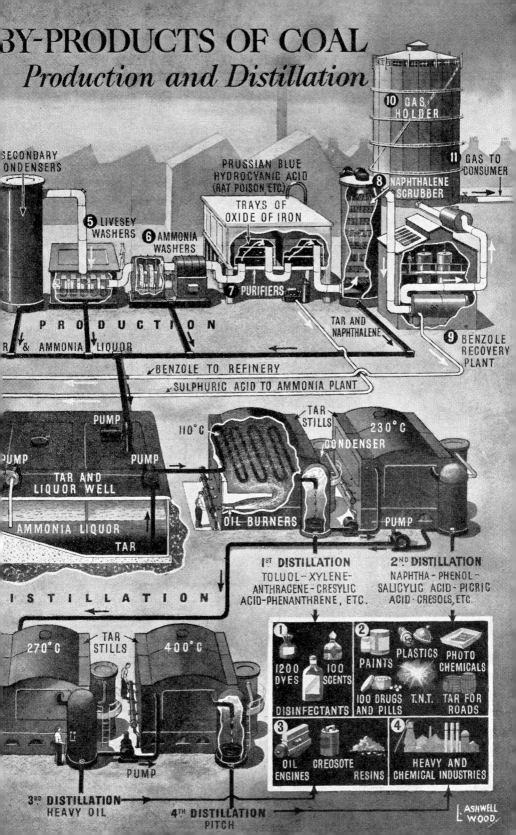

BY-PRODUCTS OF COAL
Production and Distillation

ARTIFICIAL LIGHTNING FOR SCIENTIFIC RESEARCH

Even natural phenomena are artificially produced under controlled conditions by modern scientists in order to pursue their researches and carry out tests. Above you see a sustained arc resulting from nearly one million volts, produced in Messrs. Ferranti's laboratories. This arc is, in some respects, similar to lightning. The photograph was taken at night without any other light than that supplied by this wonderful demonstration of an electrical phenomenon. The arc is slightly over 9 ft. in length. The curious cobweb effect caused by the 50-period A.C. supply can be seen. High voltages of the above order are necessary for testing insulators and switches used for the transmission of electricity.

a new type of regularity should be found and, therefore, a new scientific discovery will be made

Fundamentally Unimportant

The illustrations we have taken are all of a scientifically simple type. However important they may have been at the time when they were discovered, they would not today be regarded as of fundamental importance.   How this arises can be seen quite easily if we remember, in the first place, that each one of them is itself based on many individual experiments.

To test the truth of the law regarding the regular increase in speed of a falling body,

for example, many objects of varying types would require to be dropped from different heights. When all this evidence is collected together and it is found that the same principle appears to be at work in each case, in spite of the differences that show themselves among the various types of case, the scientist is emboldened to state the general principle. He then applies it to cases not already examined.

Process of Induction

This stating of a general principle drawn from a series of particular cases is called *Induction*, and every scientific law, elementary or complicated, is arrived at by such a process. Logically, of course, it is not justified. It does not follow from particular cases that it is true in general. Experimentally it is tried out and finds its justification in the fact that it works.

Process of Deduction

To start with the principle, on the other hand, and to use it to discover what will happen in new circumstances, is called *Deduction*. Mathematics is a highly developed apparatus of thought whose object is to apply the process of deduction to certain given principles in order to discover what these principles imply in certain stated circumstances. In this way, mathematics has played a very important role in the development of scientific inquiry.

Precisely the same process is carried through in passing from any group of simple scientific laws to a deeper and more far-reaching scientific principle. For example, careful examination of the positions of the planets that move round the sun, planets like the Earth, Mars, Jupiter, Uranus, Venus, Saturn and Pluto, shows that they all move in nearly circular paths or orbits round the sun. Actually, these paths are ellipses, oval-shaped figures with the sun occupying what is called the *focus* of the ellipses. This is one type of regularity visible among the planets.

Again, it is found that there is a systematic regularity connecting the distances of these planets from the sun, and the time taken for each planet to make a complete circuit—that is what would correspond to the year for that planet. This relation is that the "square of the times taken to make the circuit is always proportional to the cubes of the distances".

Simplifying a Complex Law

This looks like a very complex law but, in fact, it simply states that the result of an elementary piece of arithmetic conducted for each planet always gives the same result. If a planet takes two years to make a complete circuit, the square of this time is 2×2, viz. 4. If the average distance of this planet from the sun is 150 million miles, then the cube of this number is 150,000,000 $\times$ 150,000,000 $\times$ 150,000,000, which is

34 followed by twenty-three noughts. This number divided by 4, the square of the time, gives, roughly, 8 followed by twenty-three noughts. The law says that if this calculation is carried through for every planet, the number obtained is always the same.

There is a third planetary law relating to the changing speed with which a planet rotates round the sun as it moves along its path. It says that if a line were set out stretching from the planet to the sun, then, as the planet moves, this line would sweep out equal areas in equal times.

Here, then, are three regularities in the motion of the planets. At first sight they seem unconnected, independent laws. It was the great achievement of Newton to show that the single principle of gravitation, that bodies attract each other with a force that falls off with the square of their distance apart—itself a great regularity in nature—sufficed to imply the truth of all these three laws.

Advancing Science

It is not our function in this chapter to set out a detailed statement of the actual basic principles in science derived by this process of induction. Our purpose is to make the process clear and to bring out how science grows by this means. Within this past half-century, great advances have been made in this way in our understanding of the world we live in. Technical advances in the construction of apparatus and in the making of fine precision instruments have enabled the innermost secrets of the structure of matter itself to be laid bare, and made it reasonable to anticipate that in the comparatively near future the vast stores of energy locked up in the atoms of matter may be turned towards the satisfaction of man's needs on a scale hitherto unreached.

In achieving this, man has demonstrated to the full the success of the venture on which he set out in primitive times—the transformation of himself from being a mere creature of nature to its master. It remains for him finally, therefore, so to organize his social life as to take the fullest advantage of the mastery he has achieved.

GREAT SCIENTIST AT WORK

Sir Harold Spencer Jones, M.A., Sc.D., D.Phil., F.R.S., former Astronomer Royal, and contributor of Chapters II and III, surveys the heavens through a telescope at the Royal Observatory, Greenwich. In recent years the Observatory, which has been a centre of astronomical research since 1676, has been moved to Herstmonceaux Castle in Sussex.

CHAPTER II

SPACE AND TIME

IF WE look at the sky on a clear, dark night, the number of stars that we can see is by no means countless; there are not more than about 2500. The total number in the whole sky visible to the average eye is between 6000 and 7000; but only half the sky can be seen at any time and, near the horizon, only the brightest of the stars are visible. A little haze, or moonlight, or the glare from town lights, greatly reduces the number. But with field glasses or a small telescope the number is very considerably increased.

It is instructive to look at the same patch of sky, first with the naked eye and then with a pair of field glasses, and to note how many more stars can be seen in the second case. The larger the aperture of a telescope, the greater is its light-gathering power and the greater the number of stars it will reveal, especially when photography is used and long exposures are given.

Revealing the Sky's Wonders

More than a thousand million stars are within reach of the great 100-in. telescope at the Mount Wilson Observatory, with long-exposure photographs.

There is little apparent order in the arrangement of the stars. The distribution of the bright stars over the sky is irregular; but the eye naturally relates together bright stars that are in close proximity and divides them into groups. For convenience of reference or identification, the stars are divided in a somewhat arbitrary manner into groups or constellations. These constellations have been given the names of familiar objects, or of common animals, or of mythological personages, the resemblance of any constellation to its name being generally more fancied than real.

The names of most of the constellations are of great antiquity, having probably been given between four and five thousand years ago. It will add greatly to the interest of the skies if the reader will take some trouble to become acquainted with the principal constellations, with the aid of a star map, and to learn the brightest stars (Fig. 1).

By watching the sky, it can soon be seen that the stars are changing their positions relative to terrestrial objects. Take up a position so that a conspicuous bright star is in line with the top of a chimney pot, a church spire, or some other definite object; then look again from the same position after an hour or so. The star will no longer be in line, and will appear to have moved; but its position in relation to adjacent stars remains unchanged, so that these stars also must have moved.

Consequences of the Earth's Rotation

This apparent motion of the heavens is a consequence of the rotation of the earth on its axis; the rising and setting of the sun and moon and their motions across the sky are also consequences of this rotation. Some stars will be seen rising in the east, and other stars will be seen setting in the west. But not all stars rise and set. If a star were exactly on the axis about which the earth rotates, its position in the sky would not change.

The fairly bright star known as Polaris, or the Pole Star, is nearly on the axis of the earth's rotation and defines the north direction very closely. Stars near Polaris describe small circles in the sky, those farther from Polaris describe larger circles (Fig. 2).

One of the most easily identifiable constellations is the one known as the Great Bear. The Americans often term it the Dipper, from its resemblance to a bowl with a handle. Two of the stars of the bowl are called "the Pointers," because they point to the Pole Star and serve to identify it.

In the latitude of the British Isles, the constellation of the Great Bear never rises or sets, but is always above the horizon; because of the earth's rotation, it is seen sometimes above the Pole Star and sometimes below it. In the course of a few hours

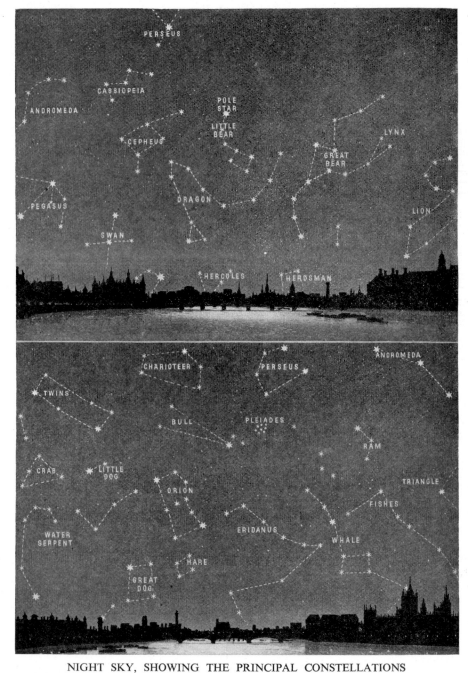

NIGHT SKY, SHOWING THE PRINCIPAL CONSTELLATIONS

FIG. 1. *Here is a representation of the night sky as seen from Westminster, London, on January 1st, at 10 p.m. At the top is a view looking north; at the bottom, looking south.*

it will be seen to change its position considerably as it circles round the Pole (Fig. 3).

Now, suppose we have fixed our standpoint so that we see a particular bright star in line with some definite mark. Let us note the line and then, a week or so later, look at the same star from the same position at the same time. It will no longer be in line the stars around the sun, we should see that the sun has a progressive motion eastwards relative to the stars, completing the circuit of the sky in the course of a year.

The reader should identify as many stars as he can on the star map and also in the sky, in winter and summer. He should note particularly the differences in colour

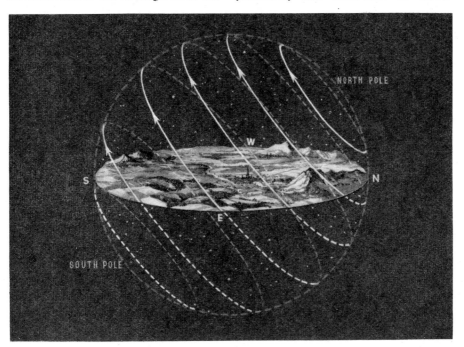

STARS AND THEIR DIURNAL COURSES

FIG. 2. *Diurnal motion of the stars caused by the earth's rotation. When on the dotted portions of the paths below the horizon they are not visible. Stars near to the north pole never set, and those that are near the south pole never rise. Other stars rise and set.*

with the mark. To see the star in the same position night by night we should have to look about four minutes earlier each night. Thus the face of the sky changes gradually through the year, and the constellations which we see in the winter sky are not the same (except for those which do not rise or set) as those which we see in the summer sky.

This is a consequence of the movement of the earth round the sun in the course of the year. The line from the earth to the sun swings completely round in the course of the year; if we could see the background of amongst the stars. Take the conspicuous and well-known winter constellation of Orion as an example. Three equally spaced bright stars form the belt, around which are four bright stars, forming an irregular quadrilateral (Fig. 4). One of these stars, Betelgeuse, has a distinct reddish colour, in contrast to the other three, which have a bluish-white colour. Or again, in the summer sky, notice Spica, bluish-white or crystalline in appearance, and the red Antares.

These differences in colour are the

consequence of differences in temperature of the stars. When molten steel is poured from a furnace it is white hot; as it cools it becomes successively yellow, yellowish-red, red, and then a dull blood red. So it is with the stars. The red stars are relatively cool stars; the blue stars are the hottest stars. The latter have surface temperatures of the

star is based upon the measurement of the apparent shift of its position relative to a more distant star, as the earth swings to and fro in its annual journey around the sun (Fig. 5). The diameter of the orbit of the earth is 186 million miles, which gives the largest available base line for measuring stellar distances. The principle involved can

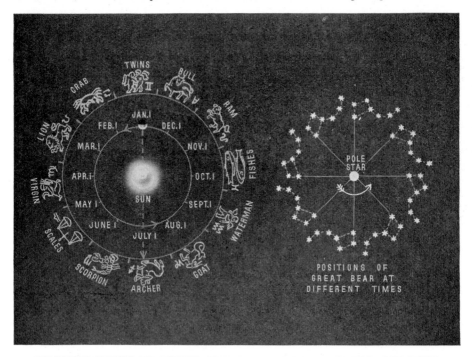

CONSTELLATIONS IN WHICH THE SUN APPEARS DURING THE YEAR

FIG. 3. *The sun appears to move round the zodiac in the course of a year, as a consequence of the orbital motion of the earth. (Left) Inner circle shows dates when the sun is in the constellations marked around outer circle. (Right) It will be seen that in whatever position the Great Bear may be its two "Pointers" always point towards the Pole Star.*

order of 30,000 deg. C. The sun, which is a yellow star, has a temperature of 6000 deg. C. The red stars are only about 2000 or 3000 deg. C.

The apparent brightness of a star gives no indication of its intrinsic brightness. A faint star will appear bright if it is sufficiently near; a bright star will appear faint if it is sufficiently far away. In order to compare the intrinsic luminosities or candle powers of two stars we must know their distances.

The measurement of the distance of a

be illustrated by how, when in a moving train, near objects in the landscape appear to move relative to distant objects which appear stationary; the nearer the object, the more rapidly it appears to move. But though the principle is simple enough, the distances of even the nearest stars are so great in relation to the size of the earth's orbit that measurements of the greatest refinement are necessary in order to measure a star's distance.

Indeed, when, in the middle of the

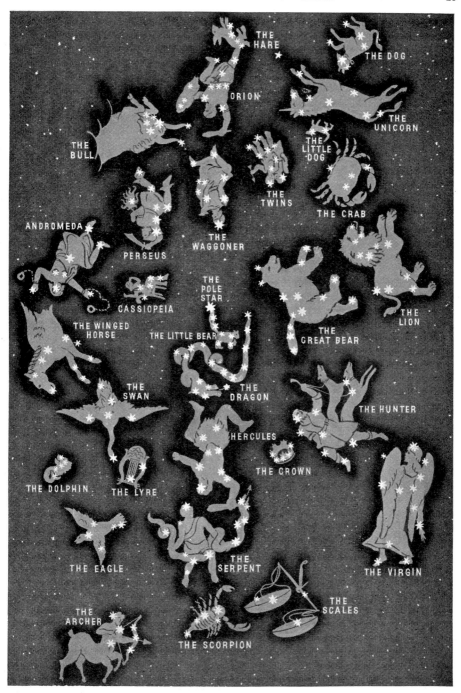

FIG. 4. *Showing the brightest stars, and their positions, in the northern constellations.*

fifteenth century, Copernicus asserted that the earth moved around the sun, in opposition to the accepted view that the earth was stationary and that the sun moved around it, his opponents objected that the distances apart of the stars would change as the earth moved around the sun and that no such changes were observed.

At that time the stars were generally believed to be just beyond the solar system; Copernicus had to assume that the stars were much more distant than had been previously supposed. It was not until the year 1838 that the first measurement of a star's distance was made.

Defining a Light Year

The nearest known star is about 25 million million miles away. It is convenient to express such a great distance in terms of the time taken by light to travel from the star to the earth. Light travels with a speed of 186,000 miles a second and in a year it travels about 6 million million miles. This is called a *light-year*. We may, therefore, say that the nearest known star is about four light-years away.

If this star were suddenly to be blotted out of existence, we should continue to see it for four years, by means of the light which was travelling on its way to us before the star ceased to shine. But the distances of most of the stars are very much greater; some are many thousands of light-years away. Space is not crowded with stars: it is comparatively empty.

If we represent the average star by a tennis ball, and scatter half a dozen tennis balls inside a hollow globe of the size of the earth, 8000 miles in diameter, we have

PARALLACTIC DISPLACEMENT

Fig. 5. *(Left) As the observer moves, nearer objects appear to change their positions relative to more distant objects. This is known as parallax. (Right) The distance of a star is determined from measurements of its displacement with respect to a more distant star when seen from opposite ends of the earth's orbit, which are 186,000,000 miles apart.*

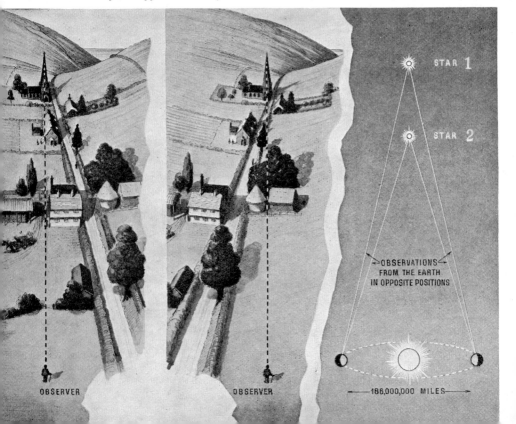

GREAT NEBULA IN ORION

One of the largest of the diffuse nebulæ, whose luminosity is obtained from the bright stars involved in them. It has a more perfect vacuum than can be produced in a laboratory.

a pretty fair representation of the density of the stars in space.

When the distance of a star is known, and also its apparent brightness, we can determine its intrinsic luminosity. There is a very great range in the luminosities of the stars: the brightest known star, S Doradus, in the Magellanic Clouds, is 300,000 times brighter than the sun; one of the faintest known, the companion to the bright star Procyon, has a brightness less than one ten-thousandth of the brightness of the sun. These are the extremes; the sun is much more typical of the average star.

Calculating Star Sizes

The sun has a diameter of 864,000 miles and could contain about 1,300,000 bodies the size of the earth; every square inch of its surface is continually sending out energy in the form of heat and light at the rate of a 62-h.p. engine.

The brightness of each square inch of the surface of a star depends upon its temperature; the hotter the star, the greater the brightness per square inch of its surface.

Having determined the luminosity and temperature of a star, it is easy to calculate the area of its surface and, therefore, the size of the star.

Again, we find that there is a tremendous range in size. Betelgeuse, the bright red star in Orion, has a diameter nearly three hundred times greater than that of the sun and could contain 24 million bodies of the size of the sun; the companion of Procyon, on the other hand, is so small that the sun could contain about 15 million bodies equal to it in size (Fig. 6).

It is thus a comparatively straightforward matter to find the distance, the luminosity and the size of a star. But to find out how much matter the star contains is not so easy; in fact, for the majority of the stars, it is impossible to find any information at all about their weight. The only means we have of finding how much matter a star contains is to measure its gravitational pull on another star.

When in ordinary life we weigh an object, we really measure the gravitational pull of the earth on it. Most stars are millions of millions of miles from their nearest neighbours and we cannot detect any gravitational influence at such great distances.

But many stars are binary systems, consisting of two stars relatively close together, the one held fast in the gravitational pull of the other. The two stars must revolve round each other; if they ceased to do so, gravitation would draw them together and they would collide. The gravitational pull of the heavier star on the lighter star is exactly equal to the pull of the lighter star on the heavier, but equal pulls will disturb the lighter star more than the heavier.

Determining the Weight of a Star

By comparing the sizes of the orbits of the two stars, we can determine the ratio of the weights of the two stars. If, in addition, we measure the distance of the system, we know the actual size in miles of the orbit of each star. We are then able to compare the weight of each of the stars with the sun. The reason is that, for any particular size of orbit, the period of revolution is determined by the weights; the heavier the stars, the faster they must move if the orbit is to remain of the same size (Fig. 7).

By such methods, a certain amount of information about the weights of the stars can be obtained. Two results of interest are found. In the first place, there is a very close correlation between the luminosity of a star and its weight; the relationship between the two quantities is determined with sufficient accuracy by the information obtained from the binary systems. This relationship makes it possible to infer the weights of stars which are single stars, which could not be determined in any other way.

In the second place, it is found that the range in the weights of the stars is not very great. We have seen that the stars differ enormously from one another in luminosity and size; but in weight they are much more nearly comparable. The great majority of the stars have weights between ten times and one-tenth of the weight of the sun. There are a few stars which are as much as one hundred times more massive than the sun, but these are exceptional.

The greatest of all contrasts between different stars is in their densities, which are determined by their mass and volume.

The average density of a giant red star like Antares or Betelgeuse is about equal to that of air in a fairly well-exhausted

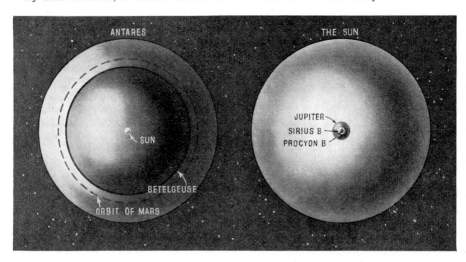

GIANT AND DWARF STARS COMPARED WITH SUN

Fig. 6. *(Left) Sun shown to scale in relation to the giant stars, Antares and Betelgeuse, with the orbit of Mars for comparison, and (right) the sun again, shown in relation to the dwarf stars, Sirius B and Procyon B, with Jupiter given for comparison.*

CLOSE-UP OF THE MOON'S SURFACE

Representation of the southern portion of the moon's surface, vividly illustrating the peculiarities in its conformation. It shows how the satellite is dotted with craters, some of which are 50 miles in diameter. Over 30,000 have been carefully recorded on maps.

vacuum, so that sufficient of the material to fill an average-sized room would weigh only a few ounces; the average density of the companion of Procyon is so great that a matchboxful would weigh more than 100 tons. Some stars are, therefore, giants: very large and extremely diffused. Other stars are dwarfs: very small and extremely dense (Fig. 6).

We have referred to the enormous output of radiation in the form of heat and light from the sun, which is an average sort of star. The output of radiation from a giant star far exceeds that from the sun. It was for a long time a great puzzle how the stars were able to maintain such enormous outputs of radiation. Not until a great deal had been learned about the structure of the atom (which is dealt with in Chapter 5) could an answer be given.

Star's Intense Internal Heat

Investigations of the internal constitution of the stars have shown that the temperature deep down in a star is many millions of degrees; at such extremely high tempera-

tures, atomic transformations can take place which release some of the vast store of energy locked up within the atom.

It has been said that the atomic bomb is the harnessing of the basic power of the universe, the force from which the sun draws its power. The explosive power of the atomic bomb is obtained by the release of subatomic energy; it is essentially the same process—the basic power of the universe—which enables the sun and the stars to maintain their radiation.

But though there is such great diversity in size, in brightness and in density amongst the stars, they are all in a sense our blood relations. By analysing the light from the stars with the spectroscope (*see* Chapter 9), it is possible to learn a great deal about their composition.

They are found to be built up of the same elements as the earth and in roughly the same relative proportions; elements which are abundant on the earth are abundant also in the stars, and elements which are rare on the earth are rare also in the stars. There is no evidence of any star containing an element which is not known terrestrially.

We have mentioned that the stars visible to the naked eye show little apparent order in their arrangement. But if we look carefully at the sky on a dark night free from haze, when the Milky Way is clearly seen, it will be noticed that the bright stars are most numerous in the regions of the sky near the Milky Way.

Stretching Across the Sky

This broad hazy belt of light stretches right across the northern sky from horizon to horizon and completes its circuit in the southern sky; its outline is irregular and its brightness is uneven. For a long time nothing was known with certainty about its nature; but in the eighteenth century, William Herschel, using improved tele-

scopes of his own construction, proved that it was composed of an innumerable number of very faint stars. These stars are individually far too faint to be seen with the naked eye, but the integrated light of the vast number becomes easily visible at night.

Herschel counted the number of stars visible in the field of view of his telescope in a large number of regions of the sky and found that the number increased rapidly towards the Milky Way. Though any given star may appear faint either because it is intrinsically faint or because it is very distant, the fainter stars will on the average be the more distant. Therefore, Herschel concluded that our stellar system has a very much flattened shape, somewhat like a millstone (Fig. 8).

The sun is near the central plane of the system, which extends to much greater

GRAVITATION IS A UNIVERSAL FORCE

Fig. 7. *The earth's gravitational pull causes objects to fall to the ground; it also causes the moon to move around the earth. The moon is continually being drawn towards the earth, instead of moving away in a straight path. Gravitation causes two stars in a twin system to revolve around their centre of mass, and provides a means for weighing stars.*

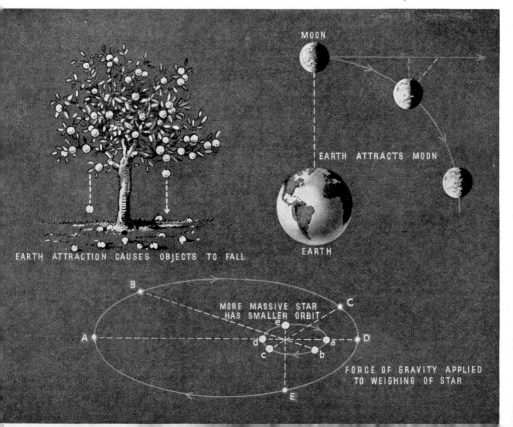

distances in any direction in the Milky Way than in other directions.

This system does not consist solely of stars. In the constellation of Orion, the three bright stars in a row form the belt; below the middle of these three are the fainter stars forming the sword. If the reader looks at these with the naked eye, he will notice that the middle one shines with a hazy light. Viewed with a telescope, this hazy-looking star is seen to be an irregular patch of greenish light.

Gaseous Nebulæ

When William Herschel made his survey of the sky, he found many other bright patches of light; he was at first inclined to think that these objects consisted of aggregations of extremely faint stars, which his telescope could not resolve into discrete stars. But he later came to the conclusion that they were essentially different in nature: this was confirmed when William Huggins proved, by the examination of their light with the spectroscope, that they were composed of glowing gas; these objects are, therefore, called "gaseous nebulæ", from the Latin word *nebula*, a cloud.

The brighter ones are objects of great beauty when seen in a telescope of sufficient power, but photography best reveals the wonderful variety and complexity of their structure. The gaseous nebulæ are found only in or near the Milky Way. They are composed of diffuse gaseous matter, which has not condensed into stars, and they shine by means of the light from the stars embedded in them, just as bright light in a fog is surrounded by a luminous halo.

"Coalsack"

Closely associated with many of these gaseous nebulæ are blank areas almost devoid of stars. Many of these are to be found in the densest regions of the Milky Way. The most striking example is called the "Coalsack", adjacent to the Southern Cross and not visible from Great Britain; it is easily seen with the naked eye and has the appearance of a small cloud hiding the portion of the Milky Way behind it.

These dark patches are caused by opaque clouds of very fine dust lying between us and the Milky Way, and screening from us the stars that lie behind them. They are, therefore, often called "dark nebulæ". This fine dust or obscuring matter is widely distributed through the central regions of the Milky Way.

For a great part of its extent, the Milky Way appears to divide into two branches; this appearance is produced by the obscuration of the central region by the dust clouds. Where the dust is sufficiently thinly scattered, the distant stars are not completely obscured, but are merely dimmed or reddened. Though the luminous nebulæ and the obscuring clouds are both of extremely low density, it is estimated that the total amount of matter in these forms is about equal to the total amount of matter in the stars; thus it appears that about half the matter in our stellar system, or galaxy, as it is often called, has condensed into stars and about half has remained in its primitive form.

The stars are continually gathering in, by their gravitational attraction, matter from the space surrounding them. They are gradually sweeping space clean, but the sweepers are few in comparison with the vast regions that have to be swept, so that the process is yet far from completion.

Through Stars to Outer Space

If we were to travel with the speed of light through our stellar universe, in the plane of the Milky Way, we should find that after some thousands of years the stars were becoming less numerous; some time later we should find only a few scattered outlying members of the system, and at last we should leave those behind and find ourselves in outer space, free from stars.

Our galaxy is not infinite in extent. Its diameter is about 100,000 light-years. The earth is near the mid plane of the system, but well away from the centre, at a distance of about 25,000 light-years. The centre of the system is in the direction of the brightest portion of the Milky Way, in the southern constellation of the Archer.

The whole system is in slow rotation about its centre, a complete revolution at the distance of the sun being completed in about 170 million years; but though the

HERSCHEL'S MODEL OF THE GALACTIC SYSTEM
Section through centre perpendicular to Milky Way

MODERN MODEL OF THE GALACTIC SYSTEM

ANCIENT AND MODERN COMPARISON OF THE GALAXY

FIG. 8. *Schematic models of galaxy according to Herschel and according to present views. The dark region in the central plane in lower figure illustrates the effect of absorbing dust in the Milky Way. Sun is placed much farther from centre in the modern model. To the naked eye, the Milky Way is a band of misty light stretching across the sky, more distinct in some parts than in others. The stars are so numerous, they cannot be counted.*

rotation is so slow, the stars in the neighbourhood of the sun have an average speed of about 170 miles a second. The total mass of the system is about 160,000 million times that of the sun and the number of stars in it is about 100,000 million (Fig. 8).

Are There Other Universes?

If we travelled on through space beyond the bounds of our galaxy, should we come to other stellar universes, or is our galaxy the one and only universe?

William Herschel, in the eighteenth century, was convinced that some of the nebulæ which he observed were island universes in space, at such great distances that they could not be resolved by his telescope into separate stars. These nebulæ do not shine with the greenish light of the gaseous nebulæ, but with a white light, more like the light from the stars.

The most easily observed of such objects can be seen with the naked eye in the girdle of Andromeda, near the Great Square of Pegasus and the Chair of Cassiopeia, appearing as a luminous patch. It was known as far back as early in the tenth century. A good pair of field glasses or a small telescope shows it as a bright oval object, shining with a silvery light. Photographs taken with a large telescope enable it to be studied in considerable detail.

Great Clusters of Stars

The Great Nebula in Andromeda, as it is called, is revealed as a flattened object, inclined to the line of sight, containing many discrete stars, aggregations of stars, gaseous nebulæ, and dark nebulæ, with a bright central condensation, in which separate stars cannot be seen. It shows all the general characteristics of our own galaxy, and, moreover, observations have revealed that, like our galaxy, it is in slow rotation.

The measurements of its distance show that its light takes about 750,000 years to reach us; therefore, it lies far beyond the bounds of the galaxy. In actual size it is comparable with, though rather smaller, than the galaxy. From the rate of its measured rotation, it is possible to estimate its mass and this proves to be about 100,000 million times that of the sun.

Extra-Galactic Nebulæ

Many other extra-galactic nebulæ (so called because they lie outside our galaxy), or island universes, are known. Some, like the Great Nebula in Andromeda, are seen inclined to the line of sight; some are seen edgewise on, when their much-flattened shape is well shown; some are seen broadside on.

The latter show a characteristic formation of two spiral arms, extending outwards from diametrically opposite points of the central nucleus; for this reason, these objects are often termed spiral nebulæ. The spiral arms can be clearly traced in the Great Nebula in Andromeda, though they might not have been recognized as such but for the clue provided by the spiral nebulæ which are seen broadside on. There is an essential continuity from the nebulæ seen broadside on to those seen edgewise on, and we can infer that these latter must also possess the spiral structure.

Velocity of Recession

The velocity of each of these systems directly towards us or away from us can be measured. The principle used for this purpose is that if a body, which is sending out radiations in the form of light, is approaching, its radiations are slightly compressed together so that their wavelengths are slightly shorter than they would be if the body were at rest; if, on the other hand, it is moving away, the radiations that we receive are all of slightly longer wavelength.

It is found that the external universes are moving away from us and that, the more distant they are, the more rapid is their velocity of recession. Apart from individual velocities of a few hundred miles a second, the velocities of recession are strictly proportional to the distance. The velocity in miles a second divided by 106 gives the distance in millions of light-years.

A distant system in the constellation of Boötes, the Herdsman, has been found to be receding with a velocity of 24,300 miles a second. We can infer that it is at a distance of about 230 million light-years. The most distant systems that have been recorded on long-exposure photographs with the great 100-in. telescope are at a distance of about 500 million light-years; within a sphere of this radius, it is estimated that there are about 100 million universes, the average distance of any universe from its nearest neighbour being of the order of a million light-years.

There is no evidence of any falling off in density at these great distances, nor of any approach to the bounds of space.

Relative Distances

The proportionality between the velocity of recession and the distance is what would be found if the universe as a whole were expanding at a uniform rate. From any point in the system, every nebula would appear to be receding with a velocity proportional to its distance; the distance between any two nebulæ whatsoever would also increase at the same rate.

It has been suggested that the separate island universes are the fragments of one large universe, which was originally very compact. An explosion occurred and the fragments were sent flying through space in all directions.

If such were the case, then, after the lapse of a considerable time, we should find that the most rapidly moving parts would be at the greatest distances and that, viewed from any one of the fragments, all the other fragments would appear to be moving away and with speeds that were faster the greater the distances. It is by no means certain, however, that this is the correct explanation, nor even that the universe is really expanding.

The recessional motions are inferred from changes in the wavelength of the light reaching us from the distant universes; these changes might also be caused by a slight loss of energy carried by the light in the course of its long journey through space, the loss being proportional to the distance travelled.

The ancients referred to the stars as "fixed stars". They believed that the stars were attached to a crystal sphere, which rotated around the earth in the course of a day.

With their crude methods of measurement, no relative changes in the positions of the stars could be detected. It was not until early in the eighteenth century that actual motions of the stars were detected by Halley.

By comparisons of photographs taken at intervals of a few years, the angular motions of stars at right angles to the line of sight can be determined. The actual linear velocities in the line of sight can be directly measured by the method used for spiral nebulæ. By statistical analysis of these motions it has been found that the sun is moving with a velocity of about thirteen miles a second towards a point in the constellation of Hercules.

Wandering Celestial Bodies

But the ancients were familiar with certain celestial bodies which moved relatively to the "fixed stars". These were called *planets*, meaning *wanderers*. The bodies which they included under this designation were the sun, the moon, Mercury, Venus,

SPIRAL NEBULA IN URSA MAJOR

Chief characteristic of the typical spiral nebula is the emergence from opposite sides of its central nucleus of two spiral arms, which wind themselves round it, as seen below.

SUN AND PLANETS TO SCALE

Fig. 9. *Smaller planets are shown above, the major planets below. Pluto is not represented, as its size is not known. Only a portion of the sun can be shown on this scale.*

Mars, Jupiter and Saturn. But the sun and moon are not now included in the list of the planets; the sun is a star, the moon is the satellite of the earth.

Planetary System

The planets, in the modern sense, are the members of the family of bodies which revolve around the sun. The earth is, therefore, to be considered as a planet. In addition to the true planets known to the ancients, Mercury, Venus, Mars, Jupiter and Saturn, there are three fainter planets: Uranus, discovered in 1781; Neptune, discovered in 1846; and Pluto, discovered in 1930; together with a large number of small bodies, termed minor planets or asteroids, which lie between Mars and Jupiter (Fig. 9).

The Greeks endeavoured to represent the observed motions of the planets by a complex combination of circular motions, being under the belief that, as the circle was the perfect curve, no other type of motion was possible for the celestial bodies.

It was left for Kepler (1571-1630) to show that the apparently complex motions of the planets could be represented by the simple assumption that each planet moved in an orbit around the sun, which was not circular but elliptical in shape, and that the sun occupied one of the foci of these ellipses (Fig. 10). Kepler found that the planets did not move with uniform speed, but moved

faster the nearer their distance to the sun, in such a way that the line joining the planet to the sun moved through the same area in the same time. In addition, Kepler found that there was a definite relationship between the mean distance of a planet and the time taken by the planet to complete one revolution of its orbit.

These laws, deduced empirically by Kepler, were shown by Newton (1643-1727) to be the necessary consequences of a universal principle of gravitation; any piece of matter attracts any other piece with a force proportional to their masses and inversely proportional to the square of their distance apart.

Double either mass and their mutual attraction is doubled; double their distance and the attraction is diminished by a factor of 4. The falling of a stone to the ground; the ebb and flow of the tides; the motion of the moon around the earth; the motion of the earth around the sun; the mutual revolution of the stars in a distant binary system; and the rotations of distant galaxies, are all controlled by the universal force of gravitation (Fig. 7).

The planets Mercury, Venus, Mars, Jupiter and Saturn have the appearance of bright stars, but can be distinguished from stars because they shine with a steady light and do not twinkle. Mercury and Venus are nearer the sun than is the earth; they can, therefore, reach to only a limited angular distance from the sun, as seen from the earth, and appear either as "evening stars" when to the east of the sun, or as "morning stars" when to the west of the sun (Fig. 11).

Mercury, because of its limited maximum distance from the sun, has to be looked for with care to be seen in the latitudes of Great Britain. Venus is easily seen, because of its brightness and its greater maximum angular distance from the sun. It shows a complete sequence of phases like the moon from a narrow bright crescent to a fully illuminated disk; its angular size changes appreciably with its phase and is least at the full phase, because Venus is then at its greatest distance from the earth. The reader will find it instructive to watch Venus with a pair of field-glasses, which will readily show its changes of phase (Fig. 11).

The outer planets, Mars, Jupiter and Saturn, can be seen at any time of the night, when suitably placed for observation. At opposition, when the earth is directly between the sun and the planet, an outer planet is on the meridian at midnight. They show no appreciable phase effects.

A pair of field-glasses will show the four major satellites of Jupiter, which were discovered by Galileo in 1610, and also the ring system of Saturn. The satellites of Jupiter will be found to change their relative positions appreciably in the course of a few hours and markedly from night to night.

Whitaker's Almanack gives useful information about the positions of the planets, their times of rising and setting, the times when they are due south and the phases of Mercury and Venus.

The outer planets, Mars, Jupiter and Saturn, have a general progressive motion eastwards amongst the stars. But occasionally the planet halts in its eastward motion, then begins to move westward for a while, comes again to rest and once more resumes its eastward motion.

The reader is recommended to note carefully the position of one of these planets relative to adjacent bright stars and to plot its position night by night on a star chart (using any good star atlas), marking the date against each position; the retrograde motion of the planet will then be revealed. This retrograde motion is a simple geometrical consequence of the planet being viewed from the earth, which is itself in motion around the sun (Fig. 12).

One of the strong arguments in favour of the Copernican theory that the earth moved round the sun was that it thereby

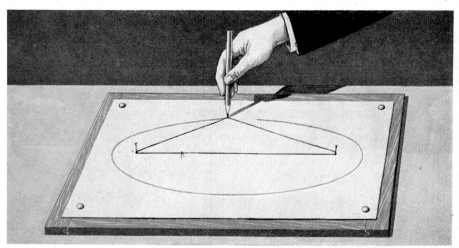

DRAWING AN ELLIPSE

FIG. 10. *Use a loop of cotton round two pins. The pins form the two foci of the ellipse. Orbits of the planets are slightly elongated ellipses; orbits of comets are very elongated ellipses; the sun is at one of the foci of each ellipse.*

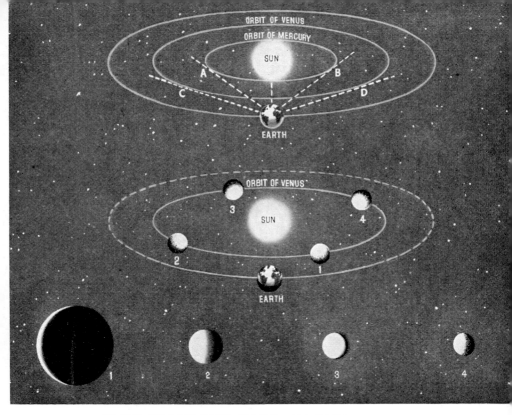

ORBITS OF MERCURY, VENUS AND EARTH

FIG. 11. *(Top) Seen from Earth, Mercury is at greatest angular distance from Sun when at A or B; Venus at C or D. Mercury's greatest angular distance is less than that of Venus. (Bottom) Changes in apparent size and phase of Venus at different positions in its orbit.*

provided a simple natural explanation of the apparent motions of the planets.

Though the planets appear like stars, they are not self-luminous as the stars are. We see them only by means of the sunlight falling upon them, which they reflect. Thus, at any time, half the surface of a planet is illuminated by sunlight, the other half being in darkness. When a portion of the illuminated face and a portion of the dark face are presented to the earth, the planet shows a phase effect. The phases of the moon have a similar explanation (Fig. 13).

The moon is the satellite of the earth and is our nearest neighbour in space, being about 240,000 miles away. It is much smaller than the earth, its diameter being about 2000 miles, or one quarter that of the earth. It is a curious coincidence that the angular diameters of the sun and moon are very nearly equal, though the sun has an actual diameter of 864,000 miles, and is at a distance of 93 million miles.

Because of the close equality of the angular diameters, it is just possible for the moon to obscure the sun completely and to produce what is termed a total eclipse of the sun; such an eclipse of the sun is only visible, however, from a small portion of the earth's surface (Fig. 13).

Moon's Eclipse by Earth's Shadow

A total eclipse of the moon, on the other hand, is caused by the moon entering the shadow of the earth thrown by the sun and is visible from the whole hemisphere of the earth facing the moon (Fig. 13). Though the direct sunlight is cut off from the moon, the moon does not become invisible, but appears of a dull coppery colour, because a certain amount of sunlight is refracted or bent by the earth's atmosphere and falls

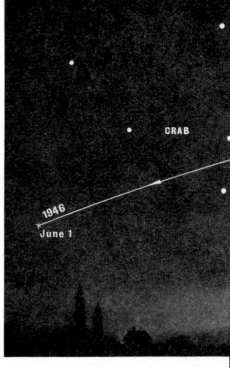

FIG. 12. *Path of Mars amongst the stars from September 16, 1945, to June 1, 1946. The motion is retrograde (westwards) from early December to late February. At the two turning points, at the ends of the loop, the planet is practically stationary relative to the stars for a few days.*

on the moon; as more blue light is lost by scattering in the earth's atmosphere than red light, it is mainly the red light which penetrates the atmosphere and is bent round to fall on the moon, so causing its ruddy colour.

The moon always turns the same face to the earth, because the period of its orbital revolution is the same as the period of its axial rotation. The surface is very mountainous and much of it is covered with numerous ring-shaped mountains or craters. These are well seen in a small telescope.

COMPARATIVE SIZES OF THE EARTH AND MOON
We shall be able better to visualize their relative sizes by studying this composite picture.

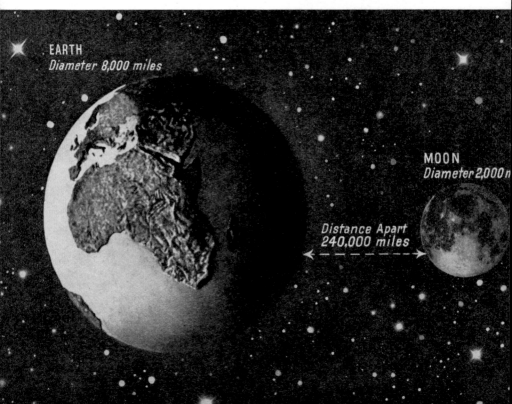

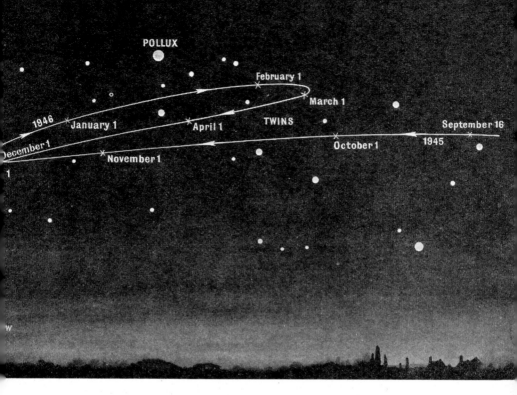

The surface is never obscured by clouds; the moon is a dry world and is completely devoid of atmosphere and, therefore, necessarily also of water vapour. This is because its gravitational pull has been insufficient to hold its atmosphere against the natural tendency of a gas to dissipate away into space. Mercury, which is a small planet, not much larger than the moon, is also devoid of any atmosphere.

Jupiter is the largest of all the planets; it could contain 1300 bodies of the size of the earth. It has an extensive and dense atmosphere, consisting mainly of hydrogen, helium, ammonia gas and methane or marsh gas. In a large telescope, a series of darkish belts parallel to its equator are seen; they show continual changes of structure and are evidently atmospheric formations, though their nature is not fully understood. Similar markings may be seen, though less clearly, on the surface of Saturn, which is the second largest of the planets.

Uranus is not a conspicuous object, but is visible to the naked eye, appearing as a faint star. Neptune is too faint to be seen without telescopic aid.

Venus shows little of interest in a tele-scope, apart from its phase changes. It has a hazy atmosphere and its surface is never visible. It is a dry world, devoid of water vapour; its atmosphere contains little or no oxygen but a large amount of carbon dioxide. As it is very similar to the earth in size and weight, it is surprising that its atmosphere is so different from our own.

Mars and its Mysteries

Mars is, in many ways, the most interesting of the planets; it is smaller than the earth but larger than Mercury, and has a thin atmosphere, through which its surface is clearly seen. The greater part of its surface is arid desert, appearing as a ruddy colour; but there are also darkish patches, which have been found by careful observation with large telescopes to show changes of coloration and of shape, and which are probably covered with a seasonal growth of vegetation.

The winter hemisphere of the planet has a white cap of ice or snow around its pole, which melts with the change of season and forms again as winter approaches. The American astronomer, Percival Lowell, developed a fanciful theory that Mars was inhabited by intelligent beings, engaged in a desperate struggle for existence on a world becoming increasingly arid; this theory is not now generally accepted. The minor planets, approaching 2000 in number, are small objects whose diameters

SOME ASPECTS OF THE SOLAR SYSTEM

FIG. 13. *A comet takes a definite path, with its tail always pointing away from the sun; the nearer the comet is to the sun, the longer is the tail. On right are shown the phases of the moon, with inner circle indicating the moon in different positions in its orbit, with one-half of its surface illuminated by the sun; appearance of the moon as seen from the earth is shown outside. Lower sketches illustrate (top) an eclipse of the sun by the moon, and (bottom) an eclipse of the moon, when the moon enters the earth's shadow.*

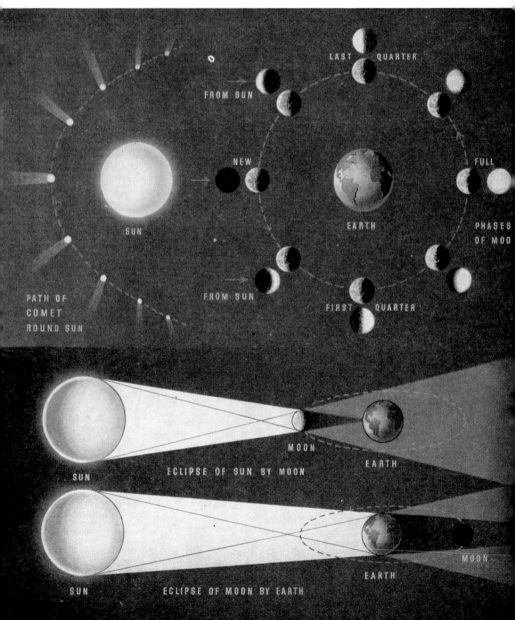

range from less than one mile to about 150 miles; their orbits lie between the orbits of Mars and Jupiter. They may be the fragments of a planet that has exploded or, on the other hand, a mass of material which failed to coalesce into a planet when the other planets were formed.

The other members of the solar system are comets and shooting stars or meteors. Comets are masses of loosely aggregated material, which move under the sun's attraction, generally in very elongated orbits. They are usually visible only in the portions of their path when they are near the sun (Fig. 13).

The characteristic feature of a comet is its tail (the word *comet* means a *hairy star*), which points away from the sun; it consists of very small dust particles, driven out from the nucleus of the comet by the pressure of the sun's radiation.

A bright comet, with a tail stretching far across the sky, is a spectacular object; it is not surprising that the appearance of a bright comet in the sky was formerly regarded as a portent of misfortune. The most famous of all comets is Halley's comet, which returns about every seventy-six years, and was last seen in 1910. Its returns have been traced back to the year 240 B.C. But the periods of revolution of most of the comets are so great that there is no record of any previous appearance.

The appearance of a shooting star is caused by a small pellet of matter entering the earth's atmosphere at a high speed (the velocity of the earth in its orbit is about nineteen miles a second), becoming intensely heated and then completely vaporized by friction in its passage through the atmosphere. The total number entering the atmosphere in twenty-four hours amounts to several millions.

Occasionally a larger mass is encountered, which does not become completely vaporized, and falls to the ground as a meteorite. Specimens of these meteorites may be seen in many museums. Sometimes a comet becomes disintegrated and the fragments scatter along its path; if the earth crosses the path of a disintegrated comet, a spectacular shower of shooting stars may be seen.

Origin of the Solar System

The solar system shows certain features of regularity. The sun, the planets and their satellites rotate in the same direction; the planets revolve around the sun in the same direction and so, also, with few exceptions, do the satellites around their parent planets. The orbits of the planets and satellites lie nearly in one plane.

These regularities prove conclusively that the solar system was not formed by chance, but that it must have had some definite origin. How it was formed is still a matter of considerable conjecture: it is thought probable that another star passed close to the sun and by its gravitational attraction drew matter out from the sun, which soon broke up and coalesced to form the planets.

Test Yourself

1. What changes in the appearance of the sky are caused: (*a*) by the rotation of the earth; (*b*) by the orbital motion of the earth?
2. Name the different classes of objects which can be seen in the sky with a large telescope.
3. What are the principal differences between a star and a planet?
4. What other movements has the earth besides rotation on its axis?
5. Do the stars differ more amongst themselves than the members of the human race and, if so, in what respects?
6. What is the cause of the appearance of the Milky Way?
7. Explain how eclipses of the sun and moon are caused.
8. The moon always turns the same face to the earth. What information can be inferred about its axial rotation?

Answers will be found at the end of the book.

PROBING A STAR'S CHEMICAL AND PHYSICAL COMPOSITION

Spectrograph attached to this "Yapp" telescope is a sensitive and delicate instrument, a kind of camera to photograph star spectra. In order to get the most accurate results, the glass prisms must be kept constantly at the same temperature, which is achieved by the casing being lined with felt and electrically heated, as shown in the picture.

CHAPTER III

APPLICATIONS OF ASTRONOMY

ASTRONOMY has practical applications in the determination of time; the fixing of positions on the earth, which forms the basis of mapping; and the determination of the position of a ship or aircraft for the purposes of navigation.

The rotation of the earth on its axis in the period of a day provides us with our fundamental unit of time. Because the rising and setting of the sun, with its alternation of light and darkness, regulates human activities, it is natural to fix the day by reference to the sun. We can then define noon or midday as the instant when the sun is due south.

As the earth makes one complete rotation, or turns through 360 deg., in twenty-four hours, it turns through 15 deg. in one hour or through 1 deg. in four minutes (Fig. 1).

Suppose the sun is on the meridian at Greenwich, so that it is noon at Greenwich; the earth is turning from west to east at the rate of 15 deg. per hour, so that one hour later a place in longitude 15 deg. west of Greenwich will have the sun on its meridian. It is, therefore, noon there, but at the same instant it is 1 p.m. at Greenwich.

Similarly, at a place in longitude 15 deg. east of Greenwich it will be noon when it is 11 a.m. at Greenwich. Thus, time is a local phenomenon; at the same instant, two places which are not on the same meridian have different local times.

It follows that at a place whose longitude is L (in degrees) east of Greenwich, the local time, corresponding to time T (in hours) at Greenwich, is $T + \frac{1}{15} L$. At a place whose longitude is L^1 (in degrees) west of Greenwich, the corresponding local time is $T - \frac{1}{15} L^1$ (Fig. 1).

The difference between the local times at the two places is, therefore, $\frac{1}{15} (L + L^1)$. But as their difference of longitude is $L + L^1$, this means that the difference in longitude is known if the difference in their local times is known. This is a result of great

importance in the determination of longitudes.

We can, if we please, reverse our ideas and think, as we usually do, of the earth being at rest and the sun describing its diurnal path across the sky. The sun is due south and it is local noon when the sun is on our meridian; one, two . . . hours previously the sun was on the meridians of places in longitudes 15 deg., 30 deg. . . . to the east of us; one, two . . . hours later, it will be on the meridians of places in longitudes 15 deg., 30 deg. . . . to the west of us. Therefore, the diurnal path of the sun across the sky can mark out for us the passage of the hours.

Measuring Time by Sundial

The sundial is a simple application of this principle. Imagine a series of planes, at angular intervals of 15 deg., to pass through the axis of rotation of the earth. The sun will cross these planes in succession at hourly intervals.

In the sundial there is a style or gnomon which is fixed parallel to the axis of the earth; the shadow of this style is thrown on to a base-plate, which is usually horizontal, but may also be vertical or in some intermediate position. The shadow marks the intersection of the plane through the earth's axis and the sun with the base-plate.

By taking planes 15 deg. apart, we can draw the lines corresponding to the positions of the shadow at hourly intervals; time at any instant can then be inferred from the position of the shadow of the style with respect to these hourly graduations (Fig. 2).

The time given by the sundial is *local true solar time*: local time because it is the time of the particular place where the sundial is set up; true solar time because it is determined by the true sun. But the time given by the sundial is not convenient for purposes of everyday life, because the days are not uniform in length, or, in other words, the

39

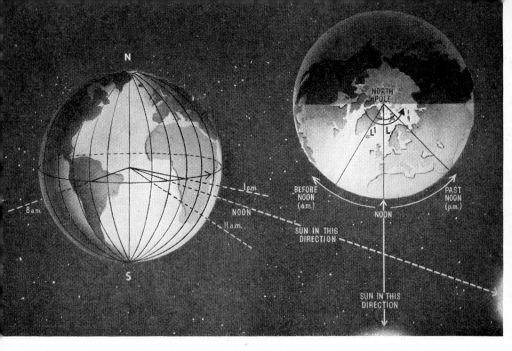

ROTATION OF THE EARTH PROVIDES A MEASURE OF TIME

FIG. 1. *At any place which has the sun on its meridian (due south), it is noon by true solar time; at places to the west it is before noon (a.m.), at places to the east it is after noon (p.m.). Time is a local phenomenon; at the same instant, different places have different times.*

interval from noon to the next noon varies throughout the year. The reason for this is twofold.

In the first place, the path of the earth around the sun is an ellipse, so that the distance of the earth from the sun changes gradually and there is a corresponding change in the rate of motion of the sun eastwards relative to the stars.

In the second place, the axis of rotation of the earth is not perpendicular to the plane of the earth's orbit; even if the orbit were circular, the apparent motion of the sun would on this account not be uniform.

Astronomers, therefore, conceive of a fictitious sun, which moves in a circular orbit at right angles to the earth's orbit; it coincides with the true sun at the spring equinox and completes a revolution in its orbit in the course of a year. The time defined by this fictitious sun is called *mean solar time*, because all the days are equal in length and equal to the mean or average of the true solar days.

The difference between true (or, as it is sometimes called, apparent) solar time and

mean solar time is called the *equation of time* (Fig. 3 (a)).

The value of the equation of time for each day of the year is given in *Whitaker's Almanack* and is sometimes marked on sundials. It must be subtracted from the sundial time to obtain the local mean solar time, or, more briefly, the local mean time. The local mean time at Greenwich is called Greenwich mean time (G.M.T.).

About the middle of February, the equation of time is nearly $-14\frac{1}{2}$ minutes; early in November it is nearly $+16\frac{1}{2}$ minutes. It thus has a range of almost 31 minutes in the course of a year.

There would be very great inconveniences if every place were to keep its own local time. Think, for instance, of the complications in the construction of railway time-tables or in listening to radio programmes. Therefore, in Great Britain, the legal time for the whole country is fixed by statute as the mean time for the meridian through the Royal Observatory, Greenwich (i.e. G.M.T.).

When correcting sundial time to obtain

G.M.T. at any place east or west of Greenwich, allowance must be made not only for the equation of time but for the difference in longitude. Penzance, for instance, is 5 deg. 33 min. west of Greenwich, and so twenty-two minutes must be added to the local mean time of Penzance to obtain G.M.T.

By international agreement, the whole world is divided into zones, 15 deg. in width, centred at longitude 0 deg. (Greenwich), 15 deg. east, 30 deg. east, . . . 15 deg. west, 30 deg. west. . . . In the central zone, Greenwich time is kept; in the zone centred at 15 deg. east (extending from $7\frac{1}{2}$ deg. east to $22\frac{1}{2}$ deg. east), the time is one hour fast on Greenwich; in the zone centred at 15 deg. west, it is one hour slow, and so on (Fig. 3 (b)).

There are certain exceptions: some countries, for instance, keep a time which is thirty minutes different from the proper zone time. Also, there are certain adjustments to suit local boundaries, and many countries advance their clocks one or two hours during the summer months.

Countries which cover a wide range of longitude, such as Canada, the United States or the U.S.S.R., cannot keep the same time throughout. These countries extend over several of the time zones and in passing from one zone to the next the time is changed by exactly one hour. The changes are noted in railway timetables and when journeying by train it is necessary to advance or retard one's watch when a different zone is entered.

Altering the Clock

Imagine a ship to be travelling eastward; the ship's clocks have to be progressively advanced and when approaching the meridian of 180 deg. they are twelve hours fast on G.M.T. A second ship travelling westward will have progressively put back its clocks until when approaching the meridian of 180 deg. they are twelve hours slow on G.M.T.

The meridian of 180 deg. east or west of Greenwich is called the *date line*; the first ship on crossing the date line will have to put its clocks back twenty-four hours, or, in other words, it must repeat a day; the second ship will have to advance its clocks twenty-four hours and, therefore, it misses a day. These changes compensate for

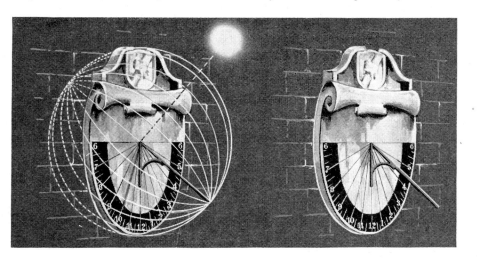

PRINCIPLE OF VERTICAL SUNDIAL ON SOUTH WALL

Fig. 2. *Imagine a sphere with its centre on the dial and its axis along the style. On this sphere are drawn the central meridian and meridians 15 deg., 30 deg., 45 deg., 60 deg., 75 deg. and 90 deg. to east and west. The planes through these meridians and the style intersect the vertical plane of the dial in the successive hourly graduations.*

the days in the first case having been shorter and in the second case having been longer than twenty-four hours. Though the repetition or missing of a day puzzles many travellers, there is nothing mysterious about it.

Sidereal Day

In the accurate determination of time, the sun is not a very convenient object to observe. It is much preferable to determine time by the stars. There are many stars but only one sun. Astronomers, therefore, define the day by means of the rotation of the earth relative to the stars. This *sidereal day* is slightly different in length from the solar day; it is the true period of the rotating earth on its axis.

Suppose we start from an instant when the sun and a particular star are both on the meridian; after one sidereal day, the star is again on the meridian, but as the earth has moved on in its orbit around the sun it has to turn a little farther before the sun is again on the meridian. The sidereal day is 3 min. 56 sec. shorter than the mean solar day; the year contains exactly one more sidereal day than mean solar days—$366\frac{1}{4}$ days instead of $365\frac{1}{4}$.

We could select a particular star and define the beginning of the sidereal day as the instant when this star is due south on the meridian. But in order to have a convenient means of converting sidereal time into mean solar time, the beginning is defined as the instant when an imaginary star, at a point in the sky where the sun is to be found at the instant of the spring equinox, is on the meridian.

Using the Star Observations

Now, suppose the positions relative to one another of a number of stars distributed around the sky have been determined. These can serve as the graduations of a clock face: as the heavens turn in their diurnal motion, the successive passages of each of these stars across the meridian determine instants of sidereal time (Fig. 3 (c)).

A telescope, termed a transit instrument, is used to determine with accuracy the times of transit; the telescope is supported by a horizontal axis, fixed in an east-west direction, so that the telescope can move in the meridian plane (*see* pages 44 and 45).

The telescope is pointed to the star to be observed, shortly before its time of meridian passage; as the earth carries the telescope with it in its rotation, the star appears as a point of light moving in a horizontal direction across the field of view of the telescope.

A number of vertical spider threads (called "wires") are fixed in the focal plane of the telescope and the time at which the star crosses each wire is recorded. For this purpose, the observer is provided with a precision clock, rated to keep sidereal time, and with an instrument called a chronograph, which is provided with a moving tape or drum, on which electric signals from the clock are recorded each second.

At the instant when the star crosses each wire, the observer presses a tapper, which closes an electric circuit and sends a signal to the chronograph. The times of each of these signals can be read off afterwards at convenience by interpolation between the adjacent clock signals.

Determining the Clock Error

In this way, the clock time of the meridian passage of the star is determined; but the true sidereal time of its passage is known. The error of the clock—how much it is fast or slow—is thus determined. The whole process of determining time reduces, in fact, merely to finding the error of the standard clock.

But it is not sufficient to know the error at a particular time: we also require to know at what rate this error is increasing or decreasing. The observations must, therefore, be repeated on a following night. Having found the error of the clock and its rate of change, the sidereal time at any instant can be obtained and this can be converted into mean solar time.

In practice, a second clock, rated as nearly as possible to mean time, is used and the error and rate of this clock are determined by comparison with the sidereal clock.

Time having been determined, for instance, at the Royal Observatory, Green-

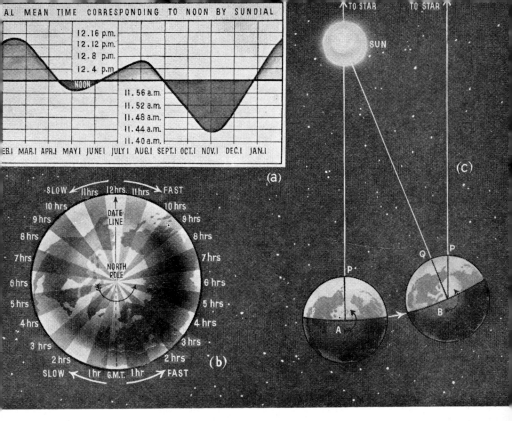

WHY TIME VARIES THROUGHOUT THE WORLD

FIG. 3. *(a) Uniform or mean time is not provided by a sundial. The diagram shows the local mean times corresponding to noon by sundial throughout the year. (b) For convenience in relating times at different places, the world is divided into twenty-four time zones, each extending over 15 deg. of longitude. The central zone keeps Greenwich mean time (G.M.T.). Successive zones to the east keep times 1 hour, 2 hours, and so on, fast on G.M.T.; those to the west keep slow on G.M.T. At the date line (180 deg. longitude) there is a discontinuity of twenty-four hours. (c) Sidereal time is determined from star observations. Sun and star are on meridian at P when centre of earth is at A. The star is again on meridian at P when centre of earth is at B. The sun is then on meridian of Q; the earth has to turn through angle PBQ before the sun is on meridian of P.*

wich, it must be made available to the public. Broadcasting provides a very convenient means of making time widely available. The B.B.C. sends out time signals, direct from Greenwich, several times daily on each of its programmes: the signals are in the form of six short dots or pips at second intervals, the last of which is the actual time signal and comes exactly at the hour (or half-hour or quarter-hour).

For those who want the correct time at any other instant during the day, the Post Office Speaking Clock can be called by telephone. This clock, controlled automatically by signals from Greenwich, announces the time at ten-second intervals.

We have mentioned that the difference in longitude of two places can be obtained from the difference in their local times. The local time at any place can be determined, as explained above; the radio time signals from Greenwich give Greenwich mean time. Hence, the longitude east or west of Greenwich can be derived.

When great accuracy is required, the time of transmission of the radio waves,

STAR AS IT APPEARS TO OBSERVER

TRANSIT

FIELD OF VIEW OF TRANSIT INSTRUMENT

REVERSIBLE TRANSIT CIRCLE

X

l

P

TO CELESTIAL POLE

p¹

l

Z

S
TO SUN

HORIZON AT 0

d

l

K

c

E

Y

FINDING LATITUDE BY ALTITUDE OF POLE STAR OR SUN

NORTH POLE OF CELESTIAL SPHE

STAR ON CELESTIAL SPHERE

DAYLIGHT LIGHTING PRISM

BUBBLE

INDEX MIRROR

FROM STAR

POSITION CIRCLE

NORTH OF EAR

BUBBLE LIGHTING LAMP

SECONDARY MIRROR

DEGREE DRUM

W

GEOGRAPHICAL POSITION OF STAR ON EARTH'S MERIDIAN

COLLIMATING LENS AND MIRROR

CLEAR GLASS MIRROR

PATH OF RAY FROM STAR

CELESTIAL   EQUATO

PRINCIPLE OF THE BUBBLE SEXTANT

MERIDIAN ON CELESTIAL SPHERE

SOUTH POL OF CELESTI SPHERE

EARTH AN CELESTIAL S

ASHWELL WOOD

NAVIGATION *by the* SUN *and* STARS

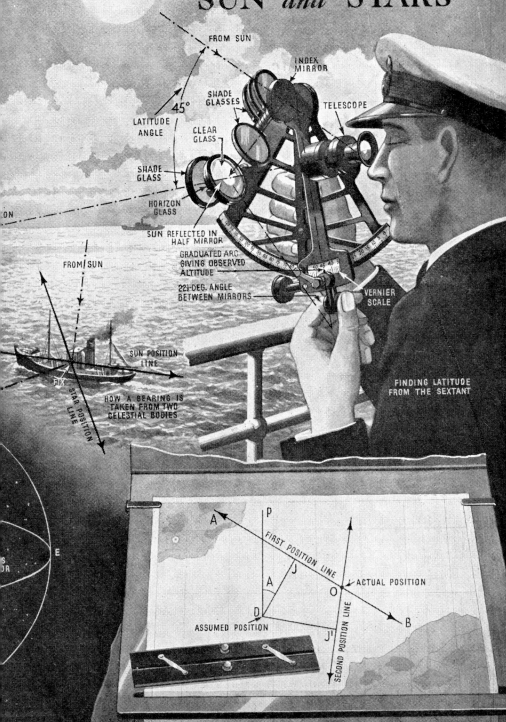

FROM SUN

INDEX MIRROR

SHADE GLASSES

TELESCOPE

45°

LATITUDE ANGLE

CLEAR GLASS

SHADE GLASS

HORIZON GLASS

SUN REFLECTED IN HALF MIRROR

GRADUATED ARC GIVING OBSERVED ALTITUDE

22½-DEG. ANGLE BETWEEN MIRRORS

VERNIER SCALE

FINDING LATITUDE FROM THE SEXTANT

FROM SUN

SUN POSITION LINE

FIX

STAR POSITION LINE

HOW A BEARING IS TAKEN FROM TWO CELESTIAL BODIES

P

A

FIRST POSITION LINE

J

A

ACTUAL POSITION

O

D

ASSUMED POSITION

J¹

SECOND POSITION LINE

B

FIXING POSITION ON CHART

which travel with the speed of light, must be allowed for. Before the days of wireless, the determination of longitude was a more complicated business, but we need not trouble to discuss methods which have now been superseded.

Parallels of Latitude

The determination of the latitude of a place is simpler than the determination of its longitude. In the sketch on pages 44 and 45, C denotes the centre of the earth, P its north pole, O a place on its surface, XOY the horizon at O. E is the point where the meridian through O meets the equator. The angle ECO is then the latitude of O, which we denote by l.

The celestial pole is seen from O in the direction OP^1, parallel to CP, because its distance can be taken as infinitely great. The altitude of the pole above the horizon at O is the angle P^1OX, which is equal to the angle OXC. But this angle is equal to the latitude l, because the addition of the angle OCP to each of them makes a right angle. Hence, we have the result that the altitude of the pole is equal to the latitude; at the north pole, the celestial pole is vertically overhead; at the equator, it is on the horizon.

Polaris is about 1 deg. from the true celestial pole. The observation of the altitude of Polaris therefore gives the latitude of a place with an error not

PRINCIPLE OF THE SEXTANT

FIG. 5. *Use of the sextant for measuring the altitude of the sun by observing, first, the horizon and then the sun. The appearance as seen in the telescope viewing mirror A, when the sextant is correctly set for each observation, is shown in the two small diagrams.*

exceeding a degree. The Pole Star table in *Whitaker's Almanack* provides a means for correcting the observation for the distance of Polaris from the pole.

The altitude may be found with a transit circle, which is a transit instrument provided with a graduated circle, whereby the angle at which the telescope is set can be read off; or it may be determined by observation with a sextant.

In the daytime, Polaris cannot be seen and it is convenient to use the sun. Suppose S is the direction towards the sun when on the meridian, let SO meet CE in K. Denote the angle SKE by d; this is the angular distance of the sun north of the equator, and is called its declination. Then the angular distance of the sun from the zenith is the angle SOZ, which is equal to the angle $COK =$ angle $OCY -$ angle $OKY = l - d$.

The altitude of the sun (SOY) when on the meridian is the complement of this angle, or (90 deg. $- l + d$). The value of d is given for each day of the year in *Whitaker's Almanack*; hence, by measuring the meridian altitude of the sun (which is its *maximum altitude*) we can deduce the latitude.

Instead of the sun we can use any convenient bright star, d then being the declination of the star. The declinations of the principal fixed stars are given in *Whitaker's Almanack*.

Positioning a Ship or Aircraft

In order to determine the position of a ship at sea or of an aircraft in flight, some modification of these methods is needed. All astronomical observations at sea or in the air are made by means of a sextant, which enables the altitude of the sun, the moon, a planet or a star to be observed. Fig. 5 shows the principle of the sextant.

The sextant carries two mirrors: *A*, which is fixed, and *B*, which can be rotated by a movable arm. Half of the mirror *A* is clear, the other half is silvered. When *A* and *B* are parallel and the instrument is turned to the horizon, the eye *E*, viewing through a low-powered telescope, sees the horizon partly direct, through the clear half of *A*, and partly by reflection from

B and from the silvered half of *A*. By turning the mirror *B*, it is possible to bring the image of the sun or of a star into coincidence with the horizon seen through the clear portion of *A*.

Advantages of the Sextant

It can be shown that the angle through which the mirror *B* is turned to secure this coincidence is half the altitude of the sun or star above the horizon; this altitude is read directly from the graduated arc of the sextant. The advantages of the sextant are that it is light and compact, easy to hold in the hand, and convenient on a moving ship for observing. A special sextant called a bubble sextant is used in aircraft, where a clear horizon is not usually visible; a small bubble is used instead of the horizon and the image of the sun or star is brought to the centre of the bubble.

What information is obtained by an observation of the altitude of a celestial body, the sun, moon, a planet or a star? The ship or aircraft carries a chronometer or watch which gives Greenwich mean time. The navigator is also provided with the *Nautical Almanac*, from which the position of the celestial body at that instant of G.M.T. can be derived.

Referring to Fig. 6, we will suppose that a star is our chosen body, and the observer is in the position indicated. The angle formed by the star, observer and Z is the angular distance of the star from the observer's zenith, which is the complement of the observed altitude, and is, therefore, known. Now, suppose we rotate the triangle made by the centre of the earth, the star and the observer about its base (star and centre of earth). The point of the observer's position will describe a circle on the surface of the earth, and it is obvious from considerations of symmetry that the angular distance of the star from the zenith at any point on this circle will be equal to the angle made by the star, observer and Z. Thus, the observation of the altitude of the star tells us that at that instant the ship or aircraft was at some point on this circle.

If the altitude of another body, star number two in the lower diagram (Fig. 6),

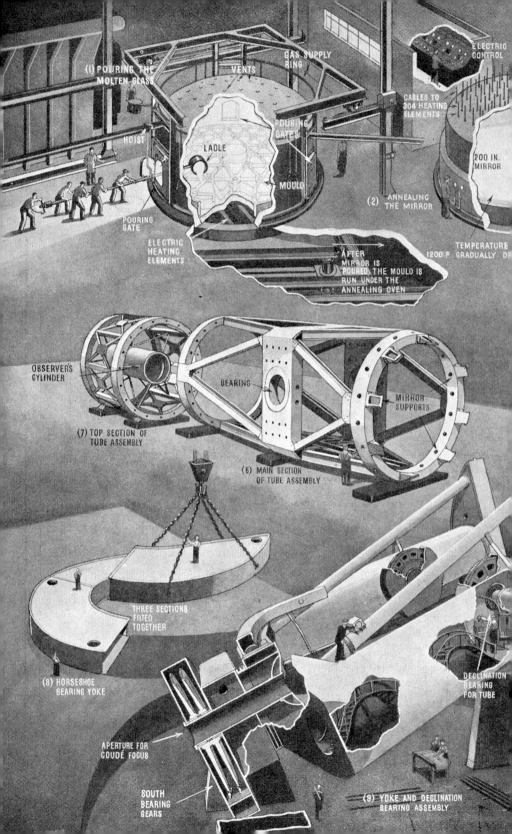

(1) POURING THE MOLTEN GLASS

VENTS

GAS SUPPLY RING

ELECTRIC CONTROL

HOIST

POURING GATES

LADLE

CABLES TO 304 HEATING ELEMENTS

200 IN. MIRROR

MOULD

POURING GATE

(2) ANNEALING THE MIRROR

ELECTRIC HEATING ELEMENTS

AFTER MIRROR IS POURED, THE MOULD IS RUN UNDER THE ANNEALING OVEN

TEMPERATURE GRADUALLY DR
1200 F

OBSERVER'S CYLINDER

BEARING

MIRROR SUPPORTS

(7) TOP SECTION OF TUBE ASSEMBLY

(6) MAIN SECTION OF TUBE ASSEMBLY

THREE SECTIONS FITTED TOGETHER

(8) HORSESHOE BEARING YOKE

DECLINATION BEARING FOR TUBE

APERTURE FOR COUDÉ FOCUS

SOUTH BEARING GEARS

(9) YOKE AND DECLINATION BEARING ASSEMBLY

Making the World's
LARGEST TELESCOPE

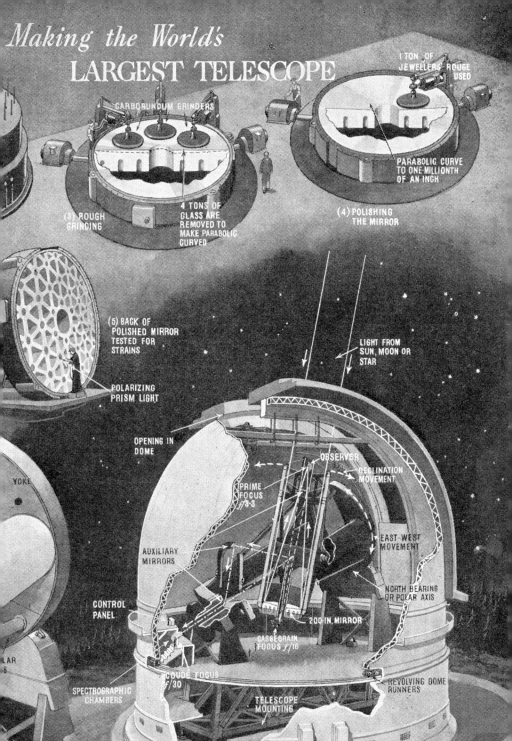

1 TON OF JEWELERS ROUGE USED

CARBORUNDUM GRINDERS

PARABOLIC CURVE TO ONE-MILLIONTH OF AN INCH

(3) ROUGH GRINDING

4 TONS OF GLASS ARE REMOVED TO MAKE PARABOLIC CURVED

(4) POLISHING THE MIRROR

(5) BACK OF POLISHED MIRROR TESTED FOR STRAINS

POLARIZING PRISM LIGHT

LIGHT FROM SUN, MOON OR STAR

OPENING IN DOME

OBSERVER

DECLINATION MOVEMENT

PRIME FOCUS f/3·3

EAST-WEST MOVEMENT

AUXILIARY MIRRORS

YOKE

NORTH BEARING OR POLAR AXIS

CONTROL PANEL

200-IN. MIRROR

CASSEGRAIN FOCUS f/16

COUDE FOCUS f/30

REVOLVING DOME RUNNERS

SPECTROGRAPHIC CHAMBERS

TELESCOPE MOUNTING

POLAR S

(10) SECTION OF COMPLETE 200-IN. TELESCOPE, MOUNTING AND OBSERVATORY, MOUNT PALOMAR, CALIFORNIA, U.S.A.

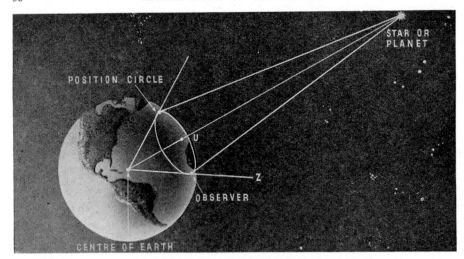

FIXING POSITION BY OBSERVATION OF STARS

FIG. 6. *(Top) Observation of a celestial body with a sextant determines its altitude (angular distance above horizon). The altitude has the same value at all points on the position circle; the line joining the centre of the earth to the celestial body passes through the centre of this circle. A single sextant observation, therefore, places the observer somewhere on this circle. (Bottom) The observation of two celestial bodies provides the information that the observer is on each of two position circles. He must, therefore, be at one or other of the two points of intersection.*

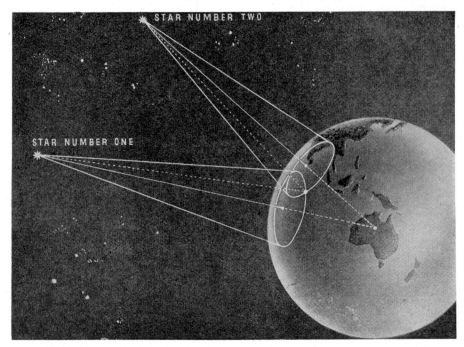

were observed at the same instant, we should know that the ship or aircraft was at some point on a second circle. Two circles intersect in two points; the two points will usually be a few thousand miles apart and it will be known that the ship or aircraft is somewhere near one of the points of intersection. It must, therefore, be at that point of intersection: its position at the moment of observation is, therefore, determined.

Navigator's Position Line

The navigator is concerned only with the portions of these circles near his actual position, which he wants to draw upon his chart. As the circles have radii of hundreds or thousands of miles, the small portion he is concerned with can be considered as a straight line; he calls this a *position line*, because it tells him that his position is somewhere on this line.

A simple dodge is used to draw the line on the chart. The navigator takes an assumed position for his ship or aircraft, which can be any convenient position where he estimates that he is. He can obtain, either by calculation or by the use of suitable tables, what the altitude of the star would have been from this position at the time of his observation. The difference between the observed altitude and this computed altitude gives him his distance from the true position line. The direction of the position line is at right angles to the direction OU, connecting the point of observation with the point U on the earth's surface which has the star in its zenith at the time of observation.

He can also calculate in a similar way (which need not be explained) the bearing of U from the observer. Suppose that D represents on his chart the assumed position at the time of observation, DP the north direction on the chart, and DJ a line drawn with the appropriate bearing A. The distance DJ is equal to the computed distance of the position line from D, so that he can mark the point J on his chart, and then a line AJB drawn through J at right angles to AJ is the required position line.

If a second position line, through the appropriate point J^1, intersects the first line in O, this is his position at the time of observation. It is not, of course, possible to observe two different objects simultaneously; but the navigator may observe star number one first, then observe star number two, and then repeat the observation of the first star so that the mean of the times of the observations of star number one agrees with the time of the observation of star number two.

If, however, he does not wish to repeat the observation of the first star, he can transfer his first position line to correspond with the line of observation of star number two; the direction of the ship or aircraft and its speed are known pretty accurately, so the navigator has merely to shift the first line parallel to itself by an amount corresponding to the distance travelled by ship or aircraft between two observations.

Test Yourself

1. The longitude of Moscow is 37 deg. 37 min. east; the longitude of Washington is 77 deg. 4 min. west. What is the difference in their local times?
2. A sundial is set up in Penzance; it is desired to obtain G.M.T. from the sundial. What corrections have to be applied?
3. What is the date line and why is a date line needed?
4. Explain why the sidereal day is shorter than the mean solar day. Calculate their difference in length.
5. Describe how the longitude and latitude of a place on the earth can be determined.
6. Explain the general principles by which the position of a ship or aircraft can be found by astronomical observations.

Answers will be found at the end of the book.

SPECTACULAR DEMONSTRATION OF NATURAL LAWS

Ascent of this 12-ton rocket missile is due to its reaction to the downward ejection of gases. The pull of gravity is overcome and the rocket reaches an upward speed of 3000 miles per hour, before its fuel is spent and gravity slows it down and brings it back to earth

CHAPTER IV

MATTER AND MOTION

OUR ideas of matter and force arose in the beginning from our sense of touch. It is easy then to understand that we can define as matter any object which, on being felt, is found to possess appreciable size and to offer resistance to being compressed. For example, when one touches objects such as chairs and tables on the theatre stage, they are found to consist of matter, whereas those on the cinema screen, despite the optical illusion, are shown to be unreal when the same test is applied.

The notion of force likewise arose from the sensation produced in our muscles. A direct illustration of this can be obtained with trial-of-strength machines on which we measure our maximum strength. But when the quantity of matter to be examined, or the force to be measured, becomes too small to be perceptible, or overwhelmingly greater than that of the strongest man, scientific machines are invented to extend the range of measurement.

Scientific progress has been so immense that those minute portions of matter known as atoms, which weigh less than a billionth part of an ounce, can be measured with great accuracy.

At the other extreme, the size and mass of the earth, and even of the entire universe, can be estimated.

Now, if a portion of matter is initially at rest and it is then subjected to a force, the motion of the matter which results depends on the quantity of that matter and the magnitude of the force.

It took several hundreds of years to establish the precise laws governing the connexion between matter, force and motion. The celebrated experiment of Galileo at the leaning tower of Pisa was a landmark in this field of work. With the aid of cannon balls of different weights, he showed that, contrary to the teaching of three thousand years, different weights all took the same time to reach the ground. Referring to Fig. 1 (b), we can easily prove Galileo's result by dropping a penny and a small flat piece of paper, considerably smaller than the penny, simultaneously from the same height. Because of air resistance, the paper takes longer to reach the ground. If, however, the piece of paper is placed on the penny and the two are gently released together, the paper, in spite of its much smaller weight, will fall to the ground as fast as the penny.

Newton's Laws of Motion

The final summary of the earlier work was achieved by Newton, who stated the famous Three Laws of Motion. Physics is sometimes defined as the science of matter and motion and, as Newton's laws form the basis of Classical Physics, we must examine them in some detail.

The First Law states: "*Every object continues in its state of rest or of uniform motion in a straight line except in so far as it is compelled to change that state by external forces.*"

The first part of the law might seem to be obvious until one considers some modern form of movement such as rocket propulsion, where the object may start from rest without the application of an external force. Further consideration, however, shows us that the motion of the rocket is produced only at the expense of its own weight, for the fuel is continually being consumed. Nevertheless, it might be better to substitute "every unchanged object" for "every object" in the first law.

The truth of the second part of the law, that of straight-line motion, is much less easy to demonstrate in common experience. An object which is gently released from a vehicle which is moving with a steady speed, in a straight horizontal line, does not continue on the same course. Instead, it traverses a swift, downward, curved path with ever-increasing velocity until it strikes the ground, as shown in Fig. 1 (a). We explain this by saying that the object is acted on by external forces, namely, the pull of the earth, which we call gravity, and also by a slight frictional air resistance. Perhaps the simplest evidence for the law is provided by the path of a smooth flat stone projected across a smooth, horizontal sheet of ice. Unless the stone meets any irregularities, its path is a straight line. Of course, the velocity gradually decreases owing to the slight frictional resistance which is present, but it does not make great demands on the belief of the experimenter to infer that, could the friction be eliminated, the stone would continue to move for ever over the ice with its original speed.

Perpetual Motion

The revolution in thought which this law achieved was that it changed the idea, "What keeps an object moving?", into "Once moving, why should not an object continue to do so, unless there is some external force to stop it or to change its direction?"

Before stating Newton's Second Law of Motion, we must note the fundamental distinction between the mass and the weight of an object. Let us suppose that a weight is hung on a spring balance and that the balance pointer reads 1 lb. If we now proceeded into the interior of the earth, for example, by descending a mine, we should find that the reading on the balance became progressively less. If we were able to carry out the experiment at ever-increasing depths, as shown in Fig. 2 (a), we should find that at the centre of the earth the balance would read zero.

The weight of an object, therefore, varies: and it does so because of the variation of the gravitational attraction of the earth. As this attraction steadily diminishes as we descend into the earth's interior, and vanishes altogether at the centre, the decrease in weight is easily understood.

Suppose now that in our fanciful region

HOW THE EFFECT OF GRAVITY IS VARIED BY OTHER FORCES

FIG. 1. *(a) Heavy object dropped from a car moving with uniform velocity in a straight line traverses a curved path. (b) Piece of paper, shielded from air resistance by resting on a penny, falls as fast as the penny; they reach the ground together when released.*

(b)

SIMPLE TEST OF THE LAW OF GRAVITY

(a)

OBJECT CONTINUES TO MOVE FORWARD WHILE FALLING

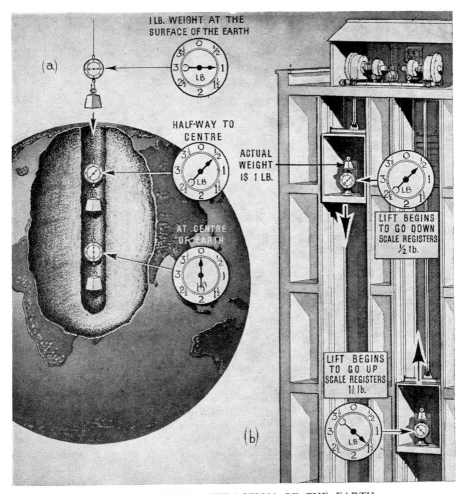

GRAVITATIONAL ATTRACTION OF THE EARTH

FIG. 2. *(a) An object weighing 1 lb. at the surface of the earth weighs only ½ lb. if situated half-way towards the centre of the earth; it weighs nothing at all if it is actually at the centre. (b) An object, such as a 1 lb. weight, registers more than 1 lb. on the dial of a spring balance when the lift starts to ascend, whereas it reads less than 1 lb. if lift starts to descend*

at the centre of the earth we had a sheet of ice. We should still find that a stone required the same force to move it as at ground level, if it is to traverse the ice with the same velocity. This inertia, which has to be overcome to cause any object to move, is, therefore, the same for the object under any conditions and it is termed the mass of the body.

Confusion sometimes arises because mass and weight are often expressed in the same units. This mistake need not arise if we realize that a given object may have a mass of 10 lb. and a weight of 10 lb. at the earth's surface, whereas the same object would still have a mass of 10 lb. at the centre of the earth, although its weight would disappear.

A more practical experiment, which shows the variable nature of weight, is

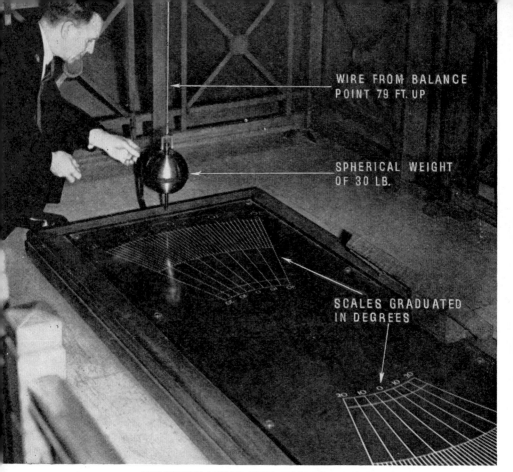

WIRE FROM BALANCE
POINT 79 FT. UP

SPHERICAL WEIGHT
OF 30 LB.

SCALES GRADUATED
IN DEGREES

DEMONSTRATING THE EARTH'S MOVEMENT

This pendulum, in the Science Museum, South Kensington, London, consists of a spherical weight suspended from a balance point. By its changing position above a graduated scale engraved on the floor, it visually demonstrates the movement of the earth about its axis.

provided by taking a small spring balance carrying a weight into a rapidly accelerating lift such as exists in some large departmental stores. It will be found that when the lift starts dropping rapidly, the registered weight is considerably less than its ordinary value and, on the other hand, when the lift suddenly rises, the registered weight is greater than its rest value.

These effects, which are illustrated in Fig. 2 (b), can be noticed from observations on our own bodies. When the lift rises suddenly, we can feel by our pressure on the floor of the lift that we have suddenly "put on weight." Owing to physiological disturbances which frequently accompany

travel in lifts, it is more exact and scientific to refer to the spring balance.

Now, supposing a stone which is moving freely over the surface of a sheet of ice with a uniform velocity is suddenly subjected to a force acting at right angles to its path. For example, as the stone passed a given position it might be given a sharp sideways tap with a hammer. What determines the amount of deflection of the path of the stone from its original direction?

Experiment shows that, provided the hammer tap always exerts the same force, a slow-moving stone of large mass can be deflected to the same extent as a fast-moving stone of small mass. Therefore, the amount of the deflection depends on both the mass and the velocity of the body. This quantity, the result of multiplying the mass by the velocity, is termed the momentum of the body, and Newton's Second Law of Motion states: *"The rate of change of the momentum is proportional to the impressed force and takes place in the direction in which that force acts."* We should, perhaps, again emphasize that, as in the First Law, the body must remain unchanged for the law to apply. This means that the force should not be so great as to splinter the stone, nor should it cause the stone to spin.

Incidentally, if the experiment is repeated several times, it will be found that a spin will always be imparted to the stone unless the direction of swing of the hammer passes through a certain point of the stone called its centre of gravity.

Newton's Third Law of Motion states: *"Action and reaction are equal and opposite."*

This may be illustrated by considering the projection of the shell from a gun resting on a smooth sheet of ice. When the shell is fired, a reaction acts on the gun and it will recoil. If we measured the masses of the shell and the gun and the velocity of projection of the shell and of recoil of the gun, we should find that the momentum of projection of the shell was exactly equal to the momentum of recoil of the gun.

This is sometimes known as the Law of the Conservation of Momentum and it follows directly from Newton's Third Law of Motion.

Calculating the Work Done

Another quantity of importance in matter and motion is Work. Scientifically defined, a force is said to do work when its point of application moves in the direction of the force, and the work done is measured by multiplying the force by the distance through which it moves. Thus, if a weight of 1 lb. is raised a distance of 1 ft., the work done on the weight is 1 ft.-lb. Conversely, if the same

MACHINE FOR DISINTEGRATING MATTER
Matter is characterized by gravitational properties and also its indestructibility under normal conditions. This American atom-smasher is used for the disintegration of nuclei.

weight is allowed to descend the same distance, the weight does 1 ft.-lb. of work.

It is the product distance times weight which determines the work done; it will, therefore, be the same when a weight of 2 lb. descends 6 in. as when ½ lb. descends 2 ft.

Finally, suppose we consider a bullet striking a thick target. The bullet penetrates a certain distance, exerting a force on the target, and it is eventually brought to rest. The work done by the bullet is the product of the force times the distance of penetration. The amount of the penetration will depend on the speed of the bullet, while the force it exerts will depend on its mass.

Experiment shows that the total work done is equal to one-half of the product of the mass and the square of the velocity. This product quantity is called the kinetic energy of the body and, quite generally, the definition of Energy is: "The capacity to do work." It is measured by finding the amount of work done and can be expressed in ft.-lb.

Suppose now that a stone is thrown straight upwards. It starts with a given kinetic energy, but it will gradually slow down until it comes to rest at its highest point. On returning to its starting point, neglecting air resistance, it will be found to have the same kinetic energy as when it started. The kinetic energy is, therefore, recoverable and we explain this by saying that since the return of the kinetic energy depends, in this instance, upon the fall of the stone from its highest point, that energy was present at its highest point, although it was, of course, latent or hidden.

Such hidden energy which depends on the position of a body is termed potential energy and we see that the kinetic energy of projection was gradually converted into potential energy, while this, in turn, was reconverted into kinetic energy as the body returned to its point of projection.

In all physical phenomena, the disappearance of energy in one form is accompanied by its reappearance in another form and no energy is lost in the conversion process. Energy is, therefore, never destroyed but merely changes from one form

into another. This is termed the Law of Conservation of Energy.

When a bullet strikes a target, its kinetic energy is destroyed, but the energy only changes into frictional heat energy, which may even be sufficient to melt the bullet. It would be difficult to reconvert this particular example of heat energy back into kinetic energy, but the operation of any steam engine is an illustration of the conversion of heat energy into mechanical energy.

In addition to the above forms, energy exists as light, sound, chemical energy, electricity, magnetism, vibration, strain and subatomic energy.

Perpetual-motion Machines

Before the laws of motion were established and the law of the conservation of energy had been verified by innumerable experiments, many attempts were made to construct perpetual-motion machines. These machines were designed to run continuously without any external supply of power and even to act as inexhaustible power supplies themselves.

One of these machines is illustrated in Fig. 3. It consists of a wheel balanced on a horizontal axle and composed of a rim together with several symmetrically placed curved spokes. Both spokes and rim were heavily grooved so that cannon balls would roll around the inside of the rim and along the spokes.

If we presume that the wheel is revolving in an anti-clockwise direction and consider the behaviour of the cannon balls in the various compartments, the argument for perpetual motion runs as follows. The cannon ball in A will roll down to the rim and, striking it with force, will exert a maximum leverage about the axle. In a compartment such as B, the cannon ball will return to the axle more or less radially and thus little leverage force will be produced when it comes to rest. Hence, a resultant leverage will be produced on the left-hand side of the wheel and it will continue to revolve indefinitely.

By the application of the conservation of energy, however, we see that as much potential energy will be destroyed by the weights descending on one side of the

FIG. 3. *Early attempt to construct a perpetual-motion machine.*

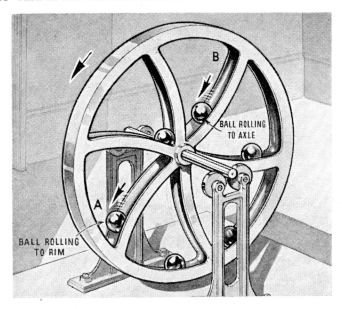

wheel as will be produced by the ascending weights on the other side. Hence, no balance of energy will remain to be converted into kinetic energy of rotation of the wheel.

Consequently, even if the wheel is initially set in motion by an external force, since this kinetic energy will eventually all be converted into heat energy by the inevitable friction at the axle bearings, the wheel will ultimately stop.

Apart from energy considerations, careful examination by the reader of the action and reaction set up throughout the entire wheel by the impact of the balls should convince him that no resultant motion can be produced in this manner. As a hint, we may mention that the problem is similar to that of the inability of anyone to raise himself by an upward pull on his own bootlaces.

In contrast to the perpetual-motion machine, which is doomed to fail in its object, we now describe some machines which serve useful mechanical purposes.

Mechanical Advantage

If we have a weight of 100 lb. and a cord which will sustain a pull of only 50 lb. without breaking, we can just suspend the weight by using two pieces of cord as shown in Fig. 4 (a), for each cord will take half the weight. By passing a somewhat stronger cord over two pulleys as shown in Fig. 4 (b), we also notice that a pull of only slightly greater than 50 lb. is required to raise the 100-lb. weight.

This arrangement of pulleys constitutes a simple machine and the ratio of the load lifted to the pull applied is termed the mechanical advantage of the machine. In the example given, the mechanical advantage is two, but by increasing the number of pulleys in the upper and lower pulley-blocks and taking the cord round and round them, the number of supporting strings becomes greater and greater. Consequently, the pull required to lift the load becomes progressively less and the mechanical advantage increases.

It is important to realize, however, that when the cord is pulled, the distance which the load moves upwards is, with two pulleys, only one-half the distance through which the end of the cord is pulled, in agreement with the conservation of energy. For example, the pull of 50 lb. must descend 2 ft. for every foot the 100 lb. rises. Hence, there is no net gain in the potential energy of the system.

The gain which the system achieves is, therefore, solely that of moving a large force with a smaller force, that is a mechanical advantage but not an increase in the total energy of the system.

Another simple machine is the inclined plane, as shown in Fig 5 (a). The load to be moved lies on the smooth plane and the pull is applied vertically. Suppose the plane is of such an inclination that every

2 ft. up the plane corresponds to a rise of 1 ft. in the vertical. Then a weight of 100 lb. on the plane will be moved by a downward vertical pull of just greater than 50 lb.

It is probable that the Egyptians made use of the inclined plane to elevate the large blocks of stone to the summits of the Pyramids, for no forces available at the time would seem to have been sufficient to raise these blocks directly.

Raising a Car

A car jack is another simple machine with high mechanical advantage which enables the weight of a car to be lifted by a single person. The basis of its operation is the use of a screw which can be regarded as an inclined plane wrapped round a vertical cylinder, as shown in Fig. 5 (b). One complete rotation of the screw raises the load resting on the jack by only the

small amount of the pitch of the screw but, by repeating the process several times, the car is eventually raised the desired distance.

By the conservation of energy, as much work will be done in raising the large weight of the car through the small distance of the pitch of the screw, as by the operator in moving the small force of his arm applied to the jack lever through the relatively large distance which this lever has to be moved in each rotation. Owing to the inevitable losses by friction in all machines, the work done by the operator must always slightly exceed the gain in potential energy of the load.

Rotation, or movement in a circle, is perhaps of even greater practical importance than movement in a straight line. One form of motion can, of course, easily be converted into the other by means of a crankshaft, as shown in Fig. 6. The laws of motion already deduced also apply to

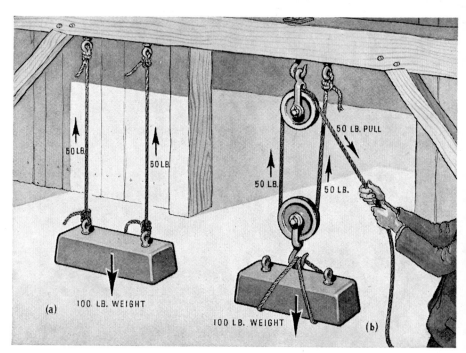

ILLUSTRATING THE PRINCIPLE OF THE PULLEY-BLOCK

FIG. 4. *(a) Two small ropes, each capable of sustaining only a 50-lb. pull, arranged so that they support a weight of 100 lb. between them. (b) Showing a simple arrangement of pulleys by which a pull, slightly greater than 50 lb., raises a weight of 100 lb.*

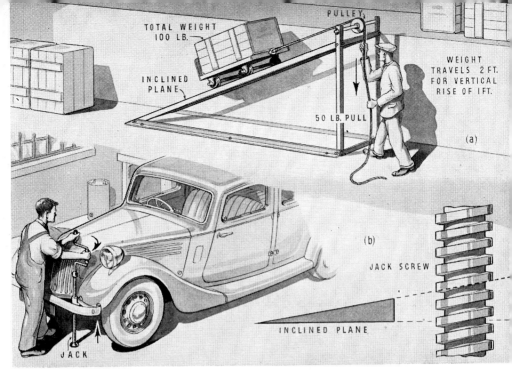

MECHANICAL ADVANTAGE OF AN INCLINED PLANE

FIG. 5. *(a) Inclined plane enables a man to raise several times the load he could raise unaided. (b) Car jack is an inclined plane wound in a spiral around a cylindrical rod.*

rotation, but certain modifications which we shall now describe are of special interest.

Since, according to Newton's First Law, every object moves automatically in a straight line in the absence of external forces, it follows that a body will follow a curved path only if there is present a force which causes it to deviate. In particular, a circular path requires a deflecting force continually directed towards the centre of the circle; otherwise the object will fly off at a tangent, that is, start to move in a straight line once more.

Let us consider a few common examples. You can move steadily on a straight moving escalator without it being necessary for you to cling to any support, but if you are seated on a joy-wheel at a fair you must cling tightly to the surface of the wheel if you are to remain on the wheel. As the speed of the wheel increases, the force, termed the centrifugal force, which is tending to fling you off, also increases. An experienced rider knows that his best chance of survival on the joy-wheel is to get to the centre, for the centrifugal force

decreases as the distance of the body from the axis of rotation decreases.

In rotational motion, therefore, besides the mass, the force and the velocity of the object being important quantities, the distance from the axis of rotation is a further factor which governs the motion of the object.

Factors Influencing Rotational Movement

Suppose now that we have a flywheel fitted with pegs at regular intervals along a radius of the wheel, as shown in Fig. 7, and that we hang a weight on one of these pegs. We should find that the rotation imparted to the wheel is greater and greater according as the selected peg lies farther and farther from the axle. The amount of rotational movement produced by a given force, therefore, depends not only on the magnitude of the force but also on its distance of application from the axis of rotation. This forms, of course, the basis of any system of leverage.

Experiment shows that the amount of rotation produced is dependent on the

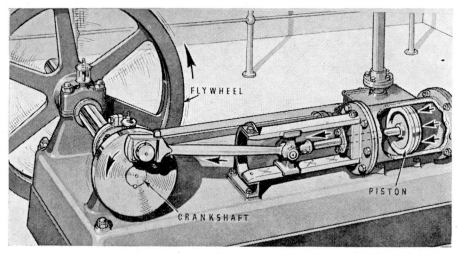

CHANGING LINEAR MOTION TO CIRCULAR MOTION

FIG. 6. *How one form of motion can be readily transformed to another form is illustrated here. The movement of a crankshaft and flywheel by means of a piston, and vice versa.*

product of the force times the perpendicular distance of the line of action of the force from the axis of rotation, and this quantity is termed the applied couple. It is quite distinct from the work done, which is also a force times a distance, for with work the force and distance are in the same direction, whereas with a couple they are at right angles.

Now, suppose we have two flywheels

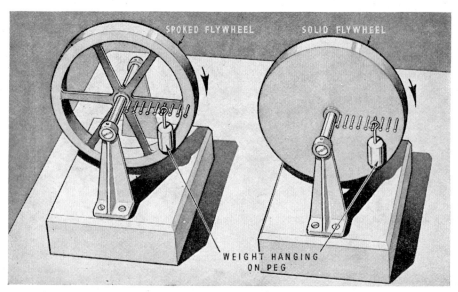

SPEED OF ROTATION IS INFLUENCED BY PATTERN OF WHEEL

FIG. 7. *Weights of the same size, if similarly placed on two flywheels of equal mass, will cause them to rotate with different speeds if the wheels are of unlike pattern.*

of exactly the same mass. One is solid and the other is spoked, but the one with spokes makes up for the lack of material between its spokes by extra weight in the rim of the wheel, as shown in Fig. 7. Will both wheels show the same rotation (for they have the same mass) if the same weight is hung the same distance from the axle in both cases?

Experiment shows that the solid wheel will rotate more rapidly than the spoked wheel. The speed of rotation, therefore, that the angular momentum imparted to a system depends on its moment of inertia about the axis of rotation, and is directly proportional to the applied couple.

We have seen by the experiment with the projected shell and the recoiling gun that linear momentum is conserved in rectilinear motion. An exactly similar law is true with angular momentum, and the result of this law has many applications in everyday life.

Suppose a prisoner, as shown in Fig. 8,

DEMONSTRATING THE LAW OF CONSERVATION OF ANGULAR MOMENTUM

FIG. 8. *Prisoner throws his arms outwards and away from the reader. His legs and body then twist towards the reader, and this twist is maintained if he now draws in his arms radially. Operation can be repeated indefinitely to produce any degree of rotation.*

depends not only upon the mass of the object but also upon the way in which this mass is distributed about the axis of rotation. These two factors combined are called the moment of inertia of the wheel about the axis of rotation.

Angular Momentum Defined

Finally, it is usual to speak of the angular velocity rather than the speed of rotation of an object, and just as the product of linear velocity and mass is termed linear momentum, so the product of the moment of inertia and the angular velocity of rotation is termed the angular momentum of a system. Summarizing the foregoing in more precise language, we say

were bound hand and foot and seated on a revolving stool facing a wall, and that it was imperative that he should turn round completely so that he could see, through a small aperture at the end of the room, what plans his captors were engaged upon. How could he effect the rotation? He could do so by applying the law of the conservation of angular momentum.

His initial angular momentum on the stool is zero; hence, by the law it will remain zero as a whole whatever he does, but it is just this fact that will enable him to rotate if he follows the correct procedure. He flings out his handcuffed arms away from his body not only radially but with a sideways movement. This gives an angular

LAWS - *The bases of* SCIENTIFIC INVESTIGATION

RIVER

GENERATOR

PENSTOCK

TURBINE

GATES

1 GRAVITATION

TAIL WATER

② CONSERVATION OF MATTER (PHYSICS)

ALL MATTER IS FOUND IN O OF THREE STATES—SOLID, LIQ OR GASEOUS. FOR EXAMPLE, W IS SHOWN HERE IN ALL THRE BUT THE MOLECULES ARE TH SAME

JET PROPULSION

FORWARD ACTION

BACKWARD REACTION

REACTION TURBINE

AIR INTAKE

④ EQUAL AND OPPOSITE LAW (ACTION AND REACTION)

GUN RECOILS IN OPPOSITE DIRECTION

FORWARD ACTION

RECOIL BACKWARD REACTION

STRAIGHT LIN ASSERTS ITSE

⑤ STRAIGHT LINE OR CENTRIFUGAL FORCE

CENTRIFUGAL CLOTHES-DRIER

MOTO

WATER IS FORCED OUT TANGENTIALLY (STRAIGHT LINE) BY REVOLVING BASK

L ASHWELL WOOD

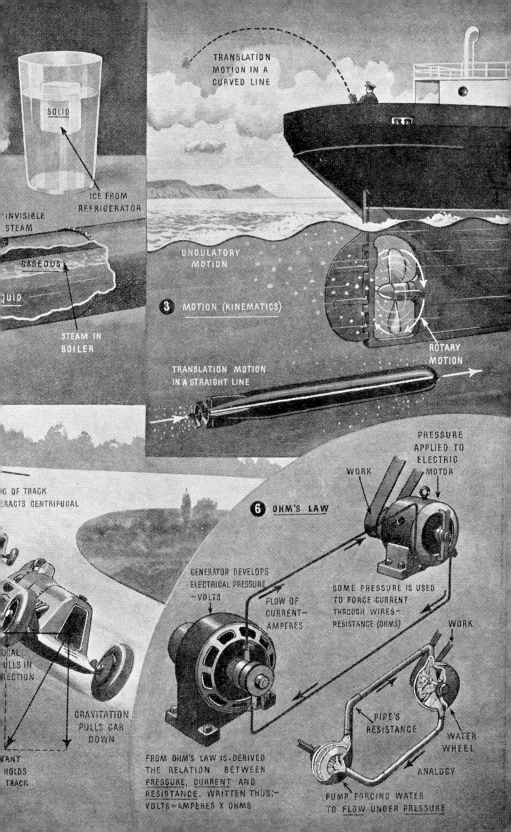

SOLID

ICE FROM
REFRIGERATOR

INVISIBLE
STEAM

GASEOUS

LIQUID

STEAM IN
BOILER

TRANSLATION
MOTION IN A
CURVED LINE

UNDULATORY
MOTION

③ MOTION (KINEMATICS)

ROTARY
MOTION

TRANSLATION MOTION
IN A STRAIGHT LINE

G OF TRACK
ERACTS CENTRIFUGAL

⑥ OHM'S LAW

PRESSURE
APPLIED TO
ELECTRIC
MOTOR

WORK

GENERATOR DEVELOPS
ELECTRICAL PRESSURE
— VOLTS

FLOW OF
CURRENT—
AMPERES

SOME PRESSURE IS USED
TO FORCE CURRENT
THROUGH WIRES—
RESISTANCE (OHMS)

WORK

UGAL
ULLS IN
RECTION

GRAVITATION
PULLS CAR
DOWN

PIPE'S
RESISTANCE

WATER
WHEEL

ANT
HOLDS
TRACK

FROM OHM'S LAW IS DERIVED
THE RELATION BETWEEN
PRESSURE, CURRENT AND
RESISTANCE, WRITTEN THUS:—
VOLTS=AMPERES × OHMS

PUMP FORCING WATER
TO FLOW UNDER PRESSURE

ANALOGY

momentum to his arms, that is, to one part of his body about the axis of the stool.

Since, by the law of conservation of momentum, the total momentum of arms, rest of body and stool was nothing to begin with, it must remain so. Consequently, the rest of his body and the stool will rotate slightly in the *opposite* direction to that in which he swings his arms. If he brought back his arms by the same route as he flung them out, his body would return again to its initial position. How then can he ensure that this slight rotation shall be permanent?

This is ensured by carefully withdrawing his arms radially without any sideways movement. In this way, no angular momentum is imparted to the system on the return journey. By imparting angular momentum on the outward journey and none on the return journey, the small backward rotation of body and stool is, therefore, cumulative when repeated and we may imagine that a lively prisoner would rapidly achieve his object. Incidentally, the more heavily he is handcuffed, the more rapidly will the result be achieved, for the moment of inertia will be correspondingly greater.

Cat and Pirouetting Dancer

The peculiar ability of a cat always to land on its feet is another illustration of the same law. Suppose it is released lying on its back. It immediately swings its legs and tail sideways and, by the conservation of angular momentum, the remainder of its body rotates slightly in the reverse direction. The cat then withdraws its extremities radially, so imparting no angular momentum to the system, and then repeats the process with great rapidity, until it has rotated sufficiently to ensure a pedestrian landing. The process can be examined in detail with a slow-motion camera.

As a final illustration, the possibility of achieving a rapid pirouette by a ballet dancer is as much dependent on the law of conservation of angular momentum as on the ability of the dancer.

The dancer commences the pirouette with outstretched arms, preferably holding some artistic but essentially heavy object. The dancer works up the maximum speed of which she is capable and then draws in her arms radially. Now this motion reduces the momentum of inertia about her axis of rotation, for the mass of the human flywheel is no longer concentrated in the rim. Consequently, since one component of the angular momentum, the moment of inertia, has been reduced, the other component, the angular velocity, must automatically increase for the angular momentum to remain constant. This happy combination of art and science gives rise to the pleasing ultra-rapid pirouette.

One of the most important practical applications of the conservation of angular momentum is the gyrostat. Any arrangement containing a heavy rotating system possesses high angular momentum and, for small disturbing forces, the system responds in such a way that the angular momentum is maintained constant both in magnitude and direction.

This explains the ability of a spinning top to "right itself" if it is temporarily disturbed. It also explains the stability of those once popular novelties, the diabolo spool and the yo-yo. Finally, it forms the basis of the gyro-compass, and of the automatic pilot which enables an unmanned aircraft to maintain its original direction in spite of air currents of variable force.

Besides the translational and rotational velocities which are imparted to matter when it is subject to a force, a further effect occurs which has hitherto been neglected. This is the deformation which the object undergoes, for no object is perfectly rigid. The study of elasticity is concerned with the changes of size and shape of an object under applied forces. A perfectly elastic object is one which regains entirely its original size and shape when the forces are removed. On the other hand, if the object entirely retains its new size and shape it is said to be perfectly plastic. These are ideal states. In practice, steel and quartz are examples of nearly perfectly elastic objects, while putty is highly plastic.

Objects of good elastic properties all show similar behaviour under applied

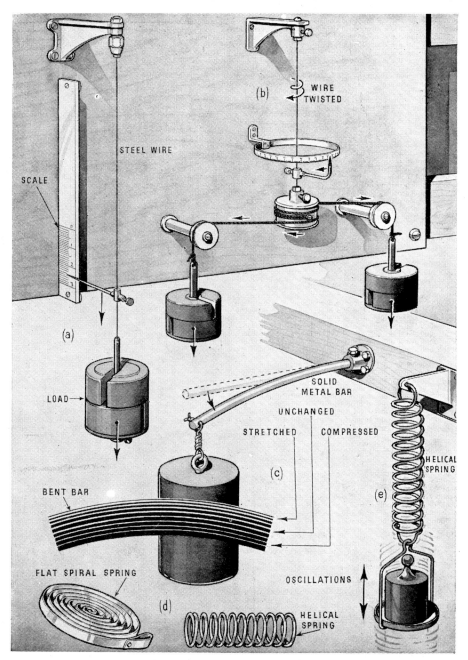

FIG. 9. (a) Stretch is proportional to the load applied. (b) Twist is proportional to the couple applied. (c) A bent beam is a special case of tension and compression. (d) Two types of spring. (e) Weight undergoing vertical oscillations on a helical spring.

forces. For example, a vertical steel wire which is held rigidly at the top, as shown in Fig. 9 (a), and stretched by increasing loads at the lower end, will at first show a stretch or strain, as it is called, proportional to the applied force. When the force passes a certain limit, however, the wire will rapidly begin to show a large increase in the strain and little further additional force will cause it to snap.

The same behaviour is observed for a steel rod undergoing compression. At first the contraction is proportional to the compressing force, but when a certain limit is passed, the rod suddenly fractures or fails by crushing.

The ratio of the applied force per unit area of cross-section of the specimen to the change in length per unit length is termed the modulus of elasticity, and is a standard characteristic of the material. The limit of the speed of revolution of any system like a flywheel is set by the breaking limit

of the material of the wheel arising from the centrifugal force acting on the various parts of the wheel. It is not possible to draw a wire or to construct a wheel of perfectly uniform elastic properties throughout and so the snapping of the wire or the bursting of the wheel takes place at the weakest point.

The elastic properties of a wire may be exhibited by other means than direct tension or compression. For example, one end of the wire may be fixed while the the other end may be twisted—Fig. 9 (b) —instead of pulled. The amount of twist is again found to be proportional to the torsional force, although, as this is a rotational problem, it is more correct to say torsional couple.

Besides tension, compression and torsion, the elastic properties of an object are involved when it is bent, and the bending of loaded beams is of great importance in structural engineering. Bending, however,

PRACTICAL APPLICATION OF CONSERVATION OF ANGULAR MOTION

A gyro-compass embodies a wheel that is rotated by an electric motor at a speed of about eight thousand revolutions per minute. Its deviation-indicating property is a mechanical one that is related to the rotation of the earth and not to the magnetic north. Those seen in this picture are being tested at the Admiralty Compass Observatory.

is a special case of tension and compression, as we can see in Fig. 9 (c). We can consider the rod or bar as composed of a very large number of parallel filaments, lying side by side, like a large bundle of spills. Before the bar is bent, these filaments are all of the same length; when the bar is bent, those filaments on the outside of the curve will be stretched, while those on the inside will be compressed. All the properties of the bent beam can then be calculated by using the experimental results already obtained on stretching and compression of wires of the same material.

The foregoing illustrates one of the chief methods by which science progresses. A new problem such as the bending of beams is turned into an old problem, the stretching and compression of wires, of which the behaviour is already well known, and so the answer to the new problem is obtained. In fact, scientific genius consists to a large extent of the ability to see which of the already solved problems is most like the new problem which it is desired to solve. In the beam problem, the key was the realization that the beam might be considered as a close bundle of parallel filaments.

Helical and Spiral Springs

Another example of elasticity of practical importance is the spring. Springs are usually helical or flat spiral in form, as shown in Fig. 9 (d). The flat type is used as the main spring and the hair spring in watches; the helical type is used in the spring balance, and in the petrol lighter to keep the flint pressed against the steel wheel.

In the helical type, the spring behaves as a long wire fixed at one end, and twisted at the other, so this is another modification of the torsional problem. The flat spring, on the other hand, operates by bending, since it gradually unwinds from a small coil to a larger one.

The energy in any elastic material under strain due to extension, torsion or bending is potential energy of strain.

The whole subject of matter and motion is sometimes divided into two parts. If the matter and the forces acting on it are at rest, it is said to be a branch of statics, whereas if motion results it is a problem in dynamics. So far we have considered only statical elasticity, but let us now consider a weight suspended on a spring as in Fig. 9 (e).

Dynamical Elasticity

Suppose the spring has stretched under the weight until an equilibrium position is reached and that the weight is now gently raised a small distance and released. It will return to its equilibrium position, but it will pass through this position until it reaches a point approximately as far below the equilibrium position as it was raised above it. It will then return again and is said to have been set in vibration.

Vibration is, therefore, a problem in dynamical elasticity, and by applying the laws of motion, together with the knowledge gained by experiment in statical elasticity, we can calculate exactly the behaviour of the vibrating object. For example, we can calculate the time required to execute one complete vibration if we know the magnitude of the suspended mass and the size, mass and the elastic properties of the material of the spring.

In this instance, a new type of motion, differing from that of uniform rotation or of uniform velocity in a straight line, is revealed. If the velocity of the mass were examined it would be found that it was, of course, nothing at the highest and lowest points of the vibration, and greatest at the centre as it passed through its position of normal statical equilibrium. Not only does the velocity vary, but the force on the mass due to the spring also changes during its vibration.

The greatest pull occurs at the lowest point when the spring is under maximum stretch, while it is nothing at the normal equilibrium position, because the pull in the spring is then exactly equal to the weight. The force causing the motion increases steadily with its distance from the equilibrium position and we now see that such a force gives rise to vibrations in which the object executes a regular motion, always passing through the same position with the same velocity and returning to that position at regular intervals of time.

Such motion is termed simple harmonic motion, and it is a fact that all forms of motion in the universe, no matter how complicated, can be regarded as mixtures of rectilinear, rotational and simple harmonic motions.

Forms of Matter

Matter can be broadly divided into three distinct classes, namely, solids, liquids and gases. As liquids and gases have many properties in common, the two together are sometimes referred to as fluids.

The solid state is noted for the difficulty with which it is compressed or divided, and by the property of maintaining its weight and shape indefinitely without any containing vessel being necessary.

Fluids, on the other hand, offer considerably less resistance than solids to a compressing or dividing force; they also require a containing vessel. Moreover, fluids have no definite shape but acquire the shape of their containing vessel, as shown in Fig. 10.

Gases have the additional property of "filling" any-size vessel in which they are placed. If a small quantity of gas is introduced into a completely exhausted container, the gas will expand to the boundaries of the container.

These three divisions of matter are to some extent arbitrary. For example, while a gem stone will maintain the same shape and size over centuries, a solid block of camphor will be found to lose weight up to as much as one-half its original value in a few months. This is because the camphor is steadily vaporizing even at room temperature; that is, the camphor is undergoing steady transition from the solid to the vapour state. In practice, this accounts for the odour of the camphor, which can be detected at some distance from the solid block.

With most substances such transitions occur in the order solid, liquid, gas, as we can see by considering the fact that rise

YOUNG SCIENTISTS INVESTIGATING THE NATURE OF MATTER

Corner of the general physics laboratory in one of the L.C.C. technical schools, where students have access to instruments and training to aid them for scientific careers.

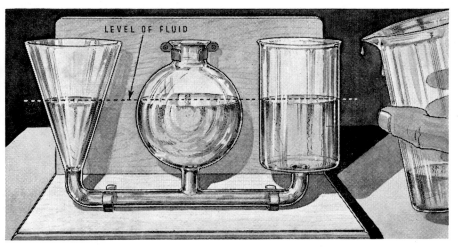

LIQUIDS IN VESSELS OF VARYING SHAPES

FIG. 10. *Fluids take the shape of their containing vessels. Although the weight of the liquid in each vessel is different, the surface level is the same in each of them.*

of temperature will cause solid ice to change to water and eventually, if the temperature is raised sufficiently, into steam. Provided that no chemical change occurs, the process is entirely reversible; the steam may be condensed to water and this in turn may be frozen into ice.

Some substances occupy an intermediate position. For example, pitch at room temperature is generally regarded as a solid, yet, if a lump of pitch is placed in a jar and set aside, after a few months it will be found to have flowed and to have taken up the shape of the jar. Similarly, liquids undergo continual evaporation to the gaseous state, even considerably below their boiling point, as shown by the drying of laundry, where the water has passed off as water vapour.

The further analysis of matter into elements, molecules and atoms is still more fundamental. To the uninitiated, there seems little connexion between the wooden leg of a dinner table and a dish of butter resting on the table. Yet although the project is not an economic one, scientists now possess sufficient knowledge to convert wood into butter.

This apparently magical transformation of one type of matter into another is, in this instance, a problem for chemistry rather than physics, but the general difficulty to be overcome is the same.

The transmutation is possible only because all the different types of matter in the universe are made of the same materials. The difference arises simply in the relative quantities of the basic ingredients which are present and the way in which they are arranged. The fact that although one may start with exactly the same ingredients, the final product may show large variations, because of difference in treatment, is illustrated every day by good and bad cooking.

These basic ingredients, out of which all matter is constructed, are about ninety-two in number and are said to constitute the elements. Most of the metals, like copper, iron, aluminium and so on, are elements, and so are such gases as hydrogen, oxygen and nitrogen. The transformation of wood into butter would first involve breaking down the wood by physical processes such as heat, and chemical processes such as solution in acids, until the elementary constituents of the wood were obtained. Such a process is termed analysis.

Similarly, the butter would be analysed into its constituents, care being taken to

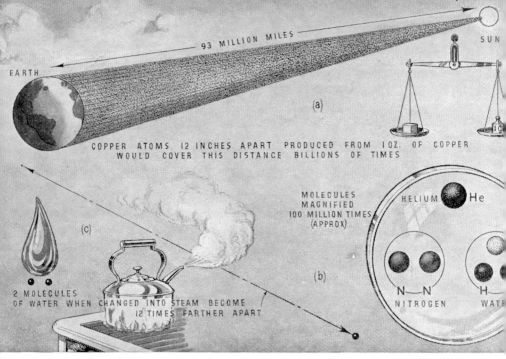

93 MILLION MILES

SUN

EARTH

(a)

COPPER ATOMS 12 INCHES APART PRODUCED FROM 1 OZ. OF COPPER
WOULD COVER THIS DISTANCE BILLIONS OF TIMES

(c)

MOLECULES
MAGNIFIED
100 MILLION TIMES
(APPROX)

HELIUM   He

(b)

2 MOLECULES
OF WATER WHEN CHANGED INTO STEAM BECOME
12 TIMES FARTHER APART

N—N
NITROGEN

H—
WAT

SOME FIGURES CONCERNING THE COMPOSITION OF MATTER

FIG. 11. *(a) There are so many atoms in a single ounce of copper, or other material, that
if they were each separated 1 ft. apart they would cover the distance from earth to sun
billions of times. (b) Molecules consist of very close associations of one or more atoms.
Helium contains only one atom in its molecule, nitrogen two, and water contains two atoms
of hydrogen and one of oxygen in close combination. (c) Average separation between two
molecules of water is increased 12 times when water is converted into steam.*

find out the way in which they were
combined. The appropriate elements would
then be taken from the analysed wood and
recombined in the correct proportions to
accomplish the synthesis of the new butter.

We shall see in Chapter 5 that the
transmutation of the elements one into
the other has now been achieved, but until
about the year 1900 this was thought to
be impossible, and it was taken as a fundamental principle in science that every element
defied further analysis. For the present,
we concentrate on an easier problem.

What occurs if we attempt simply to
divide one element, such as a strip of
copper, indefinitely? We should begin by
mechanical division with some device
such as a razor blade, but we should rapidly
find that such mechanical division still
left pieces of copper large enough to be
seen under the microscope.

However, the physicist's armoury contains far more powerful methods of attack.
By using electrical discharges, similar to
miniature lightning flashes, the small
pieces of copper could be blown into
fragments too small to be seen with the
most powerful microscope. The fundamental fact then emerges that this subdivision cannot be carried on indefinitely.
A stage is eventually reached when the
copper is divided into a number of small
equal parts which are approximately
spherical in shape and of diameter about
one-hundred-millionth of an inch. These
are the "basic bricks" out of which the
strip of copper is constructed and they are
said to be the atoms of copper.

The atoms are all identical for any one
element, but differ in weight from one
element to the next. The lightest is that of
hydrogen and the heaviest that of uranium,
which weighs about two hundred and
thirty-six times as much as a hydrogen

atom. Owing to their small size, any ordinary visible piece of an element contains millions of atoms.

If all the atoms in a single ounce of copper were to string themselves into a line 1 ft. apart and to pass the observer at the speed of the average rifle bullet, which is a few thousand feet a second, it would take over a billion years before the last atom had gone by. Similarly, as illustrated in Fig. 11 (a), they would stretch from the earth to the sun, backwards and forwards, more than a billion times.

Crystalline and Non-crystalline Forms

Examination of the way in which two or more atoms get together, to form complex groupings which eventually lead to portions of matter of visible size, is one of the most fascinating studies in physics and leads to the explanation why some substances, like sugar and soda, are crystalline in form, while others, such as butter and wood, are non-crystalline or amorphous.

In ordinary air, which consists largely of a mixture of oxygen and nitrogen gases, the atoms of each element go about in pairs of the same kind, written O_2 and N_2 respectively. The grouping which constitutes water consists of a triplet of two atoms of hydrogen together with one atom of oxygen and is written H_2O. These close groupings of the same or of different atoms are known as molecules, and substances which exist with two atoms in the molecule are termed diatomic.

A few substances, such as the rare gases like helium, which is used for non-inflammable airships, and neon, which is used for illuminated electric signs, are exceptional, as they are monatomic and will not form close groupings with atoms of the same or of a different kind. These facts are illustrated diagrammatically in Fig. 11 (b).

The realization that matter consists of atoms and molecules has led to very simple explanations of a wide variety of physical phenomena. For example, the reason that a solid is compact while a gas is less dense is easily explained on the assumption that the atoms comprising a solid are much closer together than those of a gas.

In the average solid they are about one-hundred-millionth of an inch apart; that is, the atoms are more or less in contact, whereas in a gas the molecules are about a thousand times farther apart. Liquids occupy an intermediate position, the distance mainly depending on temperature; just above the freezing point and just below the boiling point they possess every liquid property. The relative distance between two molecules of water and two molecules of steam is shown in Fig. 11 (c).

By assuming that the gas molecules have a large natural velocity, or kinetic energy, we can easily explain the automatic expansion of a gas to fill any vessel into which it is placed. Before the nature of atoms and molecules had been well established, these ideas were known as the atomic theory, and the explanation of the properties of matter by assuming the atoms to have velocity was termed the kinetic theory of matter. These "theories" are now so well established that they have become facts as real as a portion of matter which can be seen and touched.

The pressure which a gas is known to exert, as, for example, the barometric pressure of the air, is simply due to the force of impact of the air molecules continually bombarding and rebounding from the surfaces with which they come in contact, as shown in Fig. 12 (a).

The reason the atmosphere continues to exist in a layer over 200 Km. high on the earth's surface is due to the gravitational attraction of the earth for the air molecules. If gravity were to vanish, the molecules of air would dash off into space because of their gas kinetic velocity, and in a short time the atmosphere would have disappeared. The precise velocity of gas molecules depends on their temperature and nature; it can be calculated exactly, and is about 4000 ft. per second at room temperature.

The kinetic theory is of the utmost value to scientists in solving a variety of problems which could scarcely be tackled in any other way. For example, the measurement of frictional air resistance, the construction of low-pressure gauges, and the operation of rapidly exhausting air pumps, such as are essential in the production of radio valves, electric lamps and X-ray tubes, all depend on calculations based on the kinetic theory of gases.

Vibration of Molecules

To explain the type of light which is emitted by a glowing gas, such as a coal-gas flame, it may be shown that gas molecules must both rotate and vibrate, as well as possess kinetic energy of translation. For solids which maintain their well-defined outline indefinitely, the translational energy of the molecules or atoms is negligible. The atoms of a solid possess vibrational energy alone, the vibrations taking place about fixed centres (Fig. 12 (b)).

The maximum swing of these vibrations is only about as large as the size of the atoms themselves and hence the motion is invisible under the most powerful microscope. However, the steady evaporation of camphor is easily explained as due to the evaporating atoms having a swing too large for them to return to their average centre of vibration and, consequently, they break away and wander off with the translational energy of their escape.

If the temperature of a solid is raised, the atoms vibrate with larger and larger swing until, at the melting point, the atoms all break away from each other and the body loses its definite outline. It is said to melt and is converted into the liquid state. In the liquid state, therefore, the

MOTION OF ATOMS AND MOLECULES

FIG. 12. (a) Mercury column in a barometer tube is supported by the pressure exerted by the bombardment of air molecules on the mercury in the trough. As there is a vacuum in the space above the mercury column, there is no bombardment of molecules from above; the bombardment of the molecules from below just sustains the weight of the mercury column. (b) The atoms in a crystalline solid are regularly arranged, but they vibrate to and fro about centres of movement which remain fixed and form the crystalline lattice. (c) An emulsion of gamboge in water, when viewed under a microscope, shows spherical gamboge particles of various sizes moving irregularly across the field of view. The speed with which the particles dart about is much greater for the smaller particles.

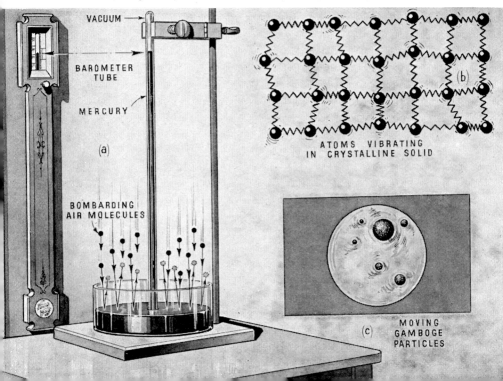

VACUUM

BAROMETER TUBE

MERCURY

(a)

BOMBARDING AIR MOLECULES

ATOMS VIBRATING IN CRYSTALLINE SOLID

(b)

(c) MOVING GAMBOGE PARTICLES

molecules possess vibrational and rotational energy and also a moderate amount of translational energy. The translational energy increases as the temperature of the liquid is raised, and ultimately becomes so large that the molecules overcome the forces of mutual cohesion and all disperse with a high translational energy. This corresponds to boiling of the liquid and the substance then exists in the gaseous state.

Brownian Motion

A remarkable proof of the truth of the kinetic theory as applied to liquids exists in what is termed Brownian motion. If an emulsion is formed by rubbing a small quantity of the resin gamboge in water and a drop of the emulsion is placed on a slide and examined under a microscope, the small particles of gamboge are seen as spherical globules of various sizes.

These globules are found to exhibit the nearest approach to perpetual motion which has yet been observed. They are found to dart in and out of the field of view, the smallest globules moving more rapidly than the larger ones. This Brownian motion, named after Brown its discoverer, is easily explained on the kinetic theory.

The globules, since they are suspended in a liquid, will be receiving a continuous bombardment of the liquid molecules which, according to the kinetic theory, have a moderate amount of translational energy. Now, any given globule will, at any instant, receive by chance more impacts on one side than another. Consequently, a resultant force will act on the globule and it will move under the impact.

The motions of the globule are directly visible under the microscope, even although the impinging molecules which cause the motion are too small to be seen. The effect is illustrated in Fig. 12 (c). The larger the globule, the more its inertia and the less will be the response, and vice versa, in agreement with experimental observation.

As the size, weight and velocity of the globules can be directly measured, the number, weight and velocity of the impinging molecules which give rise to that motion can be calculated by applying Newton's Laws of Motion, and this affords one of the methods by which we can state with precision these molecular magnitudes.

If the temperature of the gamboge suspension is gradually raised, the velocity of the globules is also found to increase. Accurate measurement reveals that the kinetic energy of the globules, and hence of the molecules which are impinging upon them, is directly proportional to the temperature.

From what has now been said, the reader will realize that many physical phenomena, such as pressure, temperature, the natural expansiveness of a gas and so on, can be accepted as physical events in themselves, or they can be interpreted in terms of the atoms of matter of which they are composed. These two ways of looking at phenomena are known as the macroscopic (large-scale) and the microscopic (small-scale) interpretations.

The atomic interpretation is, in the last resort, always more instructive and suggestive of new experiments than the older large-scale view. Nevertheless, very little additional information is obtained by interpreting some physical phenomena, like sound, in terms of atomic behaviour. Similarly, there is no particular merit in bearing continuously in mind the fact that this printed page consists of a large number of atoms in a state of continual vibration. Common sense and wide scientific experience enable us to decide when to regard a phenomenon in terms of its ultimate atomic analysis.

Two Varieties of the Same Element

Chemical analysis shows that sooty lamp-black and a diamond both consist of the same element, carbon, and nothing else. The striking difference between the two varieties of the same element can, in view of our knowledge of atoms, be due to nothing but a different arrangement of the same atoms.

In a diamond atom, the carbon atoms are, as in all crystals, arranged in a strictly ordered pattern, whereas in lamp-black they show no such order. This difference in arrangement, illustrated in Fig. 13 (a), accounts alone for all the variance in hardness, transparency and so on.

Many attempts have been made to produce diamonds from amorphous carbon by subjecting the carbon to extremes of temperature and pressure in accordance with the conditions under which diamonds are produced in the interior of the earth. The most successful of these experiments, made by Moissan, consisted in embedding the carbon in molten iron and suddenly plunging the iron into cold water. On breaking open the lump of iron, minute diamonds were found, but the process is not an economic one.

Types of Crystals

Common salt is composed of two elements, sodium and chlorine. Salt crystals are cubical in shape and the arrangement of the atoms is shown in Fig. 13 (b). Atoms of sodium alternate with atoms of chlorine and the macroscopic salt crystal is seen to be made of myriads of sub-microscopic cubical crystal cells repeated indefinitely like a honeycomb.

Each cell in this instance contains eight atoms, one at each corner, four of them being chlorine atoms and four sodium atoms. Such an arrangement is said to constitute a simple cube, but there also exist the face-centred cube and the body-centred cube, as shown in Fig. 13 (c), where, in addition to the atoms at the corners of the cube, there is one at the centre of each face or at the centre of the cube respectively.

Besides the cubic system, crystals occur in six other forms, triclinic, monoclinic, rhombic, tetragonal, hexagonal and trigonal; examples are shown in Fig. 13 (d).

By suitable processes, single crystals may be grown to almost any size. If a crystal of sugar is suspended on a piece of cotton in a sugar solution which is kept saturated as shown in Fig. 13 (e), more sugar will be deposited on the crystal and it will grow to many times its original size, but still retain its original shape.

An ordinary wire or metal bar depends for its elastic properties on the fact that it consists of a mass of crystals distributed at all angles. This lack of order is responsible for the material possessing its high elasticity. If a single crystal of copper is examined, its elastic properties are quite different from those of a copper bar. In particular, it is almost plastic; it can be distorted by a force much less than that required for the equivalent distortion of a bar of the same material.

This weakness of the elastic properties of ordered crystals is responsible for the ultimate fracture of the ordinary material under stress. If the fractured surface is examined under a microscope, a local regularity of the crystal arrangement is usually found. Incidentally, the fracture is rarely at right angles to the length of the bar in which direction the stress was applied, but at some other angle, as shown in Fig. 13 (f). The fracture is found to be due to the slipping of one regular set of crystals over another along so-called glide planes.

The remarkable toughening process produced by the addition of small quantities of other materials, for example, the addition of a little chromium to steel, may be traced to the distribution of the chromium atoms in a particularly strong arrangement among the other atoms which make up the crystal lattice. This knowledge is now used in reverse by the metallurgist, who may first examine the crystal structure of new alloys in order to predict their elastic properties.

In certain cases, the deliberate destruction of the regular crystalline arrangement is of practical importance. For example, the acquisition of high polish by a metal surface is due to the breaking down of the crystalline state of the metal by the polishing process into a completely irregular or, as it is termed, amorphous layer.

Liquid Crystals

For many years, the liquid state was considered to be characterized by complete lack of order among the constituent molecules. Recently, however, it has been found that in some liquids groups of the molecules can combine temporarily to form ordered arrangements termed liquid crystals.

If a quantity of powdered gold is stirred up in water and the mixture is passed through a filter paper, clear water emerges,

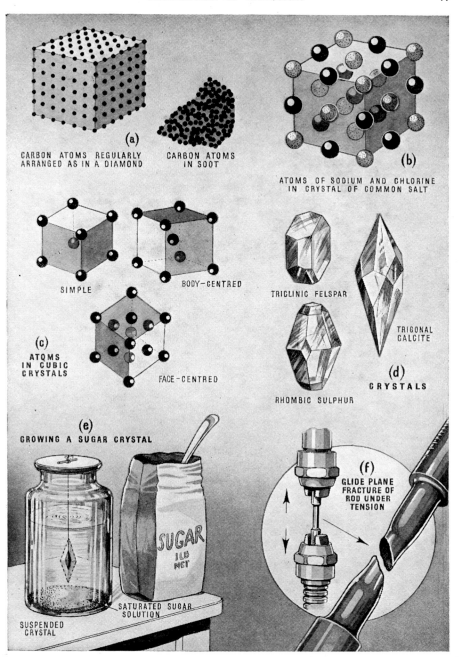

IMAGINATIVE PICTURES OF ATOMS AND CRYSTALS

FIG. 13. *(a) to (c) show diagrammatically how atoms are arranged in various substances.*
(d) Crystal forms. (e) How crystals may be developed in size. (f) Angle of fracture.

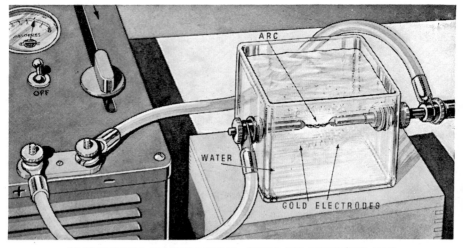

PRODUCTION OF COLLOIDAL GOLD BY ELECTRIC ARC

FIG. 14. *Colloidal gold is being produced by striking an electric arc between two gold electrodes submerged below water and connected to the power supply shown on the left.*

the gold dust remaining behind on the filter paper.

Suppose, however, that an electric arc is passed between two gold electrodes immersed beneath a water surface, as shown in Fig. 14. The water acquires a ruby red appearance and this liquid passes through the filter paper; addition of a salt to the liquid rapidly causes the red colour to disappear and at the same time gold dust is deposited on the floor of the container.

The extremely fine division of the gold which is produced by the arcing process is termed colloidal gold and the gold is said to exist in the colloidal state. As we have seen, this state is often not very stable and is easily precipitated. However, experiment shows that it can be "protected."

Complex Molecules

Many other substances can be produced in the colloidal state, but they are generally of more interest to the chemist and the biologist than the physicist. Closely associated with the colloidal state are complex molecules. These consist of molecules which contain hundreds of atoms. The upbuilding process is seen to be continuous. Starting from atoms, these may combine to form simple or complex molecules. These aggre-

gate still further to form colloids if the arrangement is irregular, or crystals if it is regular.

Vitamins consist of particular forms of grouping of complex molecules. If the liquid containing the vitamins is heated, this grouping is often destroyed, although no chemical change has taken place. No part of the liquid has in fact been destroyed, but the complex grouping which constitutes the vitamin has been broken up and lost.

Some germs or viruses responsible for diseases are large enough to be visible under a microscope. However, many viruses are known to exist which are so small that not only are they invisible under the microscope but, like colloids, they pass through a filter. These filter-passing viruses are relatively difficult to detect and to control.

One of the smallest and apparently most simple living organisms, amœba, often regarded as a single cell composed of protoplasm, is easily visible under a microscope; chemically, it is found to consist of certain complex molecules. It is by no means impossible that continued research may eventually yield the secret of life, that is, the precise arrangement responsible for a complex grouping of complex molecules turning from inert matter into the living cell.

Test Yourself

1. A spring balance carrying a weight of 1 lb. is dropped so that it is falling freely. What is the reading on the balance? (Consider what happens to the reading of the balance in a lift which starts to descend rapidly.)
2. A piece of lead and a feather are situated at the bottom of a closed glass tube from which the air has been removed. If the tube is suddenly inverted, which object reaches the bottom of the tube first?
3. Why does a stone thrown straight up continue to travel in a straight line although it traverses a curved path if it is projected at any other angle?
4. Into what forms of energy is electricity commonly converted in domestic and industrial use?
5. What difference would it make to the action of the perpetual-motion machine in Fig. 3 if the cannon balls were of unequal weights?
6. What pull would be required to sustain a weight of 96 lb. in a pulley system like that of Fig. 4 if there were four pulleys in each pulley block? What would be the mechanical advantage of the system?
7. Explain why a tension exists in a string if a weight on the end is being whirled with a circular movement.
8. What is the work done when an elephant weighing 2 tons lowers itself 2 ft. by sitting down? What is the couple exerted if the elephant's trunk pulls with a force of 2 tons at right-angles to a lever 2 ft. long? What is the difference between the two results?
9. An anti-aircraft shell is fired vertically and explodes at its highest point into two fragments only, one of which has twice the weight of the other. The larger fragment is projected due east with a velocity of 2000 ft.-sec. In what direction and with what velocity does the other fragment move? (Use the Law of Conservation of Momentum.)
10. A string, at the end of which a stone is being swung with a uniform velocity of 5 ft.-sec., is suddenly halved in length. What is the new velocity of the body?
11. A heavy object is supported by a string and a similar string hangs down from the lower side of the object. If the lower string is pulled gradually with increasing force the upper string eventually breaks, whereas if the force is applied suddenly, the lower string snaps. Explain this. (Consider the response of an object of large mass to slow and rapid forces respectively.)
12. Two men stand facing each other on two light-wheeled trucks situated a short distance apart and a common rope is gripped by each. Whether each man pulls separately or both pull together, the trucks always meet in the same place. Explain this. (Newton's Third Law of Motion.)
13. Two equal closed bottles are placed on each side of a sensitive pair of scales. Will the balance record the weight of a fly in one of the bottles and, if so, will this weight vary as the direction of flight changes or when the fly settles on the inside of the bottle?
14. What change is registered by a weighing machine if the person being weighed suddenly stoops down?
15. An expert jumper vaults a bar in such a way that his body is almost horizontal as it crosses the bar. What advantage has this over a straight vertical jump?
16. At what point of his flight, if any, is the irrevocable movement made which decides the number of somersaults a diver will achieve before reaching the water?

Answers will be found at the end of the book.

HISTORIC DEMONSTRATION OF ATOM SPLITTING

(Above) Gigantic water column, which reached 5000 ft., rises into the first phase of the characteristic mushroom following the first great under-water atom-bomb explosion at Bikini. (Below) A picture from the Mond Laboratory, Cambridge, showing adjustments being made to an atom-splitting machine. Scientists have been able to give to other substances the properties of uranium by using Cyclotrons of the type illustrated here.

CHAPTER V

WITHIN THE ATOM

As WE have said, atoms are particles of matter only about one-hundred-millionth of an inch in diameter. But atoms are constructed of even more minute particles, one hundred thousand times smaller than themselves.

Now an important point must be considered if we are to understand experiments in subatomic physics. Does it follow that because we have deduced the correct laws of motion for objects the size of cannon balls, that they are necessarily true for these minute particles? Are, for example, momentum and energy still conserved in subatomic as well as in ordinary macroscopic physics?

One of the strongest theoretical arguments for the application of the ordinary laws is that in atomic physics, such phenomena as Brownian motion and the kinetic theory of gases are found to obey the laws. If the atoms, which are particles only one-hundred-millionth of an inch in diameter, obey the laws applicable to cannon balls, are they not likely to be obeyed by particles a hundred thousand times smaller still, especially since the larger bodies are constructed out of the smaller ones?

The answer given by experiment is that in many cases the macroscopic laws *are* obeyed but, in addition, special conditions occur in which they fail. The subatomic world is, therefore, a world which, while having many features in common with the everyday world, nevertheless exhibits many startling properties and features which are quite new and which have no counterpart in ordinary life. It is these new features which, when emphasized or seen in isolation, are often liable to puzzle us at first.

. To a young child the ordinary world is a mysterious place; to the savage a radio set is a magic mystery box, and to you the subatomic world will probably at first appear fantastic. It is fantastic only because it lies outside your ordinary everyday experience. With sufficient knowledge and familiarity, the subatomic world is found to be as rational as any other part of human experience.

Naturally, we must always start by hoping that what we already know will be applicable when we come to examine what we don't know, but we must not be surprised (or the surprise should soon wear off) if we discover new facts about nature which are new basic experiences and which have no counterpart in ordinary experience and may even seem to fly in the face of "common sense." For our "common sense" is based on our common experience, which is ordinarily limited to things directly detectable by our senses. Once this common sense is enlarged to include familiarity with the subatomic world, this sensation of the fantastic departs and the universe becomes rational once more.

Splitting the Gas Atom

Until about the year 1900, it was taken for granted that the smallest particles of matter in existence were the atoms of the various elements. If, however, an electrical discharge is passed through a gas contained in a vessel at a pressure of about one-tenth of an inch of mercury, as in a glowing electric neon sign, the gas atoms are split into two parts. These two parts are electrically charged and one part is found to travel to the positive electrode, as shown in Fig. 1, while the other travels to the negative electrode.

The positively charged part has a weight and size almost equal to that of the original gas atom, but the negatively charged part is much smaller than the atom and weighs only about one two-thousandth that of the positive part.

If the discharge is passed through different gases, the same general behaviour is observed, but while the positive parts, or ions as they are called, all have different masses, the light negative parts, or electrons, have the same mass every time. Hence, every atom consists of two parts and

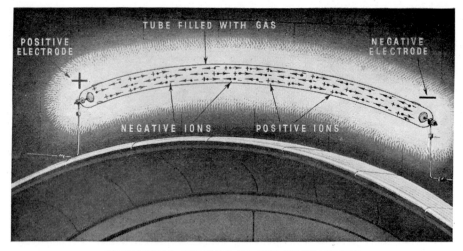

ELECTRICAL DISCHARGE THROUGH GASES

FIG. 1. *Tube is filled with a gas such as neon. When the two electrodes have correct voltage applied to them, the tube will conduct electricity. Electrical charge is conveyed along the tube by positive and negative ions travelling in opposite directions. Collision of these ions with the gas atoms excites these atoms, which then emit glowing radiation.*

of these the electron is a common constituent of all atoms. Since ordinary atoms are electrically neutral, it follows that the charge on the positive ion is equal and opposite to that on the negative electron.

Element with Simplest Atom

When most atoms are submitted to more and more violent discharges, it is found that more than one electron can be detached from the atom. Hydrogen is exceptional, yielding only one electron per atom no matter how violent the discharge. Hydrogen is, therefore, not only the lightest element, but also the element with the simplest atom, containing only one electron and one corresponding positive ion called the proton.

Now, it is well known that positive and negative electricity neutralize each other and so we conclude that the proton and the electron in the hydrogen atom cannot be in contact, but must be some distance apart. It is, however, also well known that positively and negatively charged particles attract each other. What, then, prevents the electron and proton rushing together and neutralizing each other?

The problem was solved, as so often in science, by comparison with a similar problem, the answer to which was already known. The planets are prevented from rushing towards the sun, under their mutual gravitational attraction, by the centrifugal force acting outwards because of the rotation of the planets around the sun. By supposing that the electron is revolving round the proton, a centrifugal force is called into play sufficient to oppose the mutual electrical attraction and to preserve the stability of the hydrogen atom indefinitely.

If all the elements are arranged in series according to their weight, beginning with hydrogen and ending with uranium, the fact emerges that, with exceptions, the number of electrons revolving round the positive charge at the centre is simply equal to the number of the element in the series. Thus hydrogen has one electron; the next lightest element, helium, two electrons; and so on to uranium, with ninety-two revolving electrons. Incidentally, the ordered list of elements is called the periodic table and this term will be used in future.

Space will not permit us to describe in detail the innumerable experiments, some simple and some complicated, which have been performed to verify these ideas, but these experiments are as definite in their interpretation as the original large-scale experiments on matter and motion, from Galileo onwards. We must, therefore, ask indulgence if many of the following statements seem dogmatic and to rest on slight foundations, and we would refer the reader to Chapter 13 and the Guide to Further Study at the end of the volume for additional reading of the subject.

How Atoms are Depicted

Diagrams of the hydrogen and the sodium atoms are given in Fig. 2 (a) and (b). The orbit of the single electron in the hydrogen atom is generally a circular one as shown. The diameter of the orbit is found to be about one-hundred-millionth of an inch, thus agreeing with the size of atoms deduced from the kinetic theory of matter in Chapter 4. Experiment, however, shows that the size of the electron and the proton, or central nucleus of the atom as it is termed, is only about one-hundred-thousandth that of the diameter of the orbit.

It is, therefore, sometimes said that the experiments on splitting the atom have shown that most of the atom is "empty space," for the proton and the electron occupy such a small portion of the total volume of the atom as measured by its orbital diameter.

This empty space idea is, however, very misleading. It is true that the space between the electron and the nucleus contains no other particles of matter, but this "empty" region is the seat of an intense electrical force arising from the mutual electrical attraction between the nucleus and the electron, and these electrical forces would oppose, for example, the intrusion of another portion of matter, just as though the space were already occupied.

Disposition of Electrons

Sodium is the eleventh element in the periodic table and, consequently, has eleven circulating or extra-nuclear electrons as they are termed. As a result of many cross-checking experiments, it is found that not more than one electron ever revolves in one orbit and that the number of orbits of a given size is strictly limited. Thus, in sodium there are two electrons in the two smallest equal orbits; this is followed by eight electrons in the next-sized orbits and, finally, the last electron circulates in a still larger orbit, as shown in Fig. 2 (b).

We pointed out that since every object consists of atoms, and these atoms consist in turn of central nuclei and revolving electrons, both much smaller in size than the orbits themselves, any portion of matter does in a sense consist largely of empty space, though, of course, this empty space is permeated by intense electrical forces.

An unqualified statement that a person sitting in a chair consists of one portion of largely empty space sitting on another, is not merely comical and mystifying to the average person, but it is also definitely incorrect and unscientific if it does not also add that the whole system is a complex of intense electrical forces. Moreover, the sum total of the microscopic electrical forces produces in the aggregate a mechanical force which is precisely that experienced in any large-scale experiment on matter and motion. These points are shown in Fig. 2 (c).

Space Within the Atom

The fact that the nucleus and the extra-nuclear electrons are separated by such relatively large distances, compared with their own size, is extremely fortunate, since it allows us to concentrate on each portion of the atom separately. We may note immediately that the existence of the nucleus and the extra-nuclear electrons has been demonstrated by splitting the atom and allied experiments.

The question which then arises is, can we proceed further, splitting the electron and the nucleus into smaller parts and these into still smaller parts, and so on indefinitely?

This question carries us to the very forefront of scientific progress. The nucleus has, indeed, been split into smaller portions and we discuss this later, but the electron has resisted any such attempt and is likely to do so for several generations to come.

This stability of the electron is due to the

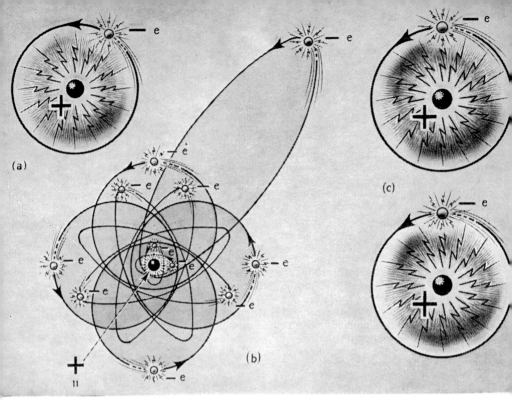

COMPOSITION OF HYDROGEN AND SODIUM ATOMS

FIG. 2. *(a) Hydrogen atom consists of a central proton carrying a positive charge, with a negatively charged electron rotating around it. (b) The sodium atom has eleven units of positive charge on its central nucleus around which revolve eleven electrons. Two of these electrons revolve in the smallest orbits, eight electrons in the next-sized orbits, and the last one in a large eccentric orbit. (c) If an attempt is made to press together the two atoms shown separated in the diagram, the intense electrical forces present in the atoms would prevent this compression beyond a very small amount.*

fact that the forces which hold it together are far greater than any forces produced by any atom-splitting machine so far devised. Any particle which cannot be further reduced is termed a fundamental particle of nature.

Originally, atoms were thought to be fundamental particles, but already in our discussion these have given way to electrons as still more fundamental. These fundamental particles, the extra-nuclear electrons, are responsible for an enormous range of physical phenomena. For example, from a knowledge of the number and size of the electron orbits we can calculate exactly the ordinary properties of matter.

Thus we can predict: (1) optical pheno-

mena such as the precise colour or wavelength of the glow when an electrical discharge passes through the gas as in a neon sign; (2) whether the substance will be crystalline or amorphous in solid form and what will be its degree of hardness, elasticity, thermal conductivity and so on; (3) all its electrical properties.

Importance of Extra-nuclear Structure

In fact, it is no idle boast to say that nine-tenths of all the known properties of matter can be calculated solely from a knowledge of the extra-nuclear structure. This is so true that the only really new discoveries to be made are those resulting from the experiments on the nucleus.

The reader may well and rightly take

exception to this, pointing out that large industrial firms are every day carrying out experiments and discovering new compounds and new properties of matter which are not essentially connected with the atomic nucleus. Why, he may ask, do not these firms shut down their experimental laboratories and employ instead an army of mathematicians to calculate and predict from the extra-nuclear structure all these new facts?

The answer is quite simply that in many cases the calculations are so long and laborious that it is quicker to carry out the experiments to attain the desired result.

The same type of problem exists in atomic as well as subatomic physics. For example, it is possible from the kinetic theory of gases to calculate exactly the frictional force exerted by the air on some irregular object like a corkscrew which is thrown across a room. The motion of the gas molecules, however, as they leave the irregular twisty surface of the corkscrew would lead to such complicated calculations that the problem would be solved far quicker by direct experiment.

But the practical reason of speed does not alter the fact that physicists now possess sufficient knowledge concerning the extra-nuclear electronic structure to explain a vast range of facts in physics, in chemistry, and in biology as well.

The scientist is often asked to define the difference between physics and chemistry, but from what has already been said we see that any such division must be a quite arbitrary one, adopted purely for convenience. The oldest definition of science was Natural Philosophy, and this all-embracing definition represents the modern view very closely, for all natural phenomena are ultimately explicable in terms of the atomic and subatomic properties of matter. Indeed, the overlapping of all branches of science is now well illustrated by the existence of certain branches such as physical chemistry, biochemistry and biophysics.

The nucleus of the hydrogen atom, the proton, is as resistant as the electron to any attempts to subdivide it still further, and the proton is, therefore, also an elementary

particle of nature. Its charge is equal and opposite to that of the electron: hence a sodium atom which contains eleven negatively charged extra-nuclear electrons must contain eleven positively charged protons in its nucleus for the whole atom to be neutral. But the sodium atom weighs twenty-three times as much as a hydrogen atom. Of what, then, does the additional weight in the nucleus, equal to that of twelve protons, consist?

Experiments, to be described later, show that it consists of twelve particles, each with a mass almost equal to that of the proton but with no electric charge. These are called neutrons and they are also fundamental particles. All atomic nuclei, except ordinary hydrogen, which is a single proton, consist of a mixture of protons and neutrons. Diagrams of some nuclei are shown in Fig. 3 (a).

Transmutation of Elements

The gas known as neon has a nucleus which contains ten protons and twelve neutrons; therefore, it occupies the tenth position in the periodic table, while its mass is 22 as compared with hydrogen. Sodium, the next element, has position 11 and mass 23 and so consists of eleven protons and twelve neutrons.

Now, by simple subtraction we see that if a proton could be removed from a sodium nucleus, the remaining nucleus would be that of neon. The accomplishment of this feat would be the transmutation of one element, sodium, into the next element, neon. This transmutation is now experimentally possible and much modern research in physics is concerned with transforming one nucleus into another. To do this, that is, to split one or more protons or neutrons from a given nucleus, requires the use of highly concentrated force, for the nucleus, as we know, is extremely small.

How this concentrated force is obtained we shall now show.

Nature herself presented us with the first clue. Everyone knows that radioactive materials, particularly radium, emit very penetrating rays which possess the power of penetrating what was regarded in the older, or classical, physics as "solid matter." For example, they will pass easily through a sheet of aluminium.

With our modern view, however, we know that aluminium consists of aluminium nuclei with circulating extra-nuclear electrons. There is, therefore, plenty of room for a ray which is small enough in size and sufficiently energetic to pass completely through the atom in the space between the nucleus and the extra-nuclear electrons, provided it can overcome the electric force in that space.

These rays from radium may be shown to consist of tiny particles travelling with high velocity and sufficiently small to pass through atoms of a solid. From what has already been said, these particles must of necessity be smaller than the atoms through which they are passing. But the only particles smaller than atoms are electrons, protons and neutrons, or neutrons and protons combined as nuclei. One group of radiations, the so-called alpha-rays (written α-rays), do, in fact, consist of helium nuclei, which having position 2 in the periodic table, and mass 4, consist of two protons and two neutrons (α is the Greek letter alpha).

What happens now if the high-speed

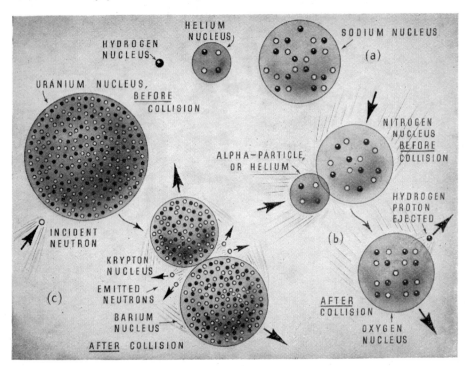

SPLITTING OF ATOMIC NUCLEI

Fig. 3. (a) Hydrogen, helium and sodium nuclei. (b) An alpha-particle collides with a nitrogen nucleus; after collision, a proton escapes, while remainder constitutes an atom of oxygen. (c) Disintegration of uranium by neutron bombardment. A slow neutron amalgamates with a nucleus of uranium 235, which contains 92 protons and 143 neutrons. The additional neutron upsets the delicate balance of forces between the neutrons and protons in the uranium nucleus and explosion occurs. Uranium undergoes fission and divides into two nuclei, krypton and barium, of unequal mass. These fragments are projected apart in almost opposite directions with very high velocity. Some additional neutrons escape at the same time, and if these fall on adjacent uranium nuclei, the whole process is continued.

CLOUD TRACKS OF ALPHA-PARTICLES

FIG. 4. *(Left) Alpha-particle, near the centre of a beam of such particles which have traversed helium gas, makes a collision with a helium nucleus. The alpha-particle goes off in one direction after the collision and the helium nucleus is projected in another direction. The collision process is shown as a fork of fog trails, a single stem representing the track of the alpha-particle before collision and two inclined branches of the fork showing the tracks of the two particles after collision. (After* Blackett and Champion.*) (Right) An alpha-particle collides with a nitrogen nucleus and disintegrates it. The ejected proton is seen as a long thin track. The shorter branch of the fork is an atom of oxygen, synthesized from the amalgamation of the nitrogen nucleus and the alpha-particle. (After* Harkins.*)*

α-particle, instead of passing between the aluminium nucleus and its attendant electrons, makes a head-on collision with the aluminium nucleus?

The answer is nuclear disintegration: the splitting of a proton from the aluminium nucleus.

The first experiment was carried out by Rutherford in 1919, using nitrogen as the element bombarded by α-rays. High-speed protons were shot out from the bursting nitrogen nuclei. But closer examination showed that we were not left with an atom of carbon, as we should expect if the nitrogen nucleus simply lost one proton (for carbon precedes nitrogen in the list of elements). Instead, an atom of oxygen remained, which is the next element *higher* in the series. The nitrogen, therefore, lost one proton but gained two in the collision. The explanation is simple: the incident α-particle does not escape from the nitrogen nucleus after causing disintegration, but is

captured, and since α-particles contain two protons, the mystery is solved. The effect is shown diagrammatically in Fig. 3 (b).

A fast α-particle will travel several inches in air before its kinetic energy is reduced to the gas kinetic value, when it mingles with the air molecules as a helium molecule. This distance of penetration is termed the range of the α-particle. Of course, ordinarily the passage through the air of a single α-particle is quite invisible and undetectable by the senses, but a remarkable invention enables the path or track of the particle to be exhibited with perfect clarity to the unaided eye.

Wilson Fog Chamber

This invention, known as the Wilson fog chamber, works on the following principle. Everyone is aware that a fog occurs when air which is moist and laden with water vapour experiences a sudden cooling. The water vapour condenses most easily on dust

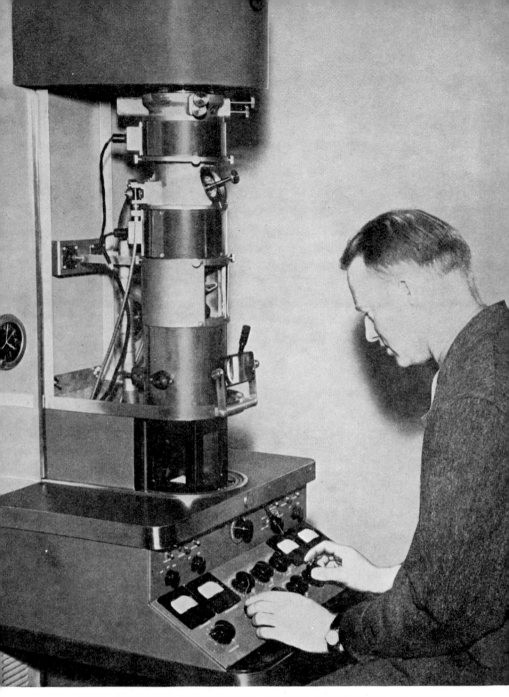

NEW ELECTRON MICROSCOPE AT THE UNIVERSITY OF WISCONSIN

Operating the new 50,000-volt electron microscope acquired by the university for use in soil, genetics, bacteriology, mining, metallurgy and other types of research. Using a stream of electrons, instead of light waves for magnification as in other microscopes, it is capable of direct magnification as high as 20,000 times and photographically to 100,000 times.

particles and grows into visible droplets which constitute the fog. Besides smoke and dust particles, electrical charges such as ions and electrons also act as centres of condensation.

When an α-particle flies through the air it disrupts the air atoms into their positive ions and electrons just like an electrical discharge. Consequently, a trail of positive and negative ions is left behind in the wake of the particle. These ions are, of course, only of atomic size or smaller, and they are still quite invisible except under one condition. If the air through which they pass is laden with moisture, but has not quite reached the saturation point sufficient to condense as a general fog, this fog will be precipitated as a line of fog along the track of the particle.

The Wilson fog chamber is a device for carrying this into effect. A sudden cooling is produced in a vessel containing air or some other gas laden with water vapour. A few α-particles are allowed to enter by moving a shutter rapidly in front of a radioactive source. Then there is, easily visible to the naked eye, a perfect set of fog lines or cloud tracks, as they are termed, showing the exact path taken by the individual α-particles. The lines are several inches long. This affords one of many methods of examining individual atoms. In Fig. 4 are reproduced some of these cloud tracks obtained by illuminating and photographing the tracks before they evaporate.

Collision of Particles

While most of the tracks are straight, every so often we obtain a forked appearance, as shown on the left. This is owing to a direct collision of the α-particle with an atomic nucleus of the gas through which the α-particle is passing. After collision, one branch of the fork is the deflected α-particle, the other is the nucleus which has been struck and projected forwards with a sufficient velocity to ionize the gas and produce a track of its own. This affords a brilliant pictorial demonstration of atomic billiards.

As the masses of the atoms are known we can calculate from the laws of motion whether the energy and momentum of the α-particle before collision are equal to the sum of the energies and momenta of the two particles after collision. In this way, direct proof has been obtained that momentum and energy are conserved in this type of subatomic process.

Tracks of Ejected Protons

The example just considered was one in which the struck nucleus was not disintegrated by the impact of the α-particle. In Fig. 4 (right), the disintegration of a nitrogen nucleus has taken place, the long thin track of the fork being that of a proton ejected during the disintegration. Measurements show that the kinetic energy of the two parts after disintegration is not equal to the energy of the incident α-particles. The difference between the two measures the energy required to explode the nitrogen nucleus.

Radium and other radioactive substances are exploding naturally with the emission of their rays. As we have seen, nitrogen may be exploded with the aid of the α-rays from radium.

By bombarding other elements with more powerful radiations, such as those from the Cyclotron to be described later, every compound nucleus has now been directly or indirectly disintegrated.

At first it seemed that protons were always the one and only type of particles emitted when the disintegration occurred, but after twelve or thirteen years of experiment it was found that a second type of disintegration was also quite common. When this occurs, a neutral particle, the neutron, with a mass practically equal to that of the proton, is released. It was from this evidence that we gradually deduced that all nuclei are built up of two fundamental types of particles only, neutrons and protons.

Owing to the fact that α-particles are helium nuclei and, therefore, have a positive charge, it is only with great difficulty that they can approach any of the heavier nuclei, for the latter contain many protons and the high accumulation of positive charge repels the positively charged α-particle. The heaviest element which can be disintegrated by α-particle bombardment is potassium which still leaves over three-quarters of the elements unaffected.

The fact that neutrons are ejected from disintegrating atoms, however, introduces a new sort of projectile; for the neutron, carrying no charge, experiences no difficulty in penetrating even the heaviest element, uranium. Further, high-energy neutrons are quite unnecessary, for the slowest neutrons can approach the nuclei, and neutrons of ordinary gas kinetic velocities are very effective in provoking nuclear disintegration.

Extensive work on nuclear disintegration has revealed no new fundamental particles; the particles which are ejected are either protons or helium nuclei, that is, α-particles. Neutrons, can, however, produce a remarkable effect, which we shall now describe, when they bombard uranium, the heaviest element.

Before we describe the effect we may pause to inquire why uranium should be the heaviest element; that is, why heavier elements should not exist containing a still greater number of those basic units, protons and neutrons. The existence of natural radioactivity supplies an explanation.

As soon as nuclei contain more protons and neutrons than make up the heavy element lead, they are no longer stable. After a shorter or longer time, such heavy nuclei automatically explode; uranium, radium, and most of the elements heavier than lead, show this instability to a greater or smaller extent. Therefore, we conclude that no heavier element exists than uranium, because once formed it would sooner or later explode again.

What, then, happens if we attempt to drive an additional neutron into the uranium nucleus by bombarding uranium with neutrons (which have in turn been produced, say, by the common process of bombarding the element beryllium with α-particles from radium)? What occurs is a new type of disintegration; the new nucleus becomes violently unstable, but instead of ejecting a simple particle like a proton or an α-particle, it splits into two large but unequal parts, as shown in Fig. 3 (c).

The two parts are none other than barium and krypton nuclei. The phenomenon producing them is called nuclear fission disintegration. Simple arithmetic shows that the original number of neutrons and protons is not accounted for by adding up the neutrons and protons in the two portions formed in the fission process. In particular, there is a balance of several neutrons and, in fact, these are emitted separately.

What will now occur if these liberated neutrons are allowed to fall on adjacent uranium nuclei? Clearly, the whole process will be repeated, and so on indefinitely! Thus, a single neutron will have started a chain reaction which will continue until all the uranium nuclei in the neighbourhood have been disintegrated. This process represents a large gain in output energy of the disintegrating uranium nuclei, above the input energy of the first incident neutron. Therefore, it holds out considerable possibilities as a source of power and is, in fact, the basis of the atomic bomb. We should, perhaps, add here that elements heavier than uranium, namely, neptunium and plutonium, have now been synthesized. They are all radioactive.

Electromagnetic Radiation

Before we can profitably consider further many additional points of interest connected both with nuclei and their extra-nuclear structure, we must introduce the important practical phenomenon of electro-magnetic radiation, or simply radiation as it is usually called.

The commonest example of radiation is light. In what way does a ray of light differ from an α-ray? Both will exert a mechanical force against, say, a lightly suspended strip of metal, though, of course, scientific appliances of the highest delicacy and sensitivity are required to demonstrate the effect.

Now we know that an α-particle is a a material particle with weight and size; do light rays, then, consist of a stream of material particles of some kind?

Newton was of the opinion that they were, but, in the intervening years, experiment showed that light or radiation exhibited so many other properties which could

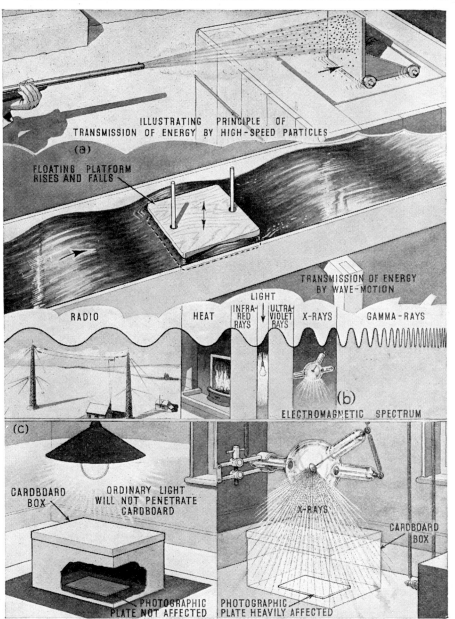

ILLUSTRATING PRINCIPLE OF
TRANSMISSION OF ENERGY BY HIGH-SPEED PARTICLES
(a)

FLOATING PLATFORM
RISES AND FALLS

TRANSMISSION OF ENERGY
BY WAVE-MOTION

LIGHT

RADIO | HEAT | INFRA-RED RAYS | ULTRA-VIOLET RAYS | X-RAYS | GAMMA-RAYS

(b)
ELECTROMAGNETIC SPECTRUM

(c)

CARDBOARD BOX

ORDINARY LIGHT
WILL NOT PENETRATE
CARDBOARD

X-RAYS

CARDBOARD BOX

PHOTOGRAPHIC
PLATE NOT AFFECTED | PHOTOGRAPHIC
PLATE HEAVILY AFFECTED

TRANSMISSION OF ENERGY BY RADIATION AT DIFFERENT WAVELENGTHS

FIG. 5. *(a) Energy is conveyed to the target by the impact of fast-moving particles, and the floating platform receives energy from the wave-motion taking place underneath it. (b) The only difference between radio waves, radiant heat, light, X-rays and gamma-rays is the wavelength of the radiation. (c) Radiation in the form of X-rays and gamma-rays, which, for instance, will penetrate materials that are opaque to ordinary light.*

not be explained if they consisted simply of particles, that before we jump to any conclusions we must search our common experience to see if energy can ever be conveyed in any way other than by high-speed particles.

In everyday experience, energy is conveyed from one place to another in only two ways; namely, by moving particles, often of high speed, such as rifle bullets, or as a wave-motion, as shown in Fig. 5 (a). The destructive force on a sea-wall is not due to the particles of water far out at sea travelling inshore with high speed and flinging themselves on the wall. It is the wave of energy which is transmitted through the water, the particles of which simply oscillate up and down as the wave passes by. Only those particles which have all the time been in close proximity with the wall are eventually flung upon it by the force of the wave when it reaches them.

Here, then, is another method of conveying energy and pressure, and as until about 1900 the observed behaviour of light was much more like that of waves than particles, it was taken for granted that radiation consisted of waves. Further, by passing light through magnetic and electric fields, effects were produced showing that light had magnetic and electric properties and light was very confidently felt to be an electromagnetic wave-motion.

Electromagnetic Spectrum

With the discovery of wireless waves, which are produced electrically in such a way that they must consist of electromagnetic waves, and the demonstration that wireless waves travelled with the same speed as light, every part of the puzzle seemed to interlock. The difference between wireless waves and light waves was attributed entirely to wavelength, which could be measured with great precision. Soon, all sorts of other forms of radiation were joined in the general scheme to produce a chart of electromagnetic radiation (Fig. 5 (b)).

If the waves are very long, that is, several yards, or even miles, from one crest to the next, they are wireless waves. As the wavelength becomes shorter, the waves possess the property of warming bodies on which they fall. They are, in fact, invisible rays of radiant heat.

As we know, when a body is warmed, it emits no light until its temperature first causes it to go dull red. Hence, we infer that red rays are the longest light waves, as shown in Fig. 5 (b), and so we proceed through the visible spectrum which we note constitutes only a minute fraction of the total chart of electromagnetic radiation. By this time, the waves are getting quite short in wavelength; in fact, there are some hundred thousand crests to the inch. They are not yet, however, of atomic dimensions. Passing on, we come to X-rays and, finally, γ-rays, which are emitted from radioactive substances, and the wavelength of these is definitely of atomic size and even approaching nuclear dimensions.

Radiations of Different Wavelength

In this chapter we shall be concerned with waves of wavelengths comparable with the size of the atom. From our chart, therefore, we are concerned with radiation in the form of visible light, ultra-violet light, X-rays and γ-rays. Now, one remarkably consistent new phenomenon is found to occur as we proceed from visible light, down the scale of wavelength. While a piece of cardboard, as shown in Fig. 5 (c), is opaque to visible light and ultra-violet light, as the wavelength is still further reduced, radiation begins to penetrate ordinary opaque objects like cardboard and human flesh to a considerable depth and γ-rays will penetrate an inch of lead. Thus, although the entire chart is that of electromagnetic radiation, different portions have different properties according to wavelength. In 1900, a revolutionary feature of electromagnetic radiation had been established beyond doubt by many converging experiments. If a sheet of sodium metal is illuminated with radiation of wavelength shorter than about half-way up the visible spectrum, as shown in Fig. 6 (a), it starts to emit electrons with appreciable velocity; this is called the photo-electric effect.

We know that the electron is a material particle of minute size, only one-hundred-thousandth that of an atom. The wavelength of the light which can give the

MILLION-VOLT VACUUM DISCHARGE TUBE

Apparatus used for subatomic research by scientists at Cambridge. It includes a 1,000,000-volt vacuum discharge tube, made by the Metropolitan-Vickers Electrical Co.

electron its energy of emission may, however, be a million times greater. How, then, is the energy from the wave communicated to the electron?

In everyday experience, the problem is like that of a cork floating on the sea on the surface of which are rolling waves whose wavelength is several yards. Now we know the energy in these waves is considerable, as seen by the damage they can do when they are eventually stopped. Yet the cork merely oscillates up and down.

We should be very surprised if the energy in the large wave could all suddenly be concentrated on the small cork and project it up in the air with tremendous velocity. Yet this is precisely what occurs in the photo-electric effect when the light wave hits an electron in a metal.

This experiment, and many others of different types, have forced us to conclude that light and radiation do not always behave as waves. They can sometimes behave, as in the photo-electric effect, as highly concentrated bundles of energy, these bundles being sufficiently small to act on a single electron and give the electron a kinetic energy exactly equal to the bundle of radiant energy. These bundles of radiant energy are termed photons, by analogy with similar bundles of matter, the electrons, protons and neutrons.

Radiation's Dual Aspect

Radiation is, therefore, said to exhibit a dual aspect; sometimes it behaves as waves and sometimes as photons. Fortunately, the rules of its two-faced nature are well known and its double life causes us no embarrassment.

We can now predict with certainty the type of experiment in which radiation will behave as a wave-motion and that in which it will behave as a photon. A beam of radiation can be regarded either as an electromagnetic wave or as a stream of

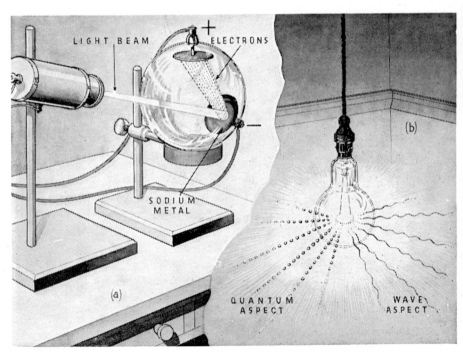

PHOTO-ELECTRIC EFFECT AND TWO ASPECTS OF RADIATION

FIG. 6. *(a) Emission of electrons by photo-electric effect when a beam of light shines on sodium metal. (b) Light and radiation either behave as quanta or as wave motion.*

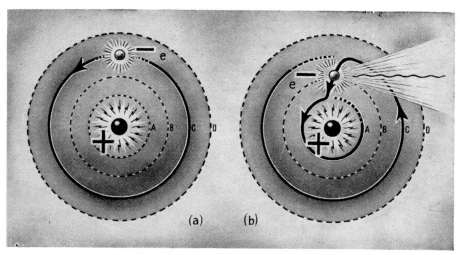

HYDROGEN ATOM AND ITS EXTRA-NUCLEAR ELECTRON

FIG. 7, (a) Negatively charged electron rotates around the positively charged proton in the hydrogen atom. The only orbits which can be occupied have radii in the ratio 1:4:9:16, etc. Therefore, if A is the smallest orbit which exists, the next possible orbit is C; while it is possible to imagine such orbits as B and D, such orbits do not exist as possible paths to be traced by the rotating electron. The diagram (not to scale) shows the electron revolving in the first level above the ground state, just prior to jumping down to that state. (b) The electron in (a) is in the process of jumping down to the ground state, or lowest possible level, in the hydrogen atom. Energy is released in the process in the form of ultra-violet radiation, which is emitted by the atom. This radiation may be detected photographically in a hydrogen discharge tube when an electrical discharge is sent through it.

photons (Fig. 6 (b)); in fact, we commonly mix the two views and talk of the wavelength of a given photon. In the photoelectric effect, each photon acts on only one electron. The shorter the wavelength of the photon, the greater the energy of ejection of the photo-electron; the energy of electrons ejected by X-rays or γ-rays is accordingly larger than the energy of those ejected by visible light.

The bundles of radiant energy or photons are also known scientifically as quanta of light, and the "theory" that regards radiation as quanta is termed the quantum theory of radiation, as opposed to the older wave theory of radiation. As with the kinetic "theory" of matter, the theory is so well established that it is now an experimental fact.

The reader may have noticed the frequent introduction of the year 1900 into this chapter. It was in this year that Planck first

proposed the quantum theory of radiation and, as X-rays were discovered in 1895, radioactivity in 1896 and the electron in 1897, we choose for convenience 1900 as the year in which the experimental and theoretical basis of Modern Physics was first laid down. For three hundred years previous to that, Newton's Laws of Motion were sufficient to explain physical phenomena, and those phenomena which can still be adequately explained on the basis of these laws are termed Classical Physics.

We shall now show that while Newton's Laws of Motion explained the orbits of the planets round the sun, they were not quite sufficient to explain the orbits of the electrons round the nucleus of an atom.

We are here face to face with a new phenomenon which has no counterpart in the everyday life-size world and must be accepted as a new fact of nature.

A planet can revolve in any-sized orbit

round the sun, the only condition necessary being that the gravitational force inwards on the planet shall equal the centrifugal force of revolution outwards. It is not so with electronic orbits. It is found that the only orbits in which, for example, the extra-nuclear electron of a hydrogen atom can revolve are such as those shown at A and C in Fig. 7 (a).

There is a quite definite closest-allowed orbit, known as the ground state, and ordinary hydrogen gas is in a condition where all the electrons are revolving around their nuclei in their ground states. If a mild electrical discharge is passed through hydrogen gas, it glows and emits light.

Production of Light

Now, we have claimed that we can explain a large part of all physical phenomena from our planetary theory of the atom, so we now proceed to explain how this light originates. First the electrical discharge lifts the electron from the ground state to one or other of the higher-allowed orbits. These higher orbits, however, are not occupied indefinitely and, quite suddenly, the electron jumps down to its comfortable permanent ground state (Fig. 7 (b)).

Now, the mechanical energy of the revolving electron is less in its ground state than in the higher or excited states, as they are called. What, then, happens to the balance of energy? It is transformed into a photon of ultra-violet radiation, which is emitted, along with visible light, by the hydrogen gas under electrical discharge. The energy of the photon could quite easily be found by allowing it to fall on sodium metal and to eject a photo-electron whose energy could be measured, and it is by this type of cross-checking experiment that our basic ideas have been continually reaffirmed.

The existence of a restricted number of allowed or quantized orbits, accounts, of course, for the particular collection of orbits which constitutes the various atoms already depicted in Fig. 2.

Two of the basic laws of Classical Physics are that matter and energy are separately conserved in all phenomena. We have already discussed at some length

in the preceding chapter the Law of Conservation of Energy. With regard to matter, it is always found in experiments with bodies of everyday size that the weight remains unaltered throughout any physical and chemical change. For example, if a given weight of hydrogen gas and the appropriate weight of oxygen gas are combined chemically to form water (H_2O) (Fig. 8), the weight of the water equals the weights of the two gases before combination. Such behaviour is said to illustrate the law of the Conservation of Mass.

Now, Modern Physics rapidly began to show that this law was not true as it stood, especially when the masses were of atomic or electronic size. For example, it was found that an electron had a different mass when it was at rest from what it possessed when it was travelling at high speed. This increased mass was quite separate from the increased kinetic energy which still occurs and would, of course, occur on the laws of Classical Physics. This increase in mass was quite regular with speed, but it increased rapidly when the speed was very high, approaching that of light, which is about 186,000 miles a second.

For example, when the speed of any body is about 150,000 miles per second, its mass is equal to twice its mass when at rest. It was Einstein who first stated clearly that not only electrons but all matter, cannon balls and planets included, ought to show this change in mass with velocity, and the only reason it had not hitherto been observed was that the velocities ordinarily used in experiment were not large enough.

Einstein's great generalization, which followed from his Principle of Relativity, was rapidly shown to account for a small but well-known and hitherto mysterious deviation of the planet Mercury from the simple Newtonian Laws of Motion, in its journey round the sun.

Apart from this increase of mass with velocity, which in itself is suggestive of a close connexion between mass and energy, however, Einstein's relativity theory predicted something still more fundamental. It showed that mass and energy ought to be convertible one into the other, and that when this conversion took place we

FIG. 8. *Weight of water formed by the combination of oxygen and hydrogen equals the weight of the gases consumed. Actually, the flame is almost invisible.*

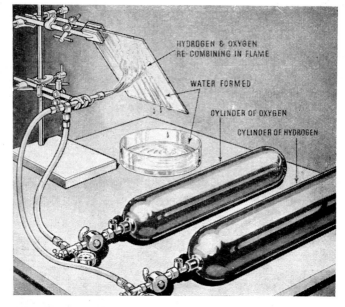

HYDROGEN & OXYGEN
RE-COMBINING IN FLAME

WATER FORMED

CYLINDER OF OXYGEN

CYLINDER OF HYDROGEN

must replace the separate Laws of Conservation of Mass and Conservation of Energy in a change into "the sum of the mass and energy of a system is the same after and before any change, but neither need be independently conserved in the change."

Einstein, moreover, showed that if any mass disappeared in a transformation, the energy which appeared in its stead was equal to the product of the disappearing mass multiplied by the square of the velocity of light!

Let us now see what all this means in concrete terms. It means that a stone of mass one pound has the possibility of either gradually or suddenly losing some portion of its mass, the mass being converted into energy. What form could this energy take up? From our previous knowledge of energy, it could suddenly appear as vastly increased kinetic energy of a smaller portion of stone which remained, or it could appear as another form of energy; in particular, as photons of radiation shot out from the dissolving stone.

In everyday experience, of course, nothing of the kind ever occurs, but in sub-atomic physics it is well known, as we shall now proceed to show. Before we demonstrate the existence of this transformation of mass into energy, however, we shall introduce another fundamental particle. This is the positive electron.

From what we have already said, if aluminium is bombarded with α-rays, either neutrons or protons are emitted when

nuclear disintegration occurs. This emission of neutrons or protons ceases immediately the α-ray beam is cut off, but careful examination shows that a very small fraction of the bombarded aluminium has been made artificially radioactive, for it continues to emit a weak stream of particles.

These instantaneous and delayed actions are shown in Fig. 9. The particles produced are found on examination to be of the same mass as ordinary electrons, but with a positive charge. What occurs to these positive electrons when they are brought to rest by collisions with other atoms which they encounter? That they cannot continue to exist for long in ordinary matter is clear, for our atomic model of a central nucleus with only negative extra-nuclear electrons is quite adequate to explain most physical phenomena, and there is no room for these positive electrons to take up any abode in either the extra-nuclear structure or the nucleus.

What happens is that they make a head-on collision with a negative electron and the two completely annihilate each other. At the instant of annihilation, a photon is born; this is of very short wavelength and is, in fact, a γ-ray. Hence, the mass of the material matter has disappeared. but electromagnetic energy has appeared: we have witnessed the transformation of pure matter into pure energy. Nor is this all, for experiment shows that this is reversible. If the γ-ray photon thus created is allowed to impinge on matter, particularly with heavy atoms like lead, there spring from the point of impact of the photon two electrons, one positive and one negative.

Mass Changed to Energy

Up to the present, no similar example has been found of the complete annihilation of the other fundamental particles, the proton and the neutron, but the partial annihilation of them, with the reappearance of the lost mass as additional kinetic energy of the mass which remains, occurs every time a nucleus is disintegrated.

Thus, for example, if in the disintegration of nitrogen we add together the mass of the α-particle and that of the nitrogen nucleus before collision, we find that the sum does not equal the sum of the masses of the ejected proton and that of the oxygen nucleus formed in the disintegration. The difference is not large, but it is easily measurable and we find it exactly equals (when multiplied by the square of the velocity of light) the difference in the kinetic energy of the system before and after collision. Again, in the disintegration of uranium by neutrons in the fission process, a relatively large net gain in kinetic energy is released in the process.

These transformations of matter into energy, and vice versa, are common at the high temperatures that prevail in the stars.

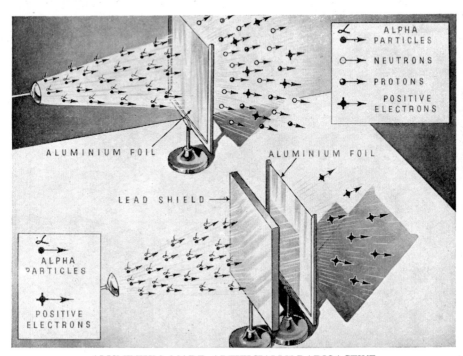

ALUMINIUM MADE ARTIFICIALLY RADIOACTIVE

Fig. 9. *Alpha-rays from a radioactive source deposited on the metal cup on the left of the diagram, cause disintegration of aluminium atoms with the emission of protons, neutrons and positive electrons. If a lead screen is interposed to cut off the alpha-ray beam, after the aluminium has been irradiated for some time, the emission of neutrons and protons stops immediately, but the emission of positive electrons continues. The aluminium is said to have been rendered artificially radioactive by alpha-ray bombardment.*

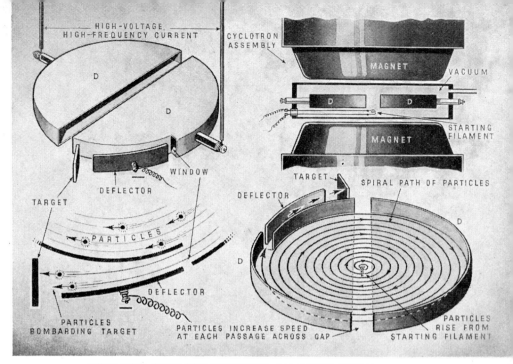

HOW THE NUCLEUS-SPLITTING MACHINE WORKS

FIG. 10. *(Top, right) Complete assembly of the Cyclotron, showing the two metal dees situated between the poles of a large electromagnet. The dees are surrounded by a chamber which can be evacuated. At the centre of the chamber is a filament or some other source of ions. (Lower, right) The ions which are produced near the centre of the chamber are accelerated every time they cross the gap between the two dees. The result is that under the combined influence of the electric field across the dees and the steady magnetic field, the ions execute a spiral path of ever-increasing radius. When they reach the edge of the dees they escape through a window and strike the target which has been selected for atomic disintegration. Deflector plates assist the escape and direction of the ions near the end of their path. (Top, left) Detailed view of dees, window and deflector plate; connexion is shown from the high-voltage, high-frequency power supply to the dees.*

Under the conditions of our own planet they are extremely rare and not detectable at all in bodies of ordinary size. The release of electromagnetic energy which would accompany the complete annihilation of an ounce of ordinary matter is enormous, and this has given rise to extravagant visions such as driving a huge modern liner across the Atlantic with the energy contained in a single penny.

There is not the slightest evidence for assuming this to be a practical possibility, for the elements which constitute a penny are extremely stable. As we have seen, uranium fission is the best yielder of energy so far discovered. This process, however, requires the exertion of so much energy to mine, smelt and purify the uranium and to prepare the neutron source, that it is doubtful if even this proposition will rapidly become an economic one. As we all know, it has been utilized in uneconomic processes such as for purposes of warfare, in the form of the atomic bomb.

Up to the present, we have considered nuclear disintegrations which have all had their origin in the natural radioactive substances, for these have formed the source of the α-rays used either directly or to produce neutrons which shall act as disintegration agents. These radioactive sources require large mining and industrial plants for their preparation and the process is extremely wasteful in energy for the

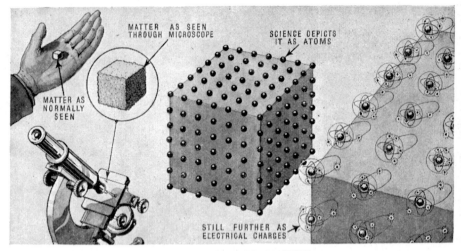

MATTER AS SEEN
THROUGH MICROSCOPE

SCIENCE DEPICTS
IT AS ATOMS

MATTER AS
NORMALLY
SEEN

STILL FURTHER AS
ELECTRICAL CHARGES

CONSTITUTION OF MATTER

FIG. 11. *Matter, the substance of which the physical universe is made, is depicted above, but not to scale, as viewed by various scientific methods, and as we normally see it.*

relatively few nuclear disintegrations which finally result.

Now, α-particles are simply high-speed nuclei: they consist, in fact, of positive helium ions and are, except for their greater speed, identical with the positive ions produced when an electrical discharge is sent through helium gas.

It is now possible to accelerate helium ions from ordinary helium gas to such a speed that they form a beam of artificially created α-particles. It is more common to use hydrogen gas; that is, to create a beam of high-speed protons. This is the aim of the newest machines which have been invented to give a stream of high-speed particles, millions of times more abundant than provided by the most intense source of ordinary natural radioactive material.

Using the Cyclotron

Perhaps the most celebrated of these machines is the Cyclotron. The operation of the machine is best described by reference to Fig. 10. Protons are produced by a quite moderate electrical discharge through hydrogen at the centre of a flat metal box similar to a large pill-box, divided into two halves like giant D's back to back.

These dees are connected to an electrical

supply so that one is positive when the other is negative, and this polarity changes with great rapidity. At the same time, the dees are situated between the poles of a large magnet. Suppose a proton produced by passing an electrical discharge through hydrogen is initially situated in the gap between the dees. Since the proton has a positive charge, it will be attracted to the negatively charged dee and repelled by the positively charged one. It will, therefore, be attracted across and will acquire a small velocity.

Now, an electrically charged particle situated in a magnetic field is bent into a circular path. The proton, therefore, traces a semi-circle and eventually arrives at the gap once more. At the instant it arrives, the polarity of the dees is reversed. Consequently, the proton is now attracted across the gap to the other dee and again its velocity is slightly increased by the attractive force. The whole process is then repeated, that is, it is bent into a circular path again by the magnetic field, but as the velocity of the proton is now greater than it was for its first half-circle, the increased centrifugal force will cause the new semi-circle to be of slightly larger radius.

Each time the proton arrives at the gap

between the dees, their polarity is changed and thus an additional increment is added to the speed of the proton. It describes larger and larger circles with ever-increasing velocity, spiralling out from the centre of the dees until it reaches their circumference with very great energy.

Situated at the edge of the dees is a separate small electric field and this pulls the protons to one side and they shoot through a window in the wall of the dee on to the target which is to be bombarded or disintegrated. Thus is produced a beam of protons, or artificial α-particles, of energy and number greatly exceeding any available from a natural radioactive source.

To summarize the ideas and facts presented in this chapter, we may say as follows. To ordinary unaided eyesight, matter appears as shown in Fig. 11 and looks much the same, except for size, as we reduce it to about one-thousandth of an inch, which is the limit of the acutest vision. With the aid of a microscope we can still detect the matter visually down to about a thousand times smaller. Much more detail is revealed.

Beyond this, eyesight fails, but our experiments on Brownian movement and so on inform us that the matter consists of atoms. With still sharper scientific eyes, the apparently solid billiard-ball-like atoms are found to consist of electrical charges, the planetary atom. This is as far as we can see with any precision, although our nuclear disintegration experiments make it certain that another sub-microscopic world exists inside the nucleus. We know it consists of protons and neutrons, but how they are arranged and just what it is like is a problem.

Test Yourself

1. Give an example of subatomic processes where the simple Law of Conservation of Energy (a) is conserved; (b) is not conserved. What happens to the energy in the second case?

2. How has the atom been split, and what products are obtained when the fracture occurs?

3. What enables the electrons and the nuclei to maintain a certain separation in spite of their mutual electrical attraction?

4. Draw a diagram of (a) the hydrogen atom; (b) the sodium atom. By what process is light emitted by such elements?

5. Criticize the statement that matter consists largely of empty space and explain why one portion of matter cannot be superposed on another.

6. What are the ultimate particles of Nature, and which of them are involved: (a) in the extra-nuclear structure; (b) in the nucleus?

7. How may an atomic nucleus be disintegrated and what is the result?

8. How may the tracks of individual atomic particles be demonstrated to the eye, and what knowledge has been gained from the examination of such tracks?

9. What are neutrons, and what particular advantage do they possess over other atomic particles in producing nuclear transmutation?

10. Upon what evidence do we conclude that light rays behave as a stream of particles? Are these material in character?

11. What is meant by the quantum theory of radiation, and in what way does it differ from the wave theory?

12. Mention two examples in which the subatomic world behaves: (a) like the everyday world; (b) unlike the everyday world.

13. What proof have we that matter and energy can be transformed one into the other?

14. By what means may the atomic nucleus be split? Describe the action of some machine devised for this purpose.

Answers will be found at the end of the book

USE OF HEAT IN INDUSTRY

Heat is encountered wherever work is done by machines or chemical processes. Frequently, it is wasteful and attempts are made to reduce it to a minimum, for excessive heat may mean an undue dissipation of energy. But here is a case where heat is itself usefully employed. The shipyard workman is employing an oxy-acetylene apparatus for welding together pieces of metal, for which process a concentration of intense heat is essential.

CHAPTER VI

HEAT

WHERE man is, there is usually need of fire for comfort and heat. Prehistoric man left blackened hearths in his cave dwellings, the cinders and debris of his cooking and primitive central heating. But down to the eighteenth century, fire and heat meant little more than warmth for comfort, heat for cooking, and fire for the destruction of your enemy and his works.

Primitive Fire-making

Yet what is it? Early man took it for granted. The old saying, "A good servant, but a bad master," expresses his respect for heat. It was feared; it was worshipped. Its spark lay hidden in the cold flint. Wood rubbed upon wood coaxed it to appear. It was a gift from heaven, or an exhibition of the anger of the gods who cast it forth upon earth with the crashing of thunder.

Yet what exactly is heat?

You can sometimes see workmen repairing tram-lines. They may hook their apparatus to the overhead conductor wire and weld a joint in the flame and sparks of an electric arc. Now and then a tram will rumble past on the other line. On one side of the road, electricity is providing power to drive a heavy tram along, on the other side, heat.

If two things are equal to the same thing, they are equal to each other. Does that hold here? Can we write equations like this?

Electricity (in the wire) = Energy (driving tram)

Electricity (in the wire) = Heat (in the arc)

∴ HEAT = ENERGY.

It becomes even more plausible after a visit to a power station. Coal goes in and fires the boilers; electricity goes out for trams, trains, motors, lights, and even for conversion back to heat in the domestic electric fire and cooker.

In fact, that equation can be written either way round. Early travellers tell us of South Sea islanders who would produce fire "in a few seconds" by rubbing a stick hard in the groove in a wooden block, or by drilling upon it with a blunt rod.

If machine bearings are not kept cool by lubrication, they will grow hot and "seize," with ruinous consequences. Windmills have burned to the ground because a strong wind caught them unprepared and drove sails and machinery so furiously that wooden bearings and axles overheated and caught fire. The barrel of a cycle pump gets warm because of the work done in compressing the air as it is pumped into the tire. This heat of compression suffices to explode the mixture in the cylinders of a Diesel motor (Fig. 1).

Examples of heat being turned into energy and work are as numerous as coal-fired steam engines. We can leave it at that. Heat *is* a form of energy. Heat and work *are* interchangeable.

The old view held that heat was a kind of fluid, the "caloric fluid," which, like water finding its own level, would always try to flow from a higher position to a lower one, that is, from the hotter to the cooler body or place.

Historic Demonstration

The death blow to this theory was given by a remarkable scientist, Count Rumford, at the end of the eighteenth century, while working in the service of Bavaria. He was engaged in reforming and refitting the army and, during the boring of cannon, was astounded at the heat developed. To the amazement of a party of onlookers, he boiled nearly two gallons of water by the heat produced in boring a gunmetal cylinder. He was struck also by "that most remarkable circumstance," as he called it, that the heat so generated by friction "appeared evidently to be *inexhaustible.*"

Later, Humphry Davy showed that ice could be melted by rubbing two pieces together, and that, when the rubbing was stopped, the pieces froze into one again. Since heat is needed to melt ice, where did the heat come from, unless it was produced in the rubbing?

The final word was spoken by James Prescott Joule in a series of classical researches from the 1840's onward. He studied the exact equivalence of heat and energy, and we shall return to his work later.

We must distinguish *heat* from *temperature*. Generally, we are concerned with whether a thing is hot or cold. We want to know whether or not the water is correct for the baby's bath, so we try it with a thermometer (or with our elbow). But this is measuring heat, and the condition or degree of heat is known as temperature.

Measurement of Temperature

It takes longer to boil a large kettle than a small one over the same gas-ring. Put half a pint of water into a kettle and time it. When you have found how long it takes to boil, empty it out and put in four times as much, a quart. This will take about four times as long to boil, for it has to take up four times as much heat, though it has to reach only the same temperature, the boiling point of water, 100 deg. C. or 212 deg. F.

Now Nature has helped us in the measurement of heat by arranging that heat shall cause a number of definite changes, generally at quite definite temperatures. First, in general, as bodies grow warmer they grow larger. Heat causes expansion—with a few most important exceptions. Second, many substances, such as ice and the metals, change from solids into liquids; they melt. If heating is continued, water begins to boil and changes into steam. Metals can be made to change into a vapour if they are heated strongly enough.

Such changes from solid to liquid, and from liquid to vapour, or vice versa, are called "changes of state," and take place at definite temperatures (degrees of heat) known as "fixed points." Here is a short list which is internationally recognized:—

SOME METHODS OF PRODUCING HEAT

FIG. 1. *(a) Friction of wood against wood, turning into fire. (b) Flint against steel strikes fire. (c) Work done on the air in the pump heats it. (d) First, compression heats the mixture until it explodes, then the heat produced by the explosion becomes energy.*

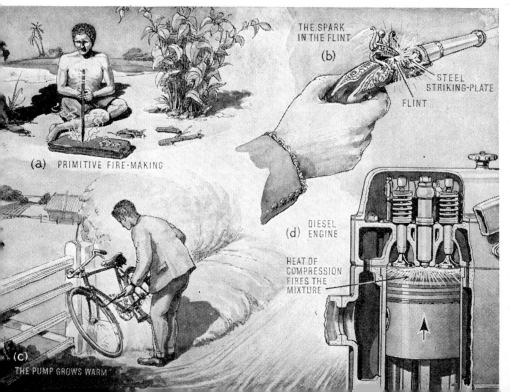

THE SPARK IN THE FLINT

(b)

STEEL STRIKING-PLATE

FLINT

(a) PRIMITIVE FIRE-MAKING

(d) DIESEL ENGINE

HEAT OF COMPRESSION FIRES THE MIXTURE

(c) THE PUMP GROWS WARM

PRODUCING A HARD SURFACE LAYER ON STEEL

Heat treatment of metals is a vital process in industry, and covers an extensive field of practical service. Picture shows case-hardening of steel at temperature of 900 deg. C.

Oxygen-point (boiling point of liquid oxygen)	−182·97 deg. C.
Ice-point . . .	0·00 deg. C.
Steam-point . .	100·00 deg. C.
Sulphur-point (boiling point of liquid sulphur)	444·60 deg. C.
Silver-point (melting point of silver) . .	960·50 deg. C.
Gold-point (melting point of gold) . .	1063·00 deg. C.

It is easy to show the effects of heat. The earliest method seems to have been due to Galileo, at the end of the sixteenth century. The principle is clear from Fig. 2 (a). Warm the flask and some air bubbles come out, because there has been expansion. Allow the flask to cool to room temperature and water will rise in the tube. Now, if the temperature rises again, the level of water will fall; if it grows cooler, the level will rise. It is a crude thermometer; but it is not

satisfactory, because the water level is affected by changes in atmospheric pressure as well as in temperature.

Fit up two flasks with good, airtight stoppers and a bent connecting tube containing a little thread of coloured water, as shown in Fig. 2 (b). If one flask is warmed, the air within it expands and the water moves away towards the cooler flask.

Fig. 2 (c) shows what is known as a thermostat. The large bulb is filled with a liquid such as toluene, which expands considerably. As it does so, it drives the mercury before it up the narrow tube, where it can be arranged to cut off the gas issuing from the jet. Such a piece of apparatus is used to control the temperature of a water bath, cutting off the heat when it rises above the desired level, and maintaining the temperature constant to a very small fraction of a degree.

Take a bar of iron, fix one end, but leave

the other free and resting on a knitting needle to which a pointer is fastened. If the bar is heated with a bunsen flame, the pointer will be found to rotate, showing that the metal has expanded.

This is the principle upon which long metal bridges are made; the ends of the girders rest on rollers which allow them a certain amount of play between winter and summer temperatures (Fig. 3).

These properties enable us to make an instrument, a thermometer, to measure temperature, instead of a thermoscope, which only indicates a change, or difference, in temperature.

A piece of glass tubing having a very fine and even bore, and with a bulb blown on one end, is filled with mercury. This is then boiled to expel the least trace of air, and the tube is rapidly sealed off just above the boiling mercury. When it has grown quite cool and settled down again, the mercury will have retreated nearly into the bulb and the thermometer is ready to be calibrated. It is placed in melting ice and the mercury level marked, next surrounded with steam, and the level marked again. If it is a Centigrade thermometer in the making, the first point is called 0 deg. C. and the second 100 deg. C., and the space between is divided into a hundred equal parts, each of which is 1 deg. C.

How the Scales are Marked

The familiar English thermometer, Fahrenheit's, calls the first of these 32 deg. F. and the second 212 deg. F., and each of the 180 divisions between is 1 deg. F. The story of how these values came to be adopted is too long to be told in full. In short, zero, 0 deg. F., was the lowest temperature obtained in a freezing mixture, the higher point was originally "the limit of the heat which is found in the blood of a healthy man," and was taken as 100 deg. F. Adjustments have given us the present values, and "blood heat," the familiar normal temperature, is now 98·4 deg. F.

The advantages of this scale are that the smaller degrees make for finer and more

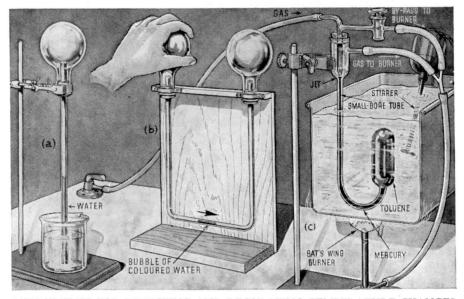

INSTRUMENTS FOR DETECTING AND REGULATING TEMPERATURE CHANGES

FIG. 2. *(a) Galileo's thermoscope, and (b) Leslie's differential thermoscope, an instrument used to detect small differences of temperature. (c) The thermostat is a device which will maintain the temperature of a water bath constant to a fraction of a degree.*

FIG. 3. *On heating the bar, expansion takes place, and, as it grows longer, the pointer moves as shown.*

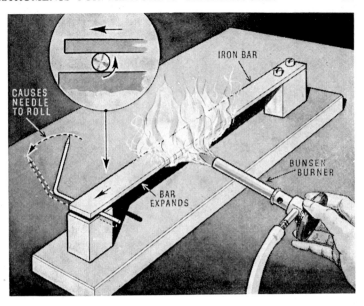

accurate readings, and also that temperatures below zero (minus readings) are rarely met with in ordinary experience. For this last reason, the Fahrenheit scale is often retained in meteorological work. The Centigrade scale, however, with its 0 to 100 simplicity, is universally employed in scientific work.

The two scales are shown side by side in Fig. 4 (a), and a more complete comparison in Fig. 4 (b).

The following formulæ show you how to convert one scale into the other:—

$$C = \tfrac{5}{9}(F - 32), \text{ or } F = \tfrac{9}{5}C + 32.$$

A mercury thermometer, specially constructed with the space above the mercury filled with nitrogen, can be used for temperatures up to about 360 deg. C. or 680 deg. F.; for higher temperatures, certain electrical effects of heat are utilized.

Electrical Thermometry

The resistance of a length of wire increases as its temperature is raised. Early experimenters used thin iron wire, but Callendar, in his resistance thermometer, replaced the iron with fine platinum wire wound into a coil and fused into a porcelain tube. Calibrated at the usual fixed points, at the sulphur point and beyond, it can be used up to 1500 deg. C.

If the junction of two wires of different metals is heated, a difference of electrical potential is set up and, if the other ends of the wire are joined, an electric current flows. A pair of metals so arranged is called a thermo-couple, and production of the current is known as the thermo-electric effect.

Take a length of copper wire and one of iron wire. Fix the iron wire to the positive terminal of a milliammeter, the copper wire to the negative terminal. If the loose ends of the wire are twisted together and heated, a current will flow through the instrument. It can be calibrated by noting the readings when the join is in boiling water, 100 deg. C., when it is plunged into just solidifying lead, 327 deg. C., and, if the copper wire just melts, as it may well do in a strong bunsen flame at about a white heat, you have reached 1000 deg. C. That is a simple, home-made pyrometer. The scientific instrument uses a couple of platinum with a platinum alloy and will read up to about 1500 deg. C. (Fig. 4 (c)).

A platinum resistance thermometer, calibrated at the oxygen point, is also used for measuring very low temperatures.

Sensitive Thermopile

The thermopile is a very sensitive instrument, used to detect and measure radiation, and the junction is between antimony and bismuth. Its construction is sufficiently clear from Fig. 5.

Steel girders, railway lines, machine parts,

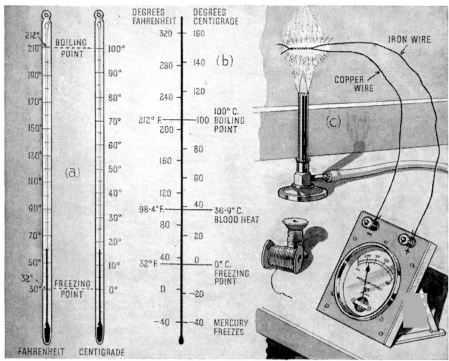

FIG. 4. *(Above) (a) Fahrenheit and Centigrade thermometers. As temperature rises and falls the mercury expands and contracts, the position of the end of the mercury thread indicating the temperature on a scale engraved on the stem. (b) The two scales compared. (c) A home-made pyrometer with which some interesting experiments can be carried out.*

FIG. 5. *(Below) The thermopile is really only a refinement of the home-made pyrometer of Fig. 4 (c), but it can be sensitive enough to measure the heat of a distant star. (a) The instrument itself. (b) Diagram of its heart. (c) Heart further dissected and explained.*

the balance wheel of a watch, a pendulum—all these will vary in length with their temperature. We must find out exactly how they vary.

It is found that they expand a definite fraction of their length measured at 0 deg. C. (we shall call this length L_o) for each degree through which the temperature changes. This fraction, a very small one, is called the coefficient of expansion, a, and it is usually accurate enough to ignore the reference to L_o and just work from the ordinary temperature. In this case, we have the following results.

If the length is L and a bar is heated

Fig. 6 (a) shows an apparatus for determining this coefficient. A metal bar is enclosed in a metal case through which ice-cold water is passed. After the length of the bar has been measured, steam is blown through the case and the change in length determined very accurately by means of a micrometer, which is set first against the bar when it is cold and then when the bar is hot.

Coefficients of expansion show considerable divergence from one metal to another. Some typical ones are as follows:—

Aluminium . . 0·000024 per deg. C.
Iron . . . 0·000012 per deg. C.

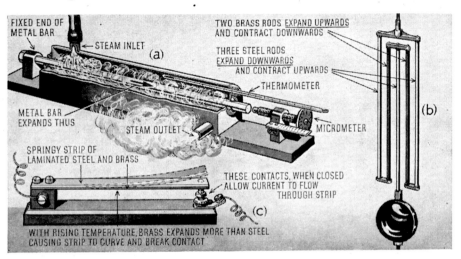

EXPANSION OF MATERIALS

FIG. 6. *(a) Determination of a coefficient. (b) Illustrating Harrison's compensated pendulum. The total lengths of the brass and iron rods are so arranged that the two expansions or contractions exactly balance each other out. (c) A bi-metal strip thermostat. As shown, it could be used to cut off a heating current if the temperature reached too great a height. Reverse the brass and iron, and it would switch on a warning bell instead.*

through t deg. C., the amount of expansion must be L times the fraction it expands for each degree times t, the number of degrees through which it is heated. That is, $x = atL$, where x is the expansion. Also, L_t must be the original length plus the amount of expansion, or $L + atL$, and we get the important formula $L_t = L(1 + at)$, in which we must remember that t stands for the number of degrees *through* which the bar has been heated, and not the final temperature.

Steel . . . 0·000011 per deg. C.
Brass . . . 0·000019 per deg. C.
Platinum . . 0·000009 per deg. C.
Glass . (approx.) 0·000009 per deg. C.
Invar . less than 0·000001 per deg. C.

One kind of invar is an alloy of iron and 36 per cent nickel and its almost negligible expansion fits it for such purposes as standard measuring rods.

These differences in expansion can be usefully balanced against each other. Fig.

6 (b) is a diagram of a compensated pendulum of brass and steel. The table shows that the expansions of the two metals are in the ratio of nearly 3 to 2. If the three steel rods expanding downwards are about the same length as the two brass ones expanding upwards, one expansion cancels the other out and the total length remains unchanged.

A compound strip of the same metals,

But with liquids a direct determination has to be made. If we find out how much liquid is driven out of a suitable, full vessel when heated, we can find the expansion.

Fig. 7 shows different types of apparatus, and a sample calculation is the best explanation. By weighing, a specific gravity bottle is found to contain 25·065 gms., or 25·065 c.c. of water at 20 deg. C., and at 40 deg.

USING HEAT FOR GAS PRODUCTION

Stoker tending a retort in a gas works; he is "slacking" out the lid, for coke removal.

riveted together, will bend and can be used to control a thermostat. If the brass is underneath, as in Fig. 6 (c), the strips curl away from the contact. When a certain temperature is reached, this would break an electric circuit and so cut off the current.

Coefficient of Cubical Expansion

If a solid cube expands, each edge increases in length according to our law and the volume becomes $L^3 (1+at)^3$, or $V_t = V_o (1+at)^3$. Since a is very small indeed, this may be written, $V_t = V_o (1+3at)$, which is within the limits of experimental error, unless t is very large. For solids, the coefficient of cubical expansion, so called, is the usual linear coefficient multiplied by three.

C., 24·928 c.c. Expansion, then, must be 0·137 c.c. over 20 deg. C., and the coefficient is $\frac{0·137}{20 \times 24·928}$, which equals 0·00027.

At this point we must note that this is the amount which the water *appears* to expand in a glass vessel which has itself expanded at the same time; it is called the "apparent" expansion. There is an "absolute" coefficient of expansion which can be found by allowing for the expansion of the glass vessel. It can also be found directly by balancing a column of the hot liquid against a cold column, as shown in Fig. 8. If a column at 100 deg. C. balances one at 15 deg. C. and their heights are 53·5 cms. and 50 cms. respectively, it can be shown that this gives us a measure of the

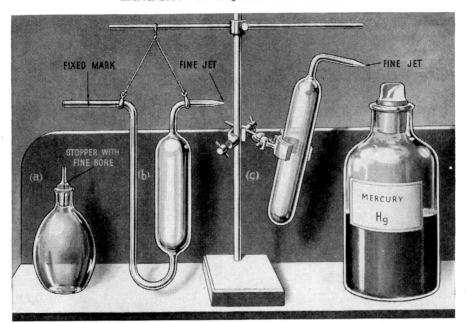

FINDING COEFFICIENT OF EXPANSION OF LIQUIDS

FIG. 7. *(a) Specific gravity bottle. (b) Pyknometer. (c) Weight thermometer, used to determine a temperature by assuming the coefficient of expansion of mercury. Fill the vessel with cold liquid, then heat to known temperature, some liquid oozes out. Weighing will give quantity of liquid used and amount lost and the amount of expansion can be found.*

HEAT DEVELOPED IN AN ELECTRIC FURNACE

Example, widely used in industry, of the useful conversion of electrical energy to heat.

MOLTEN STEEL AT A TEMPERATURE OF 2950 DEG. F.

Pouring molten steel from a basic electric arc furnace into a ladle, from which it will be poured into cast-iron moulds, at the Sheffield works of Thos. Firth and John Brown, Ltd. The light is so intense that dark-blue glasses have to be worn by the observers.

FIG. 8. *Balanced columns. Hot liquid, light, longer; cold, heavy, shorter; but both of same weight.*

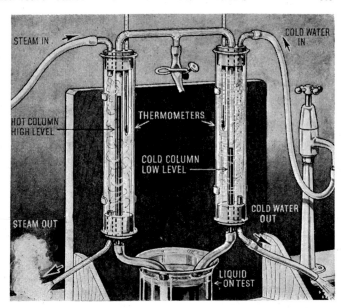

expansion by the equation, $H_{100}=H_{15}$ $(1+85a)$, 85 is 100— 15. In this case, $a=$ 0·00082 per deg. C. The expansion of a gas is a very important case. Gases are extremely sensitive to changes both of temperature and pressure, and so both these have to be taken into account. It can be seen from Fig. 9 (a) how this is done. The result is summarized in what is known as the Law of Charles, which states that, when pressure is constant, a gas expands by $\frac{1}{273}$rd of its volume at 0 deg. C. for each degree.

"Absolute Zero"

If this is written $V_t=V_o$ $(1+\frac{t}{273})$, what happens at -273 deg. C.? The formula says that the volume should become 0, which is absurd! Nature dodges the question by turning all gases into liquids and then into solids before that point is reached. It is, however, an important and significant result, and -273 deg. C. is known as the "Absolute Zero," temperatures being reckoned from it. Applied to the Law of Charles, it enables us to rewrite it in a simpler form, $\frac{V_1}{V_2}=\frac{T_1}{T_2}$, where T_1 and T_2 are measured by the Absolute scale, on which water freezes at 273 deg. A. and boils at 373 deg. A.

Increase of pressure at constant volume gives us what is known as the "constant volume gas thermometer," which is the internationally recognized standard for all checks of the highest scientific accuracy. The principle has already been illustrated, but the actual instrument has many refinements and complications which cannot be described here. Fig. 9 (a) shows the action.

It remains to be mentioned that there are cases of a quite irregular nature, for not all substances expand as regularly as has been suggested. The outstanding case is that extraordinary substance water! When ice has melted, the cold water actually contracts till it has reached a temperature of 4 deg. C., and only then begins to expand. This means that a body of water, such as a lake, must first of all cool down to 4 deg. C., then further cooling produces a layer of colder, lighter water floating on the surface, and this, with the ice that follows it, actually forms a kind of blanket which retards further freezing (Fig. 9 (b)).

The distinction between temperature and heat has already been discussed and must now be pursued a stage further. First, we need a yard-stick as a measure—and what better than water? Here are two units: (i) the Calorie, which is the amount of heat which raises 1 gm. of water 1 deg. C.; (ii) the British Thermal Unit (B.Th.U.), the amount which raises 1 lb. of water 1 deg. F. Measurements are made with a calorimeter, in its simplest form a copper can, lagged to prevent loss of heat, with thermometer and stirrer (Fig. 9 (c)).

The calorimeter will itself absorb heat

so first we find how much per deg. C. and call it the "water equivalent"; 30 gms. of water at 60 deg. C. are poured in and fall to 50·3 deg. C., while the calorimeter rises to this from 17 deg. C. The heat lost from the hot water, in calories, is $30 \times 9·7$ (the fall in temperature). This would raise $M \times 33·3$ gms. from 17 deg. to 50·3 deg., and these two must be equal; $30 \times 9·7 = M \times 33·3$, and M is 8·75 gms., the water equivalent, written W.E.

Specific Heat

Now we are ready for an important determination, a comparison of the capacities of different substances for heat. It used to be thought that their capacities depended only on their weights. A Scotsman, Joseph Black, in the mid-eighteenth century, first showed that this was not so. Everything has its own characteristic heat capacity, or specific heat, now expressed as the ratio of the amount of heat required to raise equal masses of the substance and water through equal ranges of temperature.

A piece of aluminium weighing 40 gms. is heated to 100 deg. C. and quickly dropped into our calorimeter containing 57 gms. of water at 15·5 deg. C. and the temperature rises to 24·2 deg. C. The heat gained, in calories, is 8·7 (temperature change) times $\{57+8·75\}$ (water plus W.E.). The heat lost, in calories, is 40 times 75·8 times c, where c is the specific heat of aluminium. These two must be equal, or $8·7 \times 65·75 = 75·8 \times 40 \times c$, and $c = 0·19$.

A short table of specific heats follows. Note the high value for water. Because it

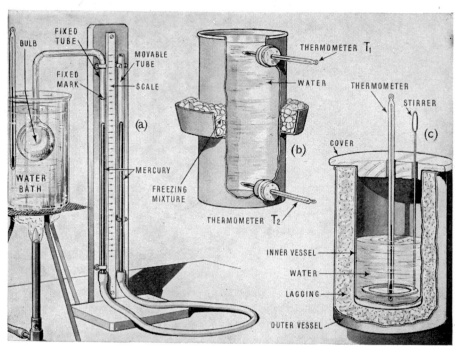

EXPANSION OF GAS AND WATER

FIG. 9. *(a) Illustrating the expansion of a gas. As shown, it is working at "constant pressure," the two mercury columns being always adjusted to the same level. If the left-hand column is always returned to the "fixed mark," it becomes a "constant volume" apparatus. (b) Irregular expansion of water. T_2 falls first. When all the water has cooled, and both T_1 and T_2 are at 4 deg. C., T_2 remains constant and T_1 falls to 0 deg. C. as freezing proceeds. (c) A calorimeter, used in the measurement of thermal constants.*

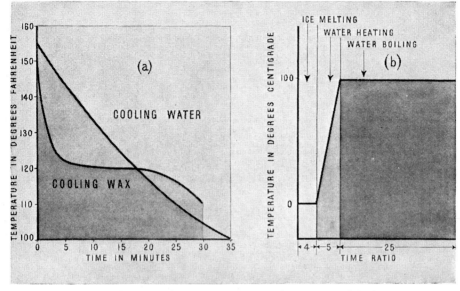

ILLUSTRATING THE EFFECTS OF LATENT HEAT

FIG. 10. *(a) Cooling curves. The water cools continuously from start to finish, but the wax sets at about 120 deg. F. and gives out heat while solidifying. This heat keeps the temperature steady until the change is complete. (b) From all ice to all steam. It takes nearly as long to melt the ice as it does to raise the water from 0 deg. C. to 100 deg. C., and about six times as long to boil it all away, though the rate of heating is constant.*

absorbs much, it can give out much. This makes it so suitable for heating systems.

Water	. .	1·00
Aluminium	. .	0·21
Copper	. .	0·094
Mercury	. .	0·033
Ice	. .	0·5
Paraffin oil	. .	0·52

A calorimeter entirely enclosed in water can have samples of fuels burned in it to determine their heating, or calorific, values. Here are some examples in B.Th.U. per lb.

Anthracite	. .	15,000
Coke	. .	11,000
Wood	. .	8,000
Motor spirit	. .	20,000
Gas	(per cub. ft.)	500

Since these units are small for commercial use, th: Therm, which is 100,000 B.Th.U., is often adopted. Coal-gas, for instance, is required by law to have a calorific value of not less than 4·5 therms per 1000 cub. ft., or 450 B.Th.U. per cub. ft.

Even food values are calculated in calories. This is because the human body is a kind of engine, burning fuel and doing work. The amount of heat developed varies according to the type of work done and may rise to over 3,000,000 calories, or 12,000 B.Th.U., a day, for heavy workers. "Stoking up" may be slang for a good meal, it is also sound science!

Latent Heat

Another important heat measurement is what is known as latent heat, also due to Joseph Black. Fig. 10 (a) shows two curves, the first of cooling water, the other of cooling melted wax. The wax remained for a long time at about 120 deg. F., giving out heat all the time; the water cooled continuously, which seems only natural. Where did the wax get its heat from?

The answer is that when anything changes its state, a large amount of heat is involved. Put some ice in a can with a steady flame underneath it, noting how long it takes to melt, how long to begin to boil, and how long to boil the water all away. The times will be roughly in the proportions 4, 5, and 25. Extra heat is needed to change ice into water and water into steam, without raising the temperature. You can find out how much by putting ice into hot water in a calorimeter, or by condensing steam in cold water and measuring the temperature changes (Fig. 10 (b)).

It takes 80 calories to melt 1 gram of ice, and another 540 to turn 1 gram of water at 100 deg. C. into steam at the same temperature. Do you wonder that our mines must produce coal by the million tons a year? Or that steam scalds so badly when it has so much heat to give up?

Radiation, Conduction, and Convection

A passing reference has been made to heating systems. A fire burns in a furnace and rooms in another part of the building are warmed by its heat. How? Three principles are involved and we will take them one by one (Fig. 11 (a)).

The fixture that delivers the heat is called a radiator. Heat will travel from one place to another, like light, through the intervening space without affecting its temperature. This is *radiation*. It can be reflected. The reflector at the back of an electric fire, as can easily be felt, reflects the heat as well as the light, and focuses it into a beam. The sun pours out light, but it also pours out heat. The heat rays are the "infra-red" rays, invisible to us, but not to a sensitive thermopile.

The outside of the radiator is hot because heat has passed through the iron from the hot water inside, making it hot in its passage. Put a poker in the fire and the handle grows hot as the heat travels along it. This is *conduction* (Fig. 11 (b)).

In general, metals are good conductors, non-metals poor, and gases very bad conductors. Clothes keep us warm not so much because cotton and wool are poor conductors, as because the air trapped in their fibres is a very bad conductor. For the same reason, heat insulation for steam pipes and refrigerators utilizes such things as asbestos, slag-wool, cork, and, in the laboratory, cotton wool.

Lastly, heat comes to the radiator be-cause the water circulates in the pipes. Drop a tiny crystal of potassium permanganate into some water warming in a glass beaker and the coloured filaments which arise show that currents are circulating. This is *convection*, which is the bodily transfer of heat by movement of the substance itself. The warm water expands, grows lighter, rises, and colder water moves in to take its place (Fig. 11 (c)).

Cut out a paper spiral and balance it on the end of a knitting needle, as shown in Fig. 11 (e). Held over the warm hand, the spiral begins to revolve in the warm, rising convection currents. Now hold it close to a window, the cold down-draught twirls it in the opposite direction. There are convection currents in liquids and gases.

Convection currents in the atmosphere keep it fresh by continuous circulation, hot air rising in the torrid zone and cold air flowing in from polar regions. Meteorology is largely concerned with the study of these currents.

Fig. 11 (d) shows a modern heating installation and hot-water supply.

Heat-energy Equation

Now, after all this, what *is* heat? The answer to this was given by Julius Robert Mayer and James Prescott Joule, from 1840 onwards. Following on the work of Rumford and others, they formed the idea that there is a definite equivalence between work and heat, and determined it. So much heat means so much energy; heat as a "Mechanical Equivalent," 4·18 times a unit called the Joule, i.e. $4·18 \times 10^7$ ergs per calorie.

Put some lead shot into a cardboard tube about a yard long and rapidly invert it a number of times. A sensitive thermometer shows that the shot grows warmer. If we know, as we do, the weight and total height the shot have fallen through, and also the rise in temperature and the specific heat, we can find two distinct quantities. We can calculate the work done, and the heat produced. These two are always found to bear the same ratio to each other.

Water is always slightly warmer at the foot of a waterfall than at the top. Joule spent a considerable part of his honeymoon scrambling about the Alps with his bride

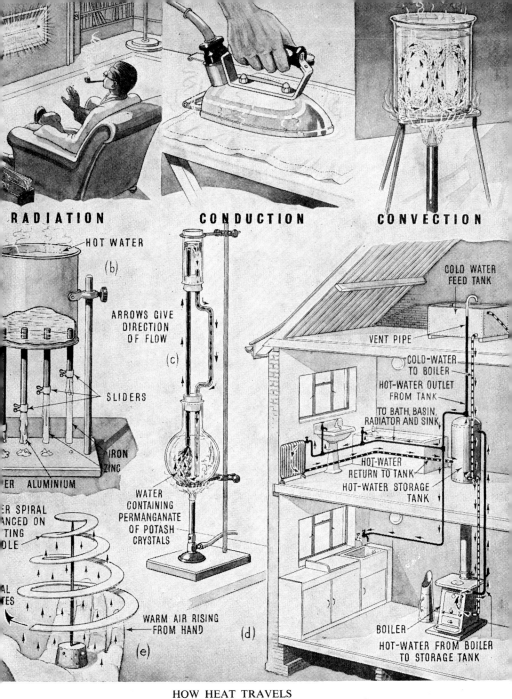

RADIATION   CONDUCTION   CONVECTION

HOT WATER

(b)

ARROWS GIVE
DIRECTION
OF FLOW

(c)

SLIDERS

IRON
ZING

ER   ALUMINIUM

ER SPIRAL
ANCED ON
TING
OLE

AL
ES

WATER
CONTAINING
PERMANGANATE
OF POTASH
CRYSTALS

WARM AIR RISING
FROM HAND

(e)

(d)

COLD WATER
FEED TANK

VENT PIPE

COLD-WATER
TO BOILER

HOT-WATER OUTLET
FROM TANK

TO BATH, BASIN,
RADIATOR AND SINK

HOT-WATER
RETURN TO TANK

HOT-WATER STORAGE
TANK

BOILER

HOT-WATER FROM BOILER
TO STORAGE TANK

HOW HEAT TRAVELS

FIG. 11. *(a) By the use of Radiation: the glow is warm and comforting; by Conduction: the
shoe of the iron grows hot and passes the heat on; by Convection: the hot substance itself
moves and carries its heat with it. (b) Showing the conduction method—but some metals
are better conductors than others. (c) Principle of convection demonstrated. (d) The
principle of convection applied. (e) The Twister! Convection in a gas (the air).*

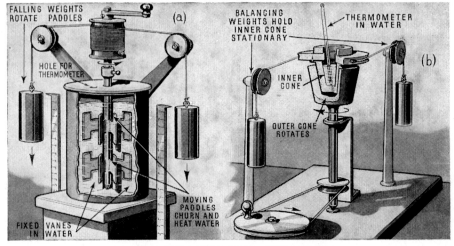

RELATION OF WORK AND HEAT

Fig. 12. *(a) Joule's paddle-wheel. The weights are wound up and allowed to fall repeatedly, churning the water round and heating it. The work done is total weight multiplied by total distance fallen and this equals the heat produced and measured in the water and machine. (b) Friction-cone machine. The outer cone is rotated rapidly at a speed which just holds the weights steady, revolutions being recorded on a counter (not shown).*

and a long thermometer investigating this question!

Fig. 12 (a) is a diagram of the kind of apparatus he used to establish this equivalent. If the weights are known, also the distance they fall through, we can calculate the work done, while the rise of temperature in the water and apparatus gives us the heat produced.

Fig. 12 (b) shows another type in which friction between metal cones is made to produce heat.

The law he formulated can be stated: $\frac{W}{Q}$ = a constant, where W is work done and Q the quantity of heat associated with the work. That constant is J, the mechanical equivalent of heat. In British units it is 778 ft.-lb. for each B.Th.U. Burning 1 cub. ft. of gas of calorific value 500 B.Th.U. produces 500×778, or 389,000 ft.-lb. of work, since the law may be written $W = JQ$. Now, 1 h.p. is 33,000 ft.-lb. per minute, so, if a gas engine uses 1 cub. ft. of gas a minute, it should produce $\frac{389,000}{33,000}$ h.p., nearly 12 h.p. In the metric system, J has the value 4.18×10^7 ergs per calorie.

This, in conclusion, can be pushed one step, but a most important one, further. Energy, force, work, these are all bound up with movement. Lord Kelvin took up this idea, so did Professor Tyndall, both of whom worked at about the same time as Joule, or a little later. Their work may be summed up in the title of Tyndall's book, *Heat as a Mode of Motion*, and the principle of the Conservation of Energy elaborated by Kelvin.

What it comes to is this. It is established that all matter consists of particles (molecules) in a state of violent agitation. If heat is supplied, their speed and energy of motion are increased and the temperature rises. They require more space. In a gas they strike the walls of the containing vessel with greater force, and pressure increases. In a liquid, they reach the surface with increasing velocity and so more and more escape; the liquid evaporates. Still more heat and a greater velocity, and their pressure becomes equal to that of the atmosphere; they will escape just as rapidly as heat can be supplied. The liquid boils. Take heat away, and contraction, or liquefaction and solidification, must follow. If *all* the heat can be taken out, all motion ceases, and that is the meaning of the Absolute Zero. It is a point, never reached yet, though almost, at which no heat remains and every molecule would be still.

By the principle of the Conservation of Energy, no energy can be created in any of those changes. The one form is changed into the other, that is all.

Test Yourself

1. (a) Why, if you *must* pour boiling water into a glass tumbler, is it safer to use a thin one?

   (b) Why are metal teapots and hot-water jugs often made with hollow or wooden handles?

   (c) Why are cork mats put under hot dishes on the dinner table?

   (d) Why wrap a blanket round a patient to keep him warm and prevent chills, and round a block of ice to keep it cool and hinder its melting?

   (e) Why do bearings get hot if insufficiently lubricated?

   (f) Why does heat turn liquids into vapours (or gases)?

2. Some temperatures are usually given as deg. C., others as deg. F. Use the formulæ given in the chapter and complete the table:—

	deg. C.	deg. F.
Absolute zero	−273	
Oxygen boils.	−183	
Mean temperature of stratosphere		−67 (approx.)
Ice-salt freezing mixture		0
Room temperature		60
Red-heat, say	700	
Oxy-acetylene blow-pipe.	3000	

3. The Forth Bridge is 5350 ft. long and is built of steel. The extremes of temperature it is subjected to are about 150 deg. F. apart. What allowance must be made for expansion? (Coefficient of expansion of steel, 0·000006 per 1 deg. F.)

4. A bungalow is 30 ft. long, 24 ft. wide, and 10 ft. high, with concrete walls 6 in. thick. Windows of glass, $\frac{1}{8}$ in. thick, occupy 90 sq. ft. Compare the amount of heat lost from the warm interior through the windows with that lost through the walls. Take the conductivity of concrete as 0·001 and of glass as 0·0025. (Comparative losses only are asked for, so no further data are needed. They will be proportional to areas and conductivities; inversely proportional to thicknesses.)

5. A gas-heated water-storage tank measures 3 ft. by 2 ft. by 1½ ft. The gas has a calorific value of 5 therms per thousand. How much must be burned to raise the temperature of the water from 50 deg. F. to 125 deg. F., assuming that half the heat only is utilized. (One cub. ft. of water weighs 62·5 lb.)

6. Ten gms. of ice cool 100 gms. of water from 90 deg. C. to 74·5 deg. C. What is the latent heat of fusion?

7. A calorimeter, water equivalent 19 gms., contains 481 gms. of water at 10 deg. C. Steam is blown in and the temperature rises to 24·1 deg. C., the calorimeter being now found to contain 492·6 gms. of water. What is the latent heat of steam? (First find calories gained by calorimeter and water in it. Calories lost by steam are in two parts: (a) 11·6 gms. condense to water, and then (b) this water cools from 100 deg. C. to 24·1 deg. C. "Heat gained equals heat lost." A similar approach solves Question 6.)

Answers will be found at the end of the book.

TRANSFORMING WATER POWER INTO ELECTRICAL POWER

View of the famous Boulder Dam, on the Colorado River. Besides serving to control floods and regulate the flow of the lower Colorado, the dam permits the gigantic potential energy of the water to be used for generating electrical power. This power is then transmitted over vast areas of the country, by means of a system of electric cables.

CHAPTER VII

POWER

THIS is the Power Age. On every hand we see devices for applying power. There are thousands of them, ranging from the housewife's vacuum cleaner to the atom bomb, from the motor cycle to the giant locomotive; and man continues the unceasing search for sources of energy, even within the atom itself, in order to harness them so that they may do work for him far beyond his own unaided power and strength to accomplish.

"We Sell Power!"

We owe many of the developments in the use of power to James Watt and those who worked with him in Boulton and Watt's foundry at Soho, just on the edge of Birmingham. He was a great craftsman and inventor. His engines, which were first used to pump water from Cornish mines, were later developed and employed to drive the machinery in the new cotton mills, and installed in the early paddle steamers. Yet it is on record that, when asked what his firm dealt in, he replied, not steam-engines, but: "We sell Power!" A proud, and true, boast.

When we talk glibly of "horse-power," we are using a term he invented, a quantity he determined and measured. When we buy a 60-watt lamp, without caring much about what a "watt" is, we are using his name, given in his honour to a measure of power.

"We sell Power." What is Power in the sense James Watt used the term, and in which it is used scientifically? Let us try to settle that point first.

In answering that question it will be best to explain as simply and clearly as possible the distinction between certain fundamental ideas with which we are all familiar, and all more or less clearly understand; although, perhaps, the emphasis should lie on the "less." They are Energy, Force, Work, and Power.

Energy is a balance at the bank; it is "capacity for doing work." Your money need not be in circulation, it need not be doing any work; if it were, we should begin to use the other terms about it as well. When it is in the bank, it awaits use.

A bold, bad baron piled stones on the battlements of his castle to hurl at attackers. Energy was there in the stones right enough, waiting to be released, but it was dormant. The scientific term for this condition is *Potential Energy*. The enemy attacks, a stone is toppled over, it falls. Its energy has become one of movement, or *Kinetic Energy*. A cheque has been drawn on the bank balance.

Force comes into the picture next when one tries to spend the cash drawn out, or when the baron's stone meets some poor wretch's skull. Force is "a push or a pull." It may be strong enough to move or change something, or it may not. You may, or you may not, have enough cash to get what you want. A horse, harnessed to a cart at the foot of a hill, tries to move, throws its weight into the collar, strains at the traces; yet for a moment or two nothing happens. Then, slowly, the cart does move and its wheels begin to turn. The bank balance has been drawn upon, applied, and done something. Force has moved a weight over a distance.

What is Work?

Work is the name for what force has accomplished. Lift a book from a table and place it on a shelf a couple of feet higher and one has performed work. Lift two books of the same weight and, obviously, one has performed twice as much work. Put them on a shelf twice as high, and one has once more clearly doubled the amount of work done. To buy twice as much, one must spend twice as much. If the price (or weight) is doubled, again one spends twice as much.

So we can make up an equation: Work = Force multiplied by the Distance moved through along the line of the force, or

$W = F \times D$. This both explains and defines the meaning of work and measures it. We say that it is so many "foot-pounds."

Power brings time in. It is the *rate* at which work is done. No more work is involved in doing a certain job in half an hour than in spending an hour over it—but one has worked twice as fast and, therefore, twice as hard. That is *Power*, the speed, or rate, at which one works.

And this is how James Watt attacked the problem. His customers wanted to know what his engines could do compared with what their horses did. So he borrowed dray horses and set them to drag a 100-lb. weight up a well shaft. He found that they could do this walking forward at about $2\frac{1}{2}$ m.p.h., which is 220 ft. per minute. By our equation, $W = F \times D$, we get Work $= 100 \times 220$, or 22,000 ft.-lb. of work every minute.

To allow for the work done in overcoming friction, and also not to over-estimate his engines' power, Watt added 50 per cent to this and said that 1 h.p. is the equivalent of raising 33,000 lb. 1 ft. in 1 minute, or is 33,000 ft.-lb. per minute. He arrived at that figure about 150 years ago, and it has remained ever since (Fig. 1 (a)). The following example may help, and will also make clear how time affects power, but not work

Time and Power

The fourth floor of a building is 64 ft. above the ground floor. A stop-watch shows that it takes $1\frac{1}{2}$ minutes to walk up, or 28 seconds to go up in the lift. If a person weighs $10\frac{1}{2}$ stones, the work done is $F \times D$, or 147 lb. $\times 64$ ft., that is, 9408 ft.-lb. The time spent walking is $1\frac{1}{2}$ minutes, so the rate of working is $\frac{9408}{1\frac{1}{2}}$, or 6272 ft.-lb. per minute.

Now 1 h.p. is 33,000 ft.-lb. per minute, so our walker has developed $\frac{6272}{33,000} = 0.19$

ORIGIN OF HORSE-POWER AS A UNIT

FIG. 1. *(a) How James Watt estimated horse-power. A horse walking forward at $2\frac{1}{2}$ m.p.h. can pull 100 lb. up a well-shaft, equivalent to 22,000 lb. lifted 1 ft. in 1 minute. He added 50 per cent and called 33,000 ft.-lb. per minute 1 h.p. (b) Pulling the airtight piston up 1 ft. is the same as lifting a 15-lb. weight 1 ft., or doing 15 ft.-lb. of work.*

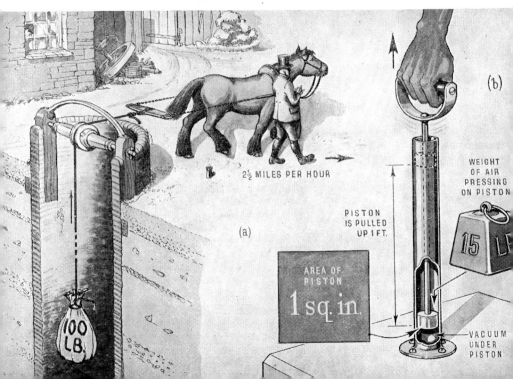

2½ MILES PER HOUR

(a)

(b)

PISTON IS PULLED UP 1 FT.

WEIGHT OF AIR PRESSING ON PISTON

AREA OF PISTON

1 sq. in.

15 LB

100 LB.

VACUUM UNDER PISTON

h.p. Put him in the lift and consider only the work done in raising him, leaving the lift itself out of the account. Work now is $9408 \times \frac{60}{28}$ ft.-lb. per minute and horse-power is $\frac{9408 \times 60}{28} \times \frac{1}{33,000}$, or 0·61 h.p.

The scientist, measuring in centimetres, grams, and seconds, uses a different unit, already mentioned, the watt. A rate of 1 h.p. is the same as 746 watts. The 60-watt lamp, then, is demanding $\frac{60}{746}$ h.p. to keep it going, say, $\frac{1}{12}$ h.p.

Here is an example. Look at all the electric lamps in your home or work-place and make a note of the number of watts given on each of them. Add these together so as to find the total wattage, or power. Divide this number by 746 and so find the horse-power needed to keep you bright! A conveniently larger unit is the kilowatt, or 1000 watts. An electric fire rated at 1 kW is taking power at the rate of $1\frac{1}{3}$ h.p.; a large modern generator, turbine-driven, may have an output as high as 100,000 kW.

Popular usage is not always scientifically accurate. We are always very liable to confuse the meanings of power and energy, though this will not matter very much if we are ready to recognize the distinction when it is necessary. For instance, we often talk about sources of power, but what we really mean is sources of energy; in daily speech the two words are almost interchangeable. And what are the sources?

Sources of Energy

The earliest, of course, was simply manpower. There was the worker with his strong right arm, or the thews and sinews of the slave. The modern problem of when to scrap and replace, and when to repair and maintain, had its counterpart in the Roman world. Is it cheaper to work your slaves literally to death and then replace them, or to be more humane and work them less strenuously so that they live longer? With such sources can be classed the use of animals—horse, ass, mule, bullock and elephant.

But, ages ago, men discovered that there were natural forces they could harness. The origins of water-wheels and windmills are lost in the mists of antiquity, but

these ingenious devices are still with us.

The windmill has a niche today, though it no longer has the place it occupied a hundred years ago when, in some parts of the country, all grinding of corn, sawing of wood, and much else, was performed by the winds of heaven.

The water-wheel has developed into the turbine of the hydro-electric plant, the source of power in some of the greatest generating stations in the world.

First Steps Into Power Age

These are forces that can be drawn upon and used; they can hardly be controlled. Consequently, the real step into the Power Age was not taken until the discovery of steam power. The steam-engine takes its power from coal-fired boilers which can be lighted, stoked, and regulated just as required. Coal also made the locomotive possible.

Here, too, a new principle is introduced. The source of power is now heat energy obtained by the burning of fuel, depending in turn on the chemical energy of combustion. The immediate source in the two other cases just discussed was the movement of wind or water, cases of what we have learned to call Kinetic Energy. Certainly it is also true that these were derived from the heat energy radiated by the sun, but that was not evident or known to those who used them.

Another source of paramount importance today is oil. Oil can be used in two ways: it can be burnt in a furnace under a steam boiler to produce heat, like coal or any other fuel; it can be used in the internal-combustion engine of the motor car or aeroplane, a method that must have further consideration. In the Royal Navy you may see, alongside each other, the great battleship with oil-fired steam engines, and the swift motor torpedo-boat driven by the internal-combustion engine.

Finally, there is the energy of the atom. The menace of the abuse of atomic energy, shattering and terrible, hangs over our world, with the riddle of its future possible uses and misuses all unsolved.

These are sources of power. How do they get to work? When we use one of the actual forces of nature, the push of wind or water, it is easy to understand; but what of a lump of black, stony stuff, or a gallon of clear liquid? Where is the power in coal or oil?

Heat as a Form of Energy

The answer is: Heat! It is heat that makes the wheels go round. Heat boils water. Heat raises the steam to a higher temperature and, if it cannot escape, to a higher pressure. The molecules of water or steam are always in a state of random, excited motion, and heat drives them faster and faster. They beat upon the prison walls of the boiler more and more furiously as they struggle to escape. Guide them, by steam pipe and valve, into the cylinder and they will urge the piston along before them.

But now the steam expands, the molecules have done a job of work, they have lost some of their store of energy and are moving more slowly. They have lost heat, but that heat, itself a form of energy, has reappeared in the movement of the cylinders, the rotation of the flywheel, and the performance of the machine.

All this can be worked out in a very neat and important formula. Suppose we have a cylinder fitted with an airtight piston, whose area is just 1 sq. in., resting on the bottom. The air is pressing on it with a weight of 15 lb., for that is atmospheric pressure, 15 lb. per sq. in. Now, it is pulled out for 1 ft. That must be the same as lifting 15 lb. up through 1 ft., assuming a perfect fit, and a complete vacuum behind the piston (Fig. 1 (b)).

We have already seen that Work is Force times Distance moved through, so we have done 15×1 ft.-lb. of work. Now, make its area 2 sq. in. and we must do twice as much work, $15 \times 1 \times 2$ ft.-lb. Move it $1\frac{1}{2}$ ft. and the 1 ft. becomes $1\frac{1}{2}$ ft., or work is $15 \times 1\frac{1}{2} \times 2$. Do this 60 times a minute and in that minute we do $15 \times 1\frac{1}{2} \times 2 \times 60$ ft.-lb.

Engineers' Formula

If we want to, we can turn this rate of work into horse-power by dividing by 33,000 and say horse-power $= \frac{15 \times 1\frac{1}{2} \times 2 \times 60}{33,000}$, or about $\frac{1}{12}$ h.p., enough for a 60-watt lamp.

This is the formula for calculating the horse-power of an engine, only the engineer uses the first letters of the words we have employed and writes Horse-Power $= \frac{P.L.A.N.}{33,000}$. Pressure of steam in lb. per sq. in., Length in ft., Area in sq. in., Number of strokes per minute. He also measures his pressure in a particular way, taking it as a kind of average between the beginning and end of the stroke.

It is interesting to note that Watt would have nothing to do with high pressures, and even tried to persuade Parliament to render the use of high-pressure steam illegal. His engines worked at about 5 to 10 lb. per sq. in. Trevithick, the Cornish pioneer railway engineer, and pioneer of high-pressure steam, used it at 50 to 75 lb. per sq. in. in his locomotives.

The short representative list below of some of the best-known express locomotive types during the last hundred years, shows how the working steam pressure has risen.

Efficiency

This is a convenient place to say something about Efficiency. What is really behind the use of higher pressures is not so much getting steam with more *push* in it, as using it at a higher *temperature*.

It is easy to determine the thermal value of a fuel as so many B.Th.U.s per lb. When we have found it, and then measured the actual amount of useful work we get

Type and Company	Date	Boiler pressure
		lb. per sq. in.
Stephenson's "Rocket" .	1829	50
G.W.R. (broad gauge) "Great Western". .	1846	100
L.N.W.R. 4-4-0 "Bloomers" . . .	1850-60	150
G.N.R. "Atlantics" .	1898	175
G.W.R. "Cities" .	1905	195
S.R. "Lord Nelson" .	1926	220
L.M.S.R. "Royal Scot" .	1927	250
L.N.E.R. "Edward Thompson" (the 2000th engine to be built at Doncaster) . .	1946	250
And, finally, two experimental locomotives:		
L.M.S. "Fury" . .	1929	1400-1800
L.N.E.R. No. 10,000 .	1931	450

POWER FOR FORGING STEEL

Here is power under exact control. This great steam hammer can beat a large piece of steel to shape and yet, despite the power available behind its blows, it can be applied with very much greater precision of pressure than could a manually operated hammer.

from it, the discrepancy appears startling. We do very well if we get one-quarter of it as work!

Thermodynamics tells us two things. The first is that, at best, much of this loss is unavoidable; a 100 per cent efficient heat engine is impossible. The second is that the higher the temperature, or, better, the wider the temperature gap between the boiler and the exhaust, the greater will be the proportion of the heat-energy we shall catch as power. That is to say, steam at high temperatures, and, therefore, high pressures, is more efficient, or economical, in its use of fuel.

Fantastic Steam-raising

Modern practice seeks to attain this increased efficiency. Special steam-raising plants may even deliver steam at the fantastic figures of 3000 lb. per sq. in. and 1200 deg. F.

When it comes to the engine, we have compound engines in which the steam is used in two, three, or even four cylinders, one after the other, in successive expansions, until it reaches the exhaust.

Importance of the Turbine

The most efficient form of all is the turbine. This has replaced the reciprocating engine entirely in electric power stations and is almost the universal practice in large marine engines. In both cases the steam does not exhaust into the open air, but into a water-cooled condenser, which gives still greater efficiency. One ton of coal can now be used to generate nearly four times as much power as it would forty years ago.

The railway engineer uses another device, streamlining the locomotive to avoid wasting power in overcoming air resistance. This is particularly valuable at high speeds. When the velocity of a head wind has to be added to the engine's speed, it may result in a saving of one-eighth, or more.

Another way to obtain power from fuel

① COAL — LATENT ENERGY

② COAL IS MINED

CONVE

UNDERCUTTER AT WORK

LOW — PRESSURE TURBINE

GENERATOR

STATOR

BLADES

EXCITER MOTOR

EXHAUST STEAM TO CONDENSER

ROTOR

⑥ MECHANICAL ENERGY TRANSFORMED INTO ELECTRICAL ENERGY BY GENERATOR

EARTH WIRE

THREE-PHASE CABLES TO TRANSFORMER

STEP-UP TRANSFORMER

L. ASHWELL WOOD.

⑦ ELECTRICAL ENERGY DISTRIBUTED BY TRANSFORMER

WONDERFUL CHAIN OF

Millions of years ago, green plants trapped the energy of the sun's heat; the earth stored it in coal-fields; now we mine it and get that heat back in the furnace. Thus the heat energy becomes kinetic energy—first in the jostling molecules of hot steam, then in the whirling

④ HEAT OF FURNACE GENERATES STEAM IN BOILER

BOILER

STEAM TO TURBINE

SUPERHEATER

AL TO SURFACE

③ COAL PRODUCES HEAT IN FURNACE

WATER TUBES

HIGH-PRESSURE TURBINE

GRATE

BLADES

STEAM

◄ VALVE CHEST

⑤ STEAM PRESSURE IS CONVERTED INTO MECHANICAL ENERGY BY STEAM ENGINE (TURBINE)

PULLEYS

BUTING S (GRID)

STEP-DOWN TRANSFORMERS

ROTOR

STATOR

MILLING MACHINE

C. TRIC TOR

⑨ ELECTRICAL ENERGY CHANGED INTO MECHANICAL ENERGY BY ELECTRIC MOTOR

ENERGY CONVERSIONS

turbines in numerous power-houses. The generators convert it to electrical energy. Distributed by the Grid system, it is tapped wherever it is wanted to do work, or to give light or warmth. It is an intriguing thought that electric lamps are in effect operated by the sun!

would be to burn the fuel inside the engine itself and cut out all the wasteful and expensive business of furnaces, boilers and steam pipes. Such engines, using gas, petrol or oil, are called "internal-combustion engines."

Birth of the Internal Combustion-engine

The 1860s and 1870s really saw their birth, though the principle was first applied as far back as 1680. Gunpowder was exploded in a cylinder and made to drive a piston, but gunpowder engines proved impracticable, as the explosions were too violent.

Experiments were made again in the early nineteenth century in which air and hydrogen were mixed and exploded in the engine cylinder.

But it was Otto, who brought out his "silent engine" in 1876, and thus made the internal-combustion engine a success. He made his engines compress a mixture of gas and air before explosion, getting greatly increased power and efficiency. He invented the "four-stroke cycle." This operates as follows: (a) Piston moves out and sucks mixture in; (b) piston moves in and compresses mixture. Next comes the explosion of the charge, followed by: (c) Piston driven out and doing work; (d) piston moves in and expels the burnt gases (Fig. 2).

In 1895, Daimler applied the same cycle to his motor-car engines, using petrol vapour instead of gas, and gave us what has become the modern internal-combustion engine of the car and the aeroplane, and of so many other uses.

Efficient Diesel Engine

Later again, the same principle gave us the Diesel engine. In this case, air only is first drawn in and then compresssed to the

FOUR-STROKE CYCLE PRINCIPLE

Fig. 2. *(a) Charging. Piston descends and draws mixture in through valve* A*; valve* B *is closed. (b) Compression. Piston rises with both valves closed and compresses the mixture. (c) Combustion. Piston descends, the spark having fired the mixture. Both valves are closed. Work is being done during this stroke. (d) Exhausting. Piston rises, driving spent gases out through valve* B*; valve* A *closed. Valves are actuated from cams on shaft.*

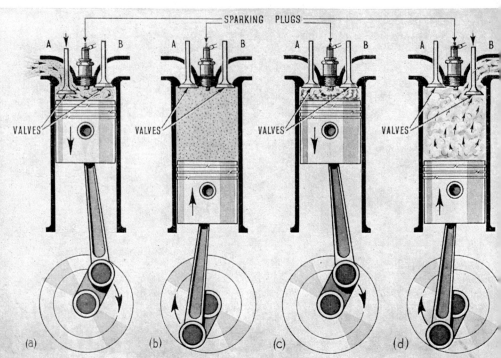

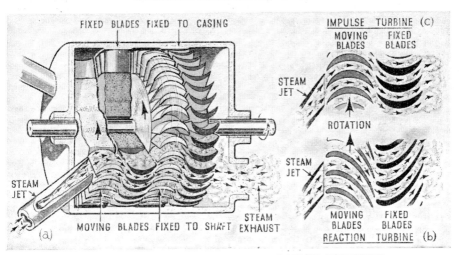

FIXED BLADES FIXED TO CASING

IMPULSE TURBINE (C)
MOVING BLADES — FIXED BLADES

STEAM JET

ROTATION

STEAM JET

STEAM JET

STEAM EXHAUST

MOVING BLADES FIXED TO SHAFT

MOVING BLADES — FIXED BLADES
REACTION TURBINE (b)

(a)

PRINCIPLES OF IMPULSE AND REACTION TURBINES

FIG. 3. *(a) Simplified view of a steam turbine, showing how the steam passes from the jet to the exhaust; a ring of rotor blades, fixed to the axle, being spun round by its passage. The stator blades, mounted on the casing, do not move; they guide the steam to the next rotor. In a turbine there are many such rings, their diameters constantly increasing as the steam expands. (b) Reaction turbine. When blades have this shape, steam issues from them faster than it enters and "kicks" them round behind it. (c) Impulse turbine. With blades so shaped, the steam "pushes" the rotor round by blowing on them.*

high pressure of about 500 lb. per sq. in. This makes it so hot that when a jet of crude oil is now shot into the cylinder it immediately fires by itself.

Engine with Highest Efficiency

Efficiency? The Diesel is the most efficient type of heat engine we have. The earliest, in 1897, had an overall efficiency of 25 per cent; thirty years later the figure had been raised to 36 per cent, and Diesel engines have since been built to yield nearly 40 per cent of the heat energy as useful work. A petrol engine has an efficiency of about 30 per cent. Our coal-fired, turbine-driven generating station gave about 25 per cent. The railway locomotive, "Royal Scot," on official test gave only just over 7 per cent, but an ordinary locomotive would give only 5 per cent overall efficiency, or even less!

This last figure makes one gasp and feel inclined to talk of the *inefficiency* of the locomotive. Well, it *is* inefficient, but look at the limitations of length, width, height

and weight which working conditions impose upon it! Its designer is hampered by them at every turn. Then, too, efficiency is measured at the draw-bar, and is based on the weight it can pull. No account is taken of the energy it uses in driving itself along, nearly 200 tons of it, at 60 m.p.h., or more. Only what is left over after that is available for the train.

Early Form of Turbine

How do turbines work? The simplest form is the ancient windmill. It has sails, or vanes, set to face the wind, but inclined at an angle to it. As the wind rushes against them, it tries to do two things. It tries to blow the vanes back against the mill and, if they were set at right angles to the wind's direction, it could do nothing else. As they are set on a slope to it, the wind also tries to brush them aside.

Or things can be pushed around in another way. There is, for example, the Catherine-wheel and the rocket. The Catherine-wheel is a spirally coiled length of firework which shoots out a high-velocity stream of gas and sparks and is driven round by the reaction. A rocket is straight and tries to fly straight. The V2 did the same; so does a jet-propelled plane. And the principle is not new, it is, indeed, very ancient; a Greek called Hero discovered it in the first century! Nature gave it ages ago to the squid and octopus.

Impulse and Reaction Turbines

Note the difference carefully. The windmill uses a ready-made wind to push its sails around. It is an *impulse* turbine. Jet propulsion makes a wind which issues from jets and pushes the jets backwards. It is a *reaction* turbine. Blow a small rubber balloon up and toss it into the air. See how the air, rushing out, drives it crazily about. Watch a sprinkler revolving on a lawn.

Both principles are utilized in modern machinery. It was Sir Charles Parsons who discovered how to apply reaction, and his turbines (really impulse-cum-reaction) have revolutionized marine engineering and power-station practice.

All this is a very much simplified attempt to explain a highly complicated machine. In use, high-pressure steam issues through jets and is led through one ring after another of blades (these correspond to the windmill sails), driving them round and expanding as it goes. The spindle which carries these blades is called the rotor. Between each of these rings there is another ring of blades, fixed to the casing, which does not turn, its purpose being to guide the steam to the next ring of revolving blades. This is called the stator (Fig. 3).

Glorified Water-wheel

Similarly, a water-turbine is a glorified water-wheel. Instead of expanding steam, we have the weight and force of flowing water brought from the heights of a water-

LARGEST COAL-FIRED GENERATING STATION IN EUROPE
One of the generating rooms at Barking Power Station, from which plant 2000 million units of electricity go out in a year, almost equal to a quarter of the units of electricity turned out for the whole of Great Britain; it also has a reserve capacity of about 500,000 kW. It is interesting to note that it uses a million tons of coal annually.

IN THE WORLD'S BIGGEST GAS WORKS

"Blower" *room of the water gas plant at the Beckton Gas Works, which claims to be the biggest gas works in the world. An operator is starting up an additional turbine. The high-speed turbine-driven fans help to produce 25 to 30 million cu. ft. of gas per day.*

fall like Niagara, or the lochs of Scotland, or the "white coal" of Norway's mountain torrents.

So far we have thought only of power for immediate use, "to be consumed on the premises," within the narrow confines of the factory or station where it is generated. It has to be transmitted from one point to another within that area, but that is all. Belts and shafting, so characteristic of a factory, can do that.

Can it be generated "to be consumed off the premises"?

Power on "Tap"

Obvious advantages would include one large central generating station, run as economically as possible, lessening transport of bulky fuels, the power being taken to the exact spot where it is wanted and, if that changes, redirected to the new site.

A gas-engine using gas from the mains would be an example. Actually, however, these engines nearly always use gas made on the spot. If it is "producer gas," it is

the result of blowing air through red-hot coke and is chiefly carbon monoxide diluted with nitrogen from the air. If it is "water gas," it is made by blowing air and steam mixed over the coke and contains hydrogen as well as the other gases. The gas-engine, then, hardly satisfies our requirements.

Strangely enough, though with reservations, water power is superior. Several of our largest cities, London, Manchester, Glasgow, for example, have hydraulic power mains. In the case of the first two, the water in them is at a pressure of 750 lb. per sq. in.; at Glasgow it is actually as high as about 1000 lb. per sq. in. Hydraulic power is most useful when very great force is required intermittently; to bend or cut a thick metal plate in a shipbuilding yard, or to compress a cotton bale, or to hoist a weight of many tons. It is easily controlled, can be worked with great precision, and needs no elaborate gearing. Its limitations are that it is unsuitable for rapid or continuous motion, and cannot economically

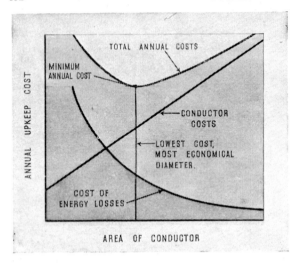

ANNUAL UPKEEP COST

MINIMUM
ANNUAL COST

TOTAL ANNUAL COSTS

CONDUCTOR
COSTS

LOWEST COST,
MOST ECONOMICAL
DIAMETER

COST OF
ENERGY LOSSES

AREA OF CONDUCTOR

FIG. 4. *"Portrait"* of a compromise. *Spending more on the conductor is good, up to a certain point; then further gain in efficiency is more than offset by the very high cost.*

be transmitted more than ten or fifteen miles.

Electricity is the form of power *par excellence* for transmission. Pylons and cables like spider webs over the countryside tell us that; or railways running for scores of miles with the electrified third rail beside the running track emphasize it. Often, too, in modern works the machines have their own individual motors alongside, dispensing with whirling shafts and belts, and only running when actually necessary.

Minimizing Inevitable Losses

The trouble with every form of transmission or distribution is that it inevitably wastes some of the power. It leaks. However scientifically lubricated, every journal, every belt, means friction, and power lost in overcoming it. It is true of hydraulic power as well, for even pure water has viscosity, and every conductor of electricity has a certain resistance. Always, for reasons such as these, apart from actual leakages arising from imperfections of construction and material, there is loss.

The transmission of electric power is too big a subject to go into at any length, too important to be missed altogether. We can glance only at some of its salient features.

The normal voltage of our Grid system is 132 kV (a kilovolt is 1000 volts). This high voltage is used because it is less waste-ful in transmission than the normal, lower voltages we are accustomed to. Whatever voltage the generator works at, and it will not be as high as this, a transformer takes over the output and steps up its pressure, or voltage, to this figure. Then it is handed over to the transmission line, the familiar cross-country cable; this is tapped where needed and transformers again alter the voltage, this time stepping it down to the familiar 230 volts for domestic use, or to whatever figure is best for the purpose in hand. (In an underground cable the voltage is lower.)

The actual transmission puts us upon the horns of a dilemma. The more efficient we make the transmission, the more costly it is; costs of erection and maintenance have to be balanced against cost of power lost. Skimp the first, and the second is inordinately high; cut the second down, and a stage is reached where the first reaches a figure which is no longer economical. A compromise has to be sought; the size and material of the cables must be chosen so as to give the best results in all the circumstances (Fig. 4).

Conductors for the "Grid"

The British Grid system uses a line of thirty strands of aluminium wire with a core of seven strands of galvanized iron wire and has an overall diameter of 0·77 in. Copper is a better conductor if you use wires of the same size; but, weight for weight, aluminium is twice as good. The small steel core is for strength.

This, then, is an outline of Power—what it is, what it does, how it is sought and applied. It is an ironical subject. Power has relieved us of much heavy labour, and "man-handling" is becoming more and more a thing of the past; women in the Potteries no longer stagger under crushing loads of wet clay; the miner, the sailor, the farmer, all have their mechanical aids.

The irony lies here. By its very nature, Power should be energy under human control, working for human ends, and so entirely humane. Yet sometimes it seems to be running away with us. It gives us new weapons of destruction such as the tank or atom bomb; it revolutionizes communications and speeds up production.

Whither Power?

But life speeds up, too, and becomes more nervous and anxious. New ways for the production and exploitation of power are found, but insecurity and apprehension grow. Fire-like, Power is an excellent servant, but an inhuman master. What is it to be, a pliant slave, or an inflexible tyrant?

Test Yourself

1. Coal is burned under the boilers in a railway power station as the ultimate source of power for the electric trains. Make as complete a list as you can of all the ways in which its energy is lost between furnace and moving train.

2. Why does a fireman, holding a hose, feel it pushing him back?

3. The height of the Niagara Falls is 160 ft. By how much is the temperature of the water raised by going over the fall? The mechanical equivalent of heat is 780 ft.-lb. per 1 deg. F.

4. A waterfall is 20 ft. high and 300 cub. ft. of water pass over it every second. If turbines are installed at the foot and $12\frac{1}{2}$ per cent of the available energy is obtained, what horse-power do they provide? 1 cub. ft. of water weighs 62·5 lb. and 1 h.p. is 33,000 ft.-lb. per minute.

5. A train weighing 250 tons and travelling at 45 m.p.h. on the level has to overcome a total resistance from friction and the air of 16 lb. per ton. What horse-power is the engine developing?

6. Average pressure of steam in a double-acting cylinder is 143 lb. per sq. in. The area of the piston is 50 sq. in. and the length of the stroke is 24 in. How much work does it do in one complete revolution? (N.B.—There are *two* working strokes to the revolution.) At 60 r.p.m., what horse-power is being developed?

7. In a room a 100-watt lamp is burning, a 450-watt electric iron is in use, and a 1-kW fire is switched on. What horse-power is being employed? 746 watts are 1 h.p.

8. An electric power station develops 65,000 h.p., this being the mean value throughout the day. If the daily consumption is 750 tons of coal, of calorific value 10,000 B.Th.U. per lb., what is the overall efficiency of the station? Take the mechanical equivalent of heat as 780 ft.-lb.

Answers will be found at the end of the book.

STROBOSCOPE
ON EDGE OF
TURNTABLE RIM

MONITORING LOUDSPEAKER

CUTTING
HEAD

WAX
BLANK

RECORDING MACHINE

MAKING SOUND IMPERISHABLE

Recording speech and music for reproducing at will. (Above) In a "His Master's Voice" studio where recording on duplicate wax blanks is about to commence. (Below) Type D recorder at the B.B.C. on which broadcast programmes are recorded for re-broadcasting as required. In reproducing from the record, the wavy grooves of the record are converted into electrical vibrations which are an electrical equivalent of the sound waves.

RECORDING HEAD
TURNED UP FOR
INSPECTION

SUCTION BOX AND
PIPE FOR SWARF
REMOVAL

MAIN INPUT
JACKFIELD

RECORDING
HEAD
TRACKING
ASSEMBLY

SPEED-CHA
HANDLE

CONTROL
PANEL

REMOVABLE AMPLIFIERS
AND POWER UNITS

CHAPTER VIII

SOUND

SOUND, as we generally understand the term, is a sensation produced at the ears. We learn to distinguish different types of sensations of sound, such as continuous sounds or noises and impulsive sounds or clicks, but all of these types are known to be caused by variations of the atmospheric pressure at the ear.

If the sound is a continuous one, it is found that the atmospheric pressure is varying continuously—if the sound is impulsive, such as a single click, it is found that the pressure change is of short duration. But all changes of pressure at the ear do not produce the sensation of sound. For example, a train travelling through a tunnel sometimes causes a change of pressure which one can feel at the ear, but it does not give the sensation we normally attribute to sound.

There are certain simple conditions that the pressure changes must satisfy before they can be heard as sound and these are as follows. Firstly, the change of pressure must be sufficiently great and, secondly, it must be sufficiently rapid, but not too rapid. Roughly, it may be said that if the pressure changes by about one-thousand-millionth part, or, in other words, by about one-thousandth part of a millionth part of the atmospheric pressure, the sensation of sound will be produced provided the change has taken place in less than $\frac{1}{10}$th of a second.

Frequency of Vibration

In the case of a continuous sound, it is found that the changes of pressure occurring at the ear alternate between increases of pressure, or compressions, called condensations, and decreases of pressure, called rarefactions, and the sensation of a continuous sound is produced when the number of these alternations, or vibrations of pressure, is greater than about 20 per second.

As the number of these vibrations per second, known as the frequency of vibration, is increased, the ear gets a sensation of rising pitch, and when the number is about 256 vibrations per second the sound is of the same pitch as middle C on the piano. The top note on the piano corresponds to a continuous vibration of a frequency of about 3500 per second.

As the number of vibrations per second is increased still further, a shriller and shriller sound is heard, until finally, at about 20,000 vibrations per second, the sound begins to appear as a hiss, and above 30,000 vibrations per second the sensation of sound ceases altogether.

Simple Experiments

The reader can make simple experiments to verify some of these facts for himself. He can close his two half-cupped hands together, gently producing an increase of pressure and flow of air which can be felt without any noise. Then, by increasing the suddenness of compression by bringing the two hands together smartly, he can produce the characteristics of an explosive sound. Similarly, by withdrawing a loosely fitting cork from a bottle no sound is heard unless the cork is pulled out rapidly, so producing a sudden rarefaction. Again, by rubbing a card on a rotating gear wheel, or drawing a stick across iron railings, he gets a series of clicks which merge into a continuous note if the interruptions are sufficiently rapid.

Physicists class all pressure vibrations as sound even when they are of too low or too high a pitch to be audible. Such inaudible sounds are referred to as subaudible sounds, or ultrasonics.

A continuous sound can always be traced to a source of vibrating energy and it helps us to understand what is happening in sound transmission if we examine the sound produced by the prongs of a tuning fork after it has been struck (Fig. 1). As each prong moves forward it compresses the air in front of it, and when it moves backward it draws the air back with it, causing a sucking action and a resulting rarefaction

Now, the compression does not stay still when the prong has produced it, but moves outwards in all directions with a speed of about 1100 ft. per second, which is 750 miles per hour, or about ⅕th of a mile per second, and each compression is followed by a rarefaction. The air as a whole does not move from its steady position in space, it is only the state of condensation or rarefaction which moves outward.

Vibrating Particles

If we could examine one spot in the air surrounding the fork we should find the particles themselves were just vibrating backwards and forwards about their steady positions, while the states of condensation and rarefaction passed through the spot at a steady rate.

Fig. 1 shows really what happens in the region of a compression and rarefaction, and it can be seen that during the existence of a compression the particles on either side of the compression have moved towards the position of the compression, while the particle actually at the compression has not moved at all and is stationary. A rarefaction can be seen to occur at a region where particles on either side have moved away from the region.

Now, it is obvious from the diagram that every forward vibration of the prong produces a compression, so that if the fork makes 100 vibrations per second, 100 condensations will have travelled outwards. The first condensation will have travelled 1100 ft. from the prong of the fork at the end of the second; from which it follows that in 1100 ft. there are 100 condensations.

The distance between neighbouring condensations (or neighbouring rarefactions) is called the wavelength of the sound and the motion of the states of compression and rarefaction outwards is known as a sound wave.

From the above reasoning it can be seen that the wavelength of a sound wave of 100 vibrations per second is 11 ft. We can see that, in general, the wavelength multiplied by the number of vibrations per second is equal to the velocity of sound. The longest wavelength we can hear (corresponding to 20 vibrations per second) is, therefore

$\frac{1100}{20} = 55$ ft., and the smallest we can hear is $\frac{1100}{30,000} = \frac{11}{300}$ ft. = about $\frac{1}{2}$ in.

The reader will have heard of wireless waves, which are not the same as sound waves, and should not be confused with them. Wireless waves are very lucidly explained in Chapter 12.

Examples of the speed of sound can be observed in ordinary life. Thunder always follows lightning, although both flash and crack occur together at the source. If one watches a cricket match at a distance, one can often hear the crack of the bat hitting the ball after the hit is observed. The noise of a train leaving a distant station reaches us after the train is seen to have started on its course.

The air is a very important link in the communication of sound from a vibrating body to the ear. It can be shown very easily that no sound reaches the ear when a body vibrates in a vacuum. But any elastic medium, solid, liquid or gas, will conduct sound. This can be observed when noises are transmitted along water pipes. Conduction of sound in water is made use of in the hydrophone for picking up the noises of submarines and for measuring the depths of ocean beds.

In the transmission of sounds through solids and liquids, condensations and rarefactions of the medium as well as motion of the particles take place just as in the case of transmission by air. The main difference is that the sound wave travels faster; for example, the velocity of sound in water is about 3200 miles per hour and it is about 11,000 miles per hour in most metals.

Sense of direction is determined by the aural system, owing to the difference in time between the sound reaching the two ears.

The sound from a source travels outwards in all directions and its vibrational pressure becomes distributed over a larger surface as it travels outwards.

As a result, the pressure, as well as the size, of vibration decreases with distance from the source. This accounts for the observed fact that the loudness of a sound diminishes as the distance from the source is increased. It should be remembered that the number of vibrations per second, or the

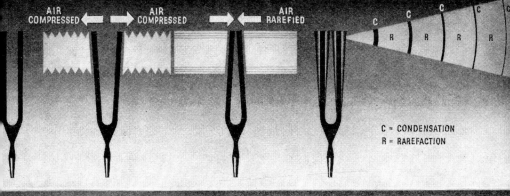

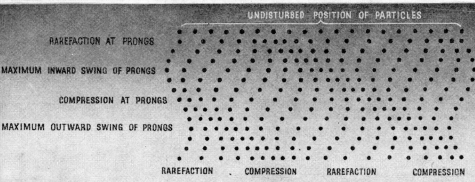

UNDISTURBED POSITION OF PARTICLES

RAREFACTION AT PRONGS

MAXIMUM INWARD SWING OF PRONGS

COMPRESSION AT PRONGS

MAXIMUM OUTWARD SWING OF PRONGS

RAREFACTION · COMPRESSION · RAREFACTION · COMPRESSION

PROPAGATION OF SOUND WAVES

FIG. 1. *Prong of a tuning fork compresses the air as it moves forward and rarefies the air as it moves backward. These disturbances move outward at a speed of about 750 miles per hour. The lower portion of the diagram shows the state of the air particles as the prong makes a complete vibration. Notice that the condensations and rarefactions move from left to right in the diagram; but in space they move out as spherical surfaces.*

pitch of the sound, does not alter with distance.

When sound falls on an object of any kind, a portion of it is scattered back or reflected. If the obstacle is soft or of a porous nature, only a very little of the sound is reflected and most of it is absorbed by the porous space of the obstacle. If, on the other hand, the obstacle is hard, such as wood or stone, almost all of the sound is reflected back.

One can notice this effect in the open air, by comparing traffic noise as reflected by a house or wall or wooden fence and that heard in front of a haystack. The latter is much quieter. Similarly, by clapping in front of a wall or in front of a haystack, one notices a tremendous difference in the loudness of the sound reflected.

An interesting effect occurs when the obstacle is quite large and some consider-able distance away from the source. Suppose, for example, one claps the hand or shouts about 36 ft. away from a large building or cliff. The sound reflected backwards will have travelled about 72 ft. before it returns to the source. It will, therefore, arrive back to the sender $\frac{72}{1100}$ths, or about $\frac{1}{15}$th, of a second after it was originally sent out.

Under these conditions, the ear hears a second sound, sharply separated from the original sound, which is known as an echo. If the object is nearer than 36 ft., the reflected sound appears as a prolongation of the original sound, because the ear is not capable of separating sounds which occur within $\frac{1}{15}$th of a second of each other. This prolongation of a sound is known as reverberation.

Echoes of quite long intervals can often be heard in hilly or mountainous country, and even multiple echoes may be heard if there are several suitably reflecting hills. In large buildings, especially cathedrals and churches, reflections of the walls and ceiling cause echoes and reverberation which are sometimes detrimental to the good hearing of speech.

Blanketing the Unwanted Sound

In such cases, acoustical engineers study the various reflecting surfaces which are mainly responsible for the long interval reflections, and place on them absorbent materials, such as porous tiles, asbestos blankets or hairfelt, to absorb this unwanted sound.

This study of sound is often referred to as architectural acoustics, and it is possible nowadays to predict the acoustic qualities of buildings before they are erected, thus saving a considerable amount of trouble that is always involved in correcting an acoustically inferior building. Musicians prefer a slight amount of reverberation, as if there is too much absorption by the surfaces reproduction of music appears rather deadened or muffled.

Some interesting phenomena occur in open country, due to the effect of different weather conditions on sound propagation. Most of us have noticed, for example, that when a gentle wind is blowing, many distant sounds on the windward side are heard quite distinctly, whereas sounds on the lee side are inaudible, even though their source is not very distant. One can notice this by listening to the noise of traffic from a distant road under different wind conditions.

The explanation of this lies not in the extra velocity given to the sound due to the wind, but in the alteration of the tilt of the sound waves produced by the change in wind speed as the height above the surface of the earth is increased. Fig. 2 illustrates the action.

Owing to the friction and resistance of obstacles and rough surfaces, the wind speed near the ground is less than that higher up. As a result, in the direction of the wind the parts of the waves high above the ground, say those parts where the compressions and rarefactions are, gain on those parts nearer the ground. The waves, therefore, tilt downwards.

In this way sound, which otherwise, in the absence of the wind, would have passed over the head of a distant observer, is now deflected downwards to him. Therefore, he hears the sound more loudly at any point and will consequently hear the noise at a greater distance from the source than in the absence of the wind.

The case of the wind blowing away from the listener is interesting, in so far that beyond a certain distance the noise will not be heard, however loud it is, since the waves will all be directed up into the atmosphere above the heads of observers on the ground.

Other interesting effects of sound transmission occur owing to reflections of upper regions of the atmosphere, where sounds are heard tens of miles from their origin. During the Second World War, for example, aircraft were heard 20 miles away, owing to favourable wind conditions, while there have been instances where aircraft have been identified at less than half a mile and yet been inaudible.

The sound from an aircraft always appears to come from a position behind it. This is because the aircraft has travelled quite an appreciable distance by the time sound which has left it reaches the ears of an observer. For example, if an aeroplane is travelling broadside to an observer at a speed of about 400 miles per hour, the sound appears to lag behind the plane by an angle of about 28 deg.

Infinitely Small Power

Sound is a form of energy, just like heat or electricity. In the case of sound waves, however, the power is remarkably small. Whereas in electricity we speak of watts and kilowatts, in sound the power we are concerned with is usually thousandths of a watt, or milliwatts, and even millionths of a watt, or microwatts.

The amount of power or energy in sound that is just audible to the ear varies with the frequency of the sound, but in the case of a frequency of about 1000 vibrations per second it is about a thousandth part of a millionth part of a microwatt. The energy

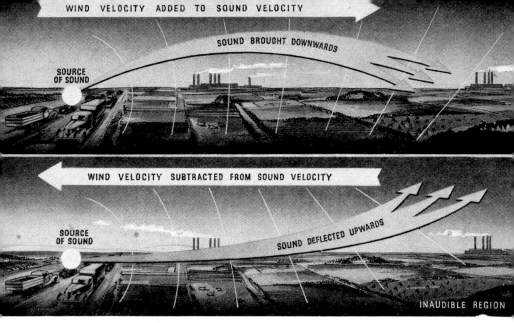

SOUND PROPAGATION AFFECTED BY WIND CONDITIONS

FIG. 2. *Velocity of a wind increases gradually with its height from the ground. Thus, the upper portions of sound waves are more affected than those near the ground. They are accelerated when they move in the same direction as the wind and always tend to be brought down to earth. Opposite effect occurs when wind blows opposite to the sound wave.*

in a whisper is about a millionth of a microwatt, and the energy due to average loud conversation 3 ft. away from the speaker is about a thousandth part of a microwatt.

When the power at the ear is about a hundredth of a watt, the sound is painful or disagreeable and may cause damage to the ear. Roughly, we may say that a whisper is about a thousand times more powerful than a sound that is just audible, and the power to produce a painful sound is ten billion times greater than the barely audible sound.

Tenfold Power Ratio

Partly because the ear deals with such an enormous range of power (actually ten billion times, i.e. 10^{13}), power ratios of tenfold have been introduced to express these colossal loudness levels. These units are called bels; thus, starting with the barely audible sound as 0 bels, a sound ten times louder, such as the quiet rustle of leaves in a gentle breeze, is said to be 1 bel louder. A whisper is a thousand times louder, i.e. $10 \times 10 \times 10$, or 3 bels louder.

The units of bels are split up in ten smaller units called decibels. The energy or power change for a decibel is about 26 per cent, that is, it corresponds to a ratio of 1·26. It can be easily shown that if we multiply 1·26 by itself ten times we get 10, which is the same as saying that a change of 10 decibels is the same as a change of 1 bel.

Notes of Identical Pitch

When two different instruments, such as a flute and a violin, sound two notes which a musician agrees are in unison, or of the same pitch, any non-musical ear can observe that there is a characteristic difference between them. When the two notes are examined by a very critical ear, it is found that the violin note appears to consist of a set of several notes, whereas the flute consists almost entirely of one note only and this note is found to be identical with the lowest note of the set of notes making up the violin sound.

This qualitative difference between two notes of identical pitch is given the term "quality," or "timbre," and it is the pitch

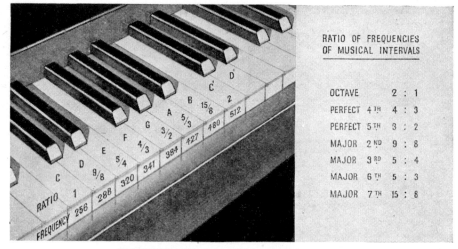

RATIO OF FREQUENCIES OF MUSICAL INTERVALS		
OCTAVE	2	: 1
PERFECT 4 TH	4	: 3
PERFECT 5 TH	3	: 2
MAJOR 2 ND	9	: 8
MAJOR 3 RD	5	: 4
MAJOR 6 TH	5	: 3
MAJOR 7 TH	15	: 8

FREQUENCIES OF SOME PIANO NOTES
FIG. 3. *Giving the arithmetical ratios between the notes of the major scale.*

of the lowest component of a sound that gives its characteristic pitch. This lowest component is called the "fundamental" and the higher components are called "overtones." A sound that consists of one note only, and cannot be split up into others, is called a "pure note." Examples of almost pure notes are the flute, tin whistle, tuning fork, overblown organ pipe and the ocarina.

With most musical notes the frequencies of the overtones are exact multiples, i.e. two, three, four, etc., times the frequency of the fundamental, in which case they are called "harmonics," since combinations of two or more of them correspond to harmonizing chords in music. There are other musical instruments, such as bells and percussion instruments, which have, as well as harmonics, but to a less extent, other overtones which are not harmonic. Any steady continuous sound can be analysed into a series of pure notes which are harmonics.

Musical Intervals

Fig. 3 gives details of the ratios of the frequencies of the different musical intervals. The notes on the piano are given

FIG. 4. *(Left) If the weight is pulled downwards and then let go, it oscillates up and down. Each particle of the spring will be observed to perform the same oscillatory motion, which*

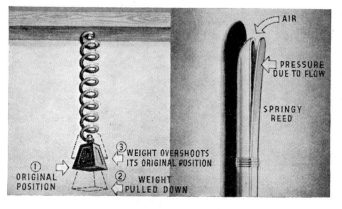

is typical of the motion of particles in a sound wave. (Right) As air is lightly blown through the slit, there is a pressure produced tending to close the slit. Thus the air flow will stop and the springy reed will fly back and the process is repeated, producing a steady sound. This is the principle of some musical instruments.

FIG. 5. *The prongs of a tuning fork send out waves of compressions and rarefactions which travel down the tube with a velocity of 1100 ft. per sec. When the waves reach the surface of the water at the bottom of the tube, they are reflected back towards the fork. If the time (or distance) of travel is correctly adjusted by*

PIECE OF GLASS OR METAL TUBE

TUMBLER OF WATER

raising or lowering the tube in the water, the reflected sound waves can be made to assist the sound from the fork and a loud sound is heard, i.e. resonance occurs. When the height AB is one-quarter of the wavelength of the sound from the fork, a loud note is emitted.

also in terms of a ratio of each note to the reference note.

We have seen that sound consists of either a sudden or an alternating change of pressure, and that, generally associated with this change of pressure, there is a to-and-fro motion of the particles. We would, therefore, expect that if by any means we could change the pressure of particles, either suddenly or oscillatorily, we should produce or generate sound. This is actually the case, and we can produce the necessary change either mechanically or electrically.

There are numerous ways of mechanically generating sound and it is possible to describe only a representative few of them. Impulsive sounds can be produced by explosions, hammer hits, collisions of objects, etc. Continuous sounds are produced by setting something of the nature of a spring into vibration.

Suppose, for example, as in Fig. 4, we have a weight fastened at the bottom of a suspended spring and we pull this weight downwards a little, we feel the spring pulling upwards, and if we leave go of the weight it moves upwards, gathering speed as it goes and overshooting its original position of rest, owing to the velocity it has acquired.

When it does finally come to rest, it is higher than its equilibrium position of rest and so it begins to come down again, gathering speed once more until it comes

to rest in almost the position to which it was pulled at the beginning of the experiment. It does not quite reach that position, because some energy is lost in friction in the material and in transfer of energy to the surrounding air.

This vibrational process goes on with gradually diminishing amplitude and, if the frequency is within the limits 20 to 30,000 vibrations per second, the transfer of energy to the air appears as audible sound. The reader will derive much value, however, by performing the experiment with a slowly-moving spring, as he will be able to observe the characteristics of this type of vibration.

In physics, this type of vibration is called a simple harmonic vibration, and, due to the fact that its amplitude or size is gradually diminishing, it is said to be damped.

Such generation of sound vibrations occurs in the case of tuning forks, plucked strings, bells and percussion instruments generally. The string of a musical instrument pulled or struck on one side behaves just like a spring and anyone can observe the phenomenon by fastening a piece of string across a room and plucking it. If the string is long and not too tightly stretched, the motion can be examined visually with ease.

In order that a steady sound with undiminished amplitude may be produced, it is necessary to supply power to make up for the power that is lost by friction and radiated as sound energy. In the case of a violin, this is accomplished by drawing a resined bow across the string. The bow first pulls the string to a deflection sufficient for the string to slip back, and after the string has completed its vibration in a direction opposite to the direction of motion of the bow, it begins to return and the bow again pulls the string and so the motion of the string is maintained.

Air Vibrations by Reed

The sound from reed instruments is maintained by the periodic interruption of a steady flow of air through an aperture holding the reed. The method of operation of a reed is shown in Fig. 4. As the air flows past the reed it carries the reed with it, thus stopping the air flow. As a result of this stoppage of flow, the reed then springs back and the air flows again. Thus a series of puffs of air occur which gives the character associated with reed instruments, such as oboes and clarinets. In the trombone the player's lips act as a reed.

As demonstrated in Fig. 5, a column of air, due to the time taken for sound to travel back and forth along it, behaves like a loaded spring, and it has certain characteristic frequencies which it will reinforce or to which it will become resonant. In organ pipes, for example, the column of air acts like a spring or reed and controls the position of the jet of air which blows on a sharp or rough edge at its lower opening. Similarly, the resonant column of the flute causes the jet of air blown from the player's lips to move periodically away from or towards the blowing hole.

One of the most interesting generators of musical sounds is the human voice. Here the sound is produced by air blown from the lungs, the air passing, in turn, three cavities. These cavities are, firstly, the larynx, secondly the pharynx

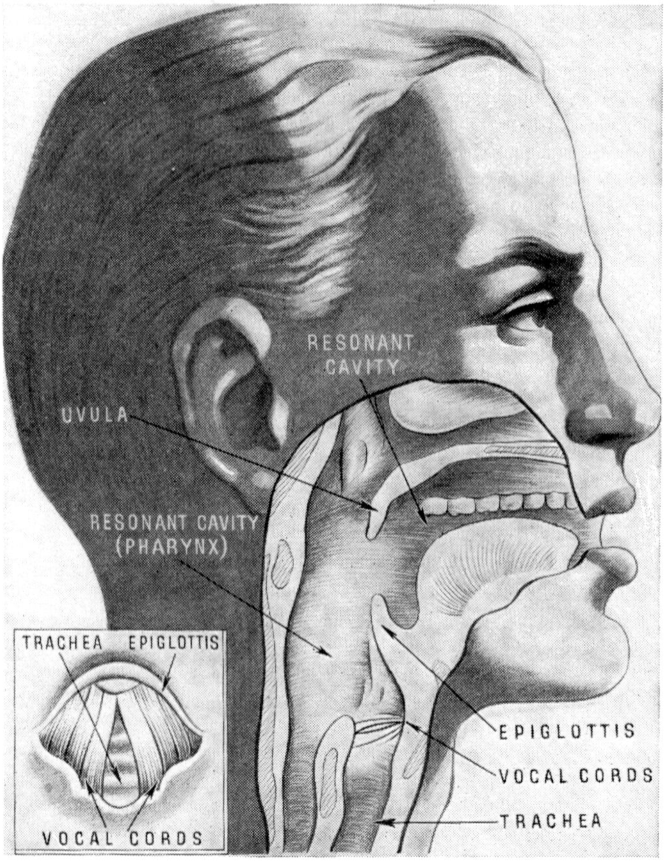

RESONANT CAVITY

UVULA

RESONANT CAVITY
(PHARYNX)

TRACHEA EPIGLOTTIS

VOCAL CORDS

EPIGLOTTIS

VOCAL CORDS

TRACHEA

FIG. 6. *In speech the vocal cords open and close at a regular rate (about 100 cycles per second for a man and about 150 to 200 cycles per second for a woman). In so doing they allow a series of puffs of air from the lungs to pass through the resonant cavities of throat and mouth.*

SYNCHRONOUS DRIVE

REPRODUCING HEAD

WASHING, RECORDING AND
SPARE REPRODUCING
HEADS SHOWN OPEN

REWIND DRIVE

TAKE-UP
SPEED
CONTROL
RESERVOIRS

STARTING
SWITCH

METHOD OF SOUND RECORDING USED BY B.B.C.
*This is the Marconi-Stille tape recording machine in operation. It transforms the speech
and music currents into varying degrees of magnetization of a steel tape.*

(throat) cavity and, thirdly, either the
mouth or the nasal cavity. In the larynx
region there is a slit formed of two mus-
cular membranes called the vocal cords,
which, if sufficiently tightly stretched, can
be caused to vibrate by the passage of air.

When vibrating as they do in ordinary
speech or in singing, the vocal cords behave
like the lips of a trombone player producing
a series of periodic puffs of air called the
laryngeal tone. This laryngeal tone is very

rich in overtones; the lowest frequency
present is about 100 cycles per second for
a man's voice and about 150 cycles per
second for a woman's voice.

Fig. 6 explains how the various parts can
be made use of in producing voice sounds.
The throat, mouth and nasal cavities act
as resonators to certain groups of the overtones and give the characteristics of vowel
sounds. When the resonators are excited by
the flow of air without the vocal cords

vibrating, we obtain whispered speech.

In modern times, the relation between sound and electricity has become very important, as, for example, in wireless and gramophone transmission, recording and reproduction and in the use of the telephone. This relation is important partly because when sound vibrations are transformed into electrical vibrations they can be controlled much more conveniently for different purposes and, by means of thermionic valves, they can be amplified to any convenient magnitude.

An instrument for converting sound vibrations into electrical vibrations is called a microphone. In making records of sounds, the sound to be recorded is allowed to fall on a microphone, and the electrical vibration produced, called the electrical output, is made larger or amplified by a series of wireless or thermionic valves.

Finally, the amplified electrical output is allowed to operate on what is known as a cutter. This is really the reverse of a microphone, as the electrical vibration causes a reed to vibrate in a way which is identical to that of the original sound. Attached to this reed is a small tool with a sharp edge, which cuts an impression in a waxed disk which is rotating at a constant speed.

Copies of this waxed record, known as pressings, are made, and can be played on a gramophone to produce sound. In this way, faithful sound records can be made, stored and reproduced at will.

In reproducing records by means of an electrical reproducer, such as a radio-gramophone, the reverse process to recording takes place. An instrument known as a pick-up, which is just like a cutter except that a smooth needle replaces the cutting edge, converts the motions derived from the grooves to an electrical amplifier and the actual conversion of electrical to sound vibration is attained by means of a loudspeaker, which, just like the cutter, acts in the reverse way to a microphone. The whole process of sound recording and reproduction is illustrated in Fig. 7.

CLOSE-UP OF A B.B.C. TYPE D RECORDER

Special large-diameter record is used, run at 33⅓ r.p.m., which compares with normal record speed of 78 r.p.m. Large record and low speed give very much longer playing time.

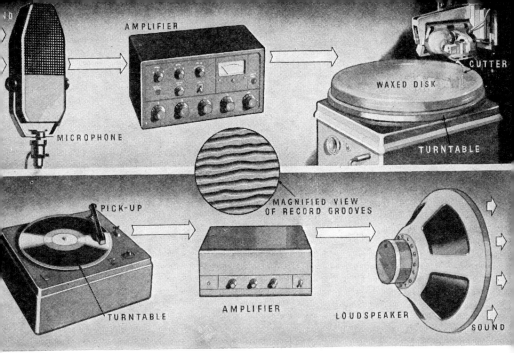

PRINCIPLES OF SOUND RECORDING AND REPRODUCING

FIG. 7. *In recording, the sound vibrations are converted to electrical vibrations of the same frequency by a microphone and made sufficiently powerful by means of a valve amplifier to operate an electromagnetic cutter. The latter has a sharp knife point which cuts an impression on a revolving waxed disk. From this original, thousands of copies can be made by a special manufacturing process. In reproducing, the needle of an electromagnetic pick-up is vibrated by the waves in the record groove, thus producing an electrical vibration. This is amplified and conveyed to a loudspeaker, which converts the electrical vibration to sound. Disk of the reproducer must be rotated at same speed as the disk of the recorder in order to get faithful reproduction of original sound.*

Test Yourself

1. Explain the following: (i) a buzzing or humming sound is heard when a flying insect approaches your ears; (ii) hammer noises on pipes in a building are heard easily in all rooms where the pipes go.
2. How are echoes produced in buildings and hilly countries? Why do large buildings reverberate when sounds are made in them and cause difficulty in the hearing of speech? Explain why speech in a room sounds louder than in the open air.
3. Why does a violinist move his finger up and down the strings as he plays? Why does he rub resin on the hairs of his bow?
4. If you blow on the edge of a sheet of paper or a blade of grass you sometimes get a noise of a definite pitch. Why?
5. People who do not hear well, sometimes use appliances to help them. Can you explain the operation of these?
6. Why is a megaphone used to give directions on a ship? What is the advantage of loudspeaker announcements on railway stations?
7. Why is thunder always heard after lightning is seen? Can you give any other instances illustrating the same phenomenon?

Answers will be found at the end of the book.

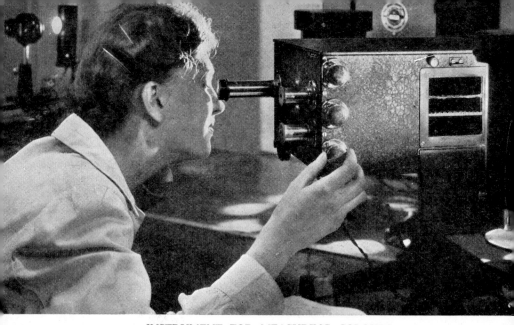

INSTRUMENT FOR MEASURING COLOURS

Adjusting a Donaldson colorimeter, which is a device for providing measurements of colours. Optical instruments of this nature are of vital importance in the dye industry where it is necessary to determine colour values in accordance with precise standards.

HILGER-NUTTING INDUSTRIAL SPECTROPHOTOMETER

This instrument is used for the measurement of the light absorption of coloured substances in different parts of the spectrum and for providing the data from which a curve relating absorption with spectrum wavelength can be drawn, and from which the colour of the object can be determined. Among its typical uses is the study of organic substances.

CHAPTER IX

LIGHT

IF we imagine ourselves in a picturesque part of the country on a pitch-dark night, without moon or stars being visible, and then consider the impressions conveyed to the brain by the eye as the day unfurls itself from, say, an early misty and cloudy twilight to a bright sunny day, we have a demonstration of what light means to us.

As dawn breaks, grey, uncoloured forms of uncertain definition gradually change to more brightly coloured objects of clear outline. As the sunlight appears, shadows become more definitely defined and formed, and these alter their size and orientation as the sun moves in the sky to a final sunset with glorious coloured sky effects.

Such are the sensations conveyed to us by light, and in the physical study of light we are concerning ourselves with an explanation of the agent of nature which is responsible for these phenomena.

The source of the agent which renders these visible effects is quite frequently found to be a hot body as well as a luminous one, but this is not always the case. A glow-worm, for example, seems to give out light without itself being hot; similarly, substances like decaying vegetable matter occasionally glow in the dark without any apparent heat being present—in other words, they phosphoresce like the chemical phosphorus when exposed to air.

Electromagnetic Waves

Early physicists, especially Sir Isaac Newton, believed the sensation of light to be due to the emission of myriads of luminous particles from the bright body giving out the light, and many experiences can be explained on this principle. There are, however, certain phenomena which cannot be so explained, and physics has now come to the conclusion that luminous and hot bodies emit forms of a common radiation which are known as electro-magnetic waves, which in addition to light

and heat include X-rays, wireless waves, ultra-violet light and infra-red radiations.

These waves travel with an enormous velocity, which has been measured in a number of ways and found to be 186,000 miles per second. They carry the energy associated with the radiation. They are not identical with waves on water or sound waves, as the actual particles of the medium through which the light is transmitted do not vibrate. In fact, light and radiation generally are transmitted freely through a vacuum.

The waves really consist of an oscillating electric and magnetic field of force, which is analogous in its behaviour to material waves. The lengths of the waves are determined by the distances between successive regions of space, where the field is the same at the same time, and these wavelengths lie between $\frac{8}{10}$ths of a millionth of a metre for red light and $\frac{4}{10}$ths of a millionth of a metre for violet light.

Polarized Light

Ordinary light is supposed to consist of waves with the vibrations occurring in all directions in the surfaces of the waves, but there are certain substances, such as Iceland spar and tourmaline, which have the property of allowing vibrations to be transmitted through them in one direction only. They are said to produce "polarized light." Ordinary glass produces a certain amount of polarized light by reflection, especially when the angle of reflection is about 60 deg. Different types of sugars have the property of rotating the direction of polarization of light and this property is made use of in commerce and medicine for estimating the amounts of sugars in liquids.

Light waves themselves are invisible and their presence is revealed only by being reflected by the bodies or particles on which they fall. For example, if a beam of light is sent through a clear atmosphere or liquid its course cannot be observed, but if the atmosphere contains dust or smoke particles, the course of the beam is made visible.

A projector in a cinema shows the effect very well, due to the impurities in the air. Similarly, if a little milk is added to clear water, the path of the beam of light which was previously unobserved can be made visible.

It is because different substances reflect light by different amounts that we see their character at all, and if all objects were perfect reflectors we should be unable to distinguish one body from another. But, in addition to being reflected, light is transmitted and absorbed differently by different materials, thus giving all the effects we appreciate, including opacity, brightness, roughness, polish and colour.

An opaque body is one which absorbs all the light entering or falling on it and a translucent body is one which transmits light falling on it.

The term transparent is used in the general sense for bodies in which the form is clearly distinguishable, such as a piece of window glass, whereas a piece of ground or frosted glass is said to be translucent; similarly, a solution of milk and water is said to be translucent.

In the physics of light, however, a medium is said to be transparent if light travels through it without its course being impeded. Thus the medium of clear glass is said to be transparent, however irregular its outward form may be.

Light waves, being carriers of energy, can be converted into forms of energy other than heat; for example, the green plant makes use of light to supply the energy to make starch, and light will alter the chemical constitution of certain chemicals such as potassium ferricyanide and silver salts in the photographic emulsions on plates and films. Light also has the property of causing the emission of electrically charged particles from some bodies—a phenomenon called photo-electricity.

The waves of light energy can be represented by spherical surfaces radiated from the source and travelling outwards with a velocity of 186,000 miles in one second. It must be remembered, however, that these surfaces do not really exist. What really exists is a combination of electric and magnetic fields of force, so that as the wave passes through any point in space the electric and magnetic fields oscillate in magnitude and direction, and every time a spherical surface passes the point the values of these fields repeat themselves.

These oscillations take place very rapidly, actually about a thousand billion times per second (10^{15}), which means that a thousand billion of these imaginary surfaces pass through any point in one second. The velocity of 186,000 miles per second is the velocity of light in air or in a vacuum. The velocity is different in other media; for example, it is only three-quarters of this in water, and two-thirds of it in crown glass.

We shall see later that this property is made use of in prisms, lenses (such as in spectacles, telescopes and microscopes), and nature makes use of it in the eye.

What Happens on Impact

When we represent these waves on paper we can draw them as circles or rings emanating from the source, as in Fig. 1. Now, when these rings fall on different obstacles, as we have mentioned previously, they may be reflected, transmitted and absorbed by the material of the obstacle.

In Fig. 1 we see what happens to the wave when it falls on a rough surface—its shape is made irregular and the wave is said to be scattered. When it falls on a plane mirror surface, it is reflected evenly and behaves as though its direction were changed and it came from a point just as far behind the mirror as the source is in front.

We call this point from which the reflected light comes, or appears to come, the "image" of the source. This term image occurs very frequently in many light phenomena.

When the wave is reflected by a spherical mirror surface, it generally changes both its direction and radius of curvature and again appears to come from an image of the source. When the wave is incident on a plane-glass surface, some of it enters the glass, but it travels more slowly and the circles have a bigger radius of curvature. This gives the impression that the waves in

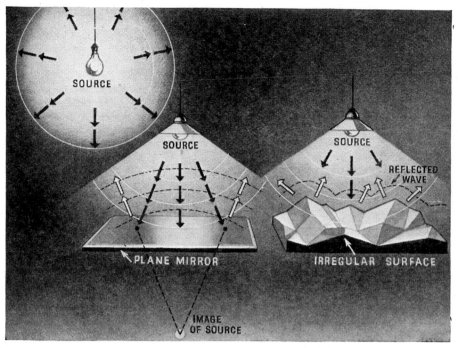

REFLECTION OF LIGHT WAVES

FIG. 1. *Light waves from a small source radiate as spheres and, when they impinge on a smooth polished surface, are reflected as spherical waves, though in a different direction. If surface is rough or irregular, the reflected waves cease to be spherical in shape, so the eye senses no definite direction and judges character of the surface to be rough.*

the glass are coming from an image which is farther away than the actual source of light.

Conversely, if a light source is in water or glass, the image appears to be nearer the surface than the source. This explains the striking trick of pouring water on a coin at the bottom of a glass bowl. Not only does the coin appear to come nearer the surface, but if the eye is placed so that it cannot quite see the coin owing to the presence of a small screen in front of the bowl, then pouring on the water renders it visible.

Similarly, a stick half-submerged in water appears to bend towards the surface. This phenomenon is called refraction. It gives a fish in a pond or river a decreased field of view of objects on the banks.

In Fig. 2 we see the effect of a non-reflecting or absorbing obstacle, such as a black stick and a black screen with a hole

in it. In the case of the black stick, those parts of the waves falling on the stick are totally absorbed and the remainder of the waves pass on. In the case of the hole, only those parts of the wave falling over the hole pass onwards.

Now, if a white screen is placed so that the transmitted waves fall on it, we get a black line or shadow in the first case and a bright spot in the second case. These effects can be drawn a little more easily by drawing lines at right angles to the wave surfaces. These lines we call "rays" and we can use rays to examine other effects. Thus, in light, if we draw surfaces at right angles to the rays, we get, generally speaking, waves which describe better what is really happening to the light energy.

Drawing rays suggests that the boundaries of shadows are always governed by the straight lines drawn from the source through the boundaries of the obstacle and on to the receiving screen, and this is the reason for the general statement that "light travels in straight lines."

The statement applies only when the path of the light is entirely in one uniform medium. It is not applicable if the density of the medium changes as the light passes through it. This is sometimes referred to as "the rectilinear propagation of light."

The phenomenon of light travelling in straight lines can be demonstrated very prettily by what is known as the "pinhole camera." If the bottom of a cocoa or biscuit tin is pierced by a small hole and a piece of thin tracing or writing paper is held at the back, well-defined images of objects can be viewed which are always clearly defined whatever the distance of the object. The images are inverted and the linear dimensions of the images vary inversely as their distances from the pinhole. This is what one would expect by drawing straight lines from the object through the pinhole on to the screen (Fig. 3).

In everyday phenomena, the rectilinear propagation of light is evident because the waves are so remarkably small. It can be shown, however, by carefully planned experiments, that the waves bend a little round the corners of any obstacle in their paths, but this bending is usually so microscopically small as to be unobservable by the unaided eye unless special means are used to magnify its effect. Thus, when a shadow is formed by light from a very small aperture falling on an obstacle, it is found that the edges of the shadow are never perfectly defined, however sharply the edges of the obstacle may be.

Similarly, if a farthing is held up by means of thin cotton about 20 ft. from an illuminated pinhole, the shadow cast a further 20 ft. away will be seen to have a bright spot in the centre. Or, if the eye is placed about 20 ft. behind the farthing, it will appear to have a small hole at its centre. This phenomenon of bending of light rays is called "diffraction," and it is studied in greater detail in advanced treatises on light.

Let us now examine how the eye sees an image by reflection in a plane mirror. The governing law in all cases of reflection by a

OPAQUE OBJECTS WILL CAST SHADOWS

Fig. 2. *Wherever rays of light are obstructed we obtain a shadow. The size of the shadow can be determined by drawing straight lines from the source of the light to the screen. Actually, the behaviour shown in these pictures is strictly true only for a point source.*

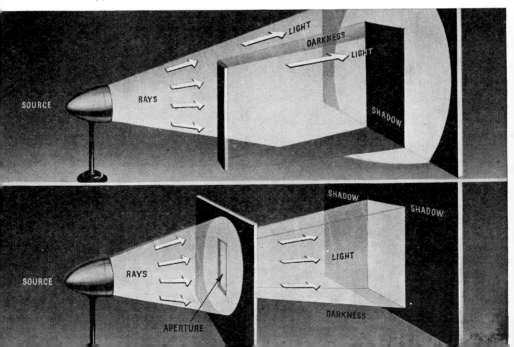

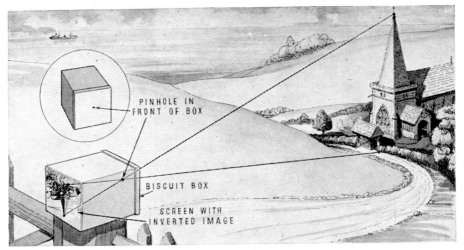

PINHOLE IN FRONT OF BOX

BISCUIT BOX

SCREEN WITH INVERTED IMAGE

PRINCIPLE OF THE PINHOLE CAMERA

Fig. 3. *Making use of the principle that light travels in straight lines, an inverted image may be produced by means of a small hole at one end of the box. If a photographic plate is placed at the opposite end, very clear photographs may be obtained on exposure.*

plane surface is that the angle of reflection must be equal to the angle of incidence, as is shown in Fig. 4. Wherever the eye is placed, the rays it receives are those which have struck the mirror at such an angle of incidence that they pass through the eye. All the other rays are not seen by the eye.

Now, if we consider an extended object, such as the letter L, we see that each part of the object has an image point and the final extended image is one which is reversed. As another example, if we look in a plane mirror we see our left side on our right.

Reflection from a Plane Mirror

Also, if we examine, in front of a plane mirror, blotting paper which has been used for blotting wet writing, we can often read the writing. The blotted impression is equivalent to a plane mirror reflection, so that another reflection brings it to the right disposition.

If more than one mirror is used, multiple reflections occur and some interesting effects are shown, as illustrated in Fig. 5. If the mirrors are parallel, a large number of images is seen. Further, whenever the angle is an exact sub-multiple of 360 deg., an exact number of images is seen.

Thus, a very simple rule emerges, i.e. that the number of images together with the object is equal to this sub-multiple. If the angle is 90 deg., three images and one object are seen; if the angle is 72 deg., the total number is five, and so on.

This is the principle of the charming child's toy, the "kaleidoscope," where a few pieces of coloured glass or paper placed between mirrors set at 72 deg., 60 deg., or 45 deg. give a beautiful symmetrical pattern, the number of points of symmetry being equal to 5, 6 or 8. An infinite number of delightful modifications is obtained, simply by shaking the toy each time a new variety is wanted.

Spherical reflecting surfaces produce specially interesting results. When the mirror surface is such that an incident parallel beam is reflected as a divergent beam it is said to be convex, and when an incident parallel beam is reflected as a convergent beam the mirror is said to be concave.

With both of these mirrors a distant object has an image at a point called the focus, which is half-way between the centre of curvature and the surface of the mirror. In the concave mirror this image can be produced on a screen, but the image due to

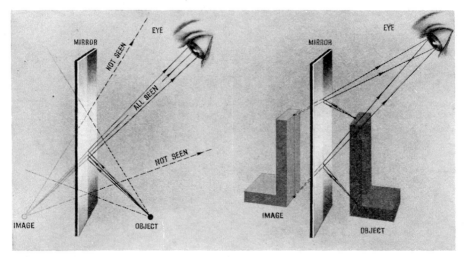

HOW THE EYE SEES IMAGES BY REFLECTION

FIG. 4. *(Left) Pictorial explanation of reflection by a plane mirror. (Right) An extended image, such as writing or a human figure, appears to be reversed in one dimension.*

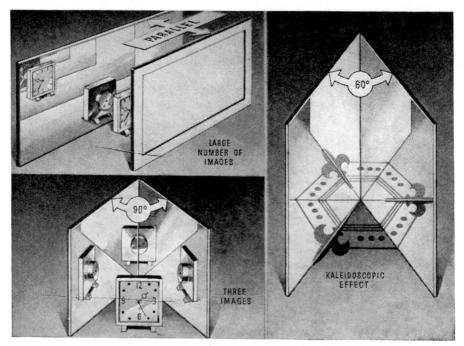

REPRODUCING SYMMETRICAL FIGURES BY REFLECTION

FIG. 5. *(Left) How mirrors, mounted at varying angles, give a series of multiple images. When the mirrors are parallel, a very large number of images are reproduced. When they are at 90 deg., three only are seen. (Right) Principle is developed in the kaleidoscope.*

a convex mirror appears to be behind the mirror. This is due to the mirror reflecting rays so that they diverge outwards, with the result that when they fall on the eye they give the impression of coming from behind the mirror. Such an image is said to be a virtual image as contrasted with the real image, which is produced on a screen, and are shown in Fig. 6, in which these points are illustrated.

Concentrated Beam of Light

Of special interest is the searchlight mirror, which is known as a parabolic mirror. This has the property that all rays from the focal point are reflected so that

GLASS REFLECTORS IN THE MAKING

Mirror surfaces for light-ray reflection demand a high degree of skill and workmanship in manufacture. This moulding operation picture was taken in Chance Brothers' factory.

through which the rays of light actually pass.

A convex mirror always produces a diminished image which is the right way up, whereas a concave mirror can produce either an erect or inverted image, dependent on where the object is placed with respect to the focus. If the object is placed between the surface and focus of the concave mirror, the image is a virtual one, that is, behind the mirror, and it is magnified and erect. An example of this kind of image can be observed in the so-called shaving mirror. Some images, as obtained by drawing rays,

they are parallel to the axis. This is a useful property for getting a concentrated beam of light over a large distance and is used also in the motor-car headlight.

The phenomenon of change of direction due to a change of velocity when light travels from one medium to another, and which we call refraction, has already been referred to. Now, if light passes through a slab of glass with parallel faces, the light, on entering the glass, is refracted towards the perpendicular to the surface (Fig. 7).

When, however, the light leaves the glass at the second surface, it is refracted away

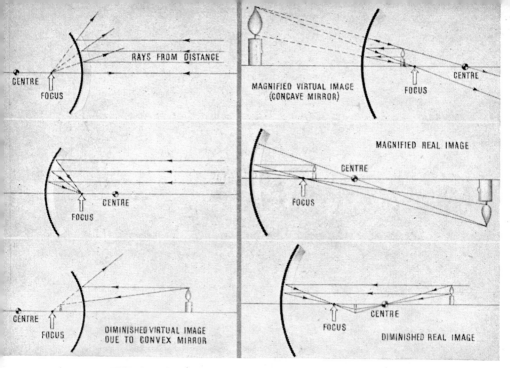

TYPES OF IMAGE PRODUCED BY SPHERICAL MIRRORS

FIG. 6. *Convex mirrors produce diminished and upright images which cannot be produced on a screen. Concave mirrors can produce magnified or diminished images on a screen.*

from the normal by the same amount, with the result that it emerges in a direction parallel to the incident direction. This accounts for the fact that when we look through a thick sheet of plate glass there is no apparent change in direction of any object in our field of view.

Deviated Light

If the two faces of a slab of glass are not parallel, that is, if they are part of a glass prism, then the refraction from air to glass is not equal to the oppositely directed refraction from glass to air, with the result that the emergent light is not parallel to the incident light. We then say the light is deviated.

If we proceed further and consider what happens when a series or beam of rays parallel to the base of the prism passes through it (i.e. what we know as a parallel beam of light), we see that all the rays emerge as a parallel beam striking the base line at different points.

If, instead of having a single prism, we use a series of prisms of gradually increas-

ing angles, beginning with a parallel-faced slab at the bottom, the points at which these rays hit the base line are much nearer together. It is obvious, therefore, that by a suitable choice of the angles of these prisms we could make all the rays hit the base line at one point only.

It is found that when we do this the sides of all the little segments of prisms approximate to a spherical surface, so that when the number of prisms is infinitely large we get the limiting case. This limiting form is called a lens, and it is found that these bounding surfaces need not be of the same radius of curvature to give this property of bringing all the rays to a point or focus.

In fact, one surface could be plane and one surface could be oppositely curved to the other—the only requirement is that, in order to bring the rays to a focus, the lens must be thicker in the middle than at the edge. This type of lens is called a convex or converging lens. In optical work it is called a positive lens. The various types of convex lenses are called bi-convex, plano-convex and concavo-convex, dependent on

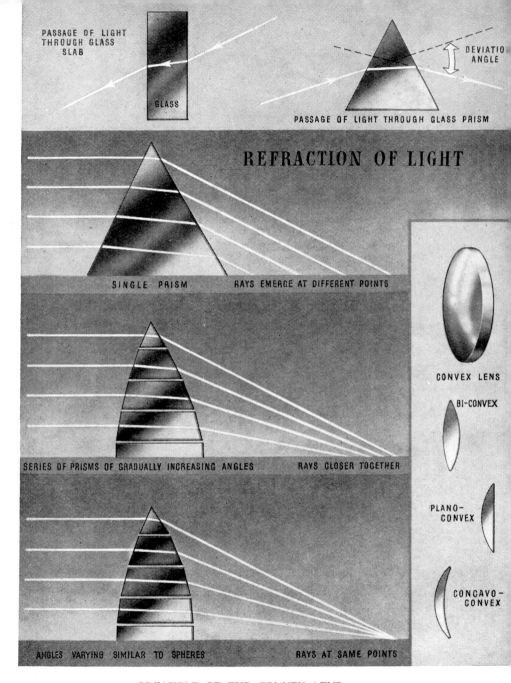

PASSAGE OF LIGHT THROUGH GLASS SLAB

GLASS

DEVIATION ANGLE

PASSAGE OF LIGHT THROUGH GLASS PRISM

REFRACTION OF LIGHT

SINGLE PRISM

RAYS EMERGE AT DIFFERENT POINTS

SERIES OF PRISMS OF GRADUALLY INCREASING ANGLES

RAYS CLOSER TOGETHER

ANGLES VARYING SIMILAR TO SPHERES

RAYS AT SAME POINTS

CONVEX LENS

BI-CONVEX

PLANO-CONVEX

CONCAVO-CONVEX

PRINCIPLE OF THE CONVEX LENS

FIG. 7. *When a ray of light passes from one medium to another medium it generally changes its direction, and is, therefore, said to be affected by refraction, or to be refracted. A section through a convex lens can be looked upon as made up of a series of small prisms. Provided the angles of the prisms increase at the same rate as a spherical surface, they will have a common focusing point, as is shown diagrammatically here.*

the forms of the two bounding spherical surfaces.

Conversely, we can lead, by a similar argument and taking prisms with the bases upwards, as shown in Fig. 8, to a lens which causes a parallel beam of rays to become a divergent beam which, when produced backwards, appears to diverge from a focus on the same side of the lens as the incident light. Such a lens is called a concave lens and it exists in the forms of bi-concave. plano-concave and convexo-concave.

Images of objects can be brought to a focus on a screen by means of a convex lens, and it will be found that images of objects beyond a certain distance are all clearly formed at the focus of the lens. Objects nearer the lens have images which are farther away from the surface.

Use of the Concave Lens

On the other hand, a concave lens, on its own, can never be used to produce a real image. It can, however, be used to produce a real image in combination with a convex lens. When we view objects through a concave lens, we only apparently see the image, since the rays give the appearance to the eye of diverging from a point on the same side of the lens as the object.

Important examples of the use of the simple convex lens are the magnifying glass, the camera and the eye.

In the case of the camera, a lens with a shutter is separated from a ground-glass focusing screen by means of flexible light-proof leather bellows. Dependent on the distance of the object to be photographed, the distance between the lens and screen is adjusted until a clear, well-defined image is formed on the screen. This is called focusing the camera. When the focusing has been accomplished, a photographic plate or film is substituted for the screen and an exposure made.

Some cameras have graduated scales on them which avoid the necessity of viewing the image before the exposure is made, and some cameras of the box type have no adjustment for focusing. These cameras make use of a lens with a very short focal length which will give clear images over a large range of distances, provided the film or plate is placed at the focal point.

Eye Compared with Camera

The eye is, in many ways, similar to a camera. The lens itself is flexible. The part corresponding to the photographic screen is called the retina, which is a sensitive surface connected by nerve fibres to the optic nerve, which in turn sends the sensations of light to the brain.

Instead of focusing objects by varying the distance between the lens and the retina, as is done in the camera, there are muscles attached to the lens called ciliary muscles, which, by varying the tension on the flexible lens, can alter its focal length and so bring objects of varying distances to a focus on the retina.

In a normal eye at rest, the lens is so adapted that distant objects are in focus on the retina. The muscles which adjust the lens are, in this condition, relaxed, but when near objects are required to be viewed the ciliary muscles contract, causing the lens to bulge in the middle so that it becomes more convex than it was before.

In the normal healthy eye, objects can be clearly focused to within about 10 in. from it. When viewing objects as close as this, the eye-lens has been thickened to the maximum and in a normal eye attempts to focus on a nearer object produce a serious strain.

The most common defects of the eye are due to defects in the mechanism of adjustment of the lens or to abnormal distances between the lens and the retina. In short sight (myopia), the eyeball is too long and the image of a distant object is formed in front of the retina. Objects much nearer the eye than 10 in. can be focused. These defects are equivalent to the lens being too powerful and it is necessary to reduce the effective convexity by placing a concave spectacle lens in front of the eye.

In hypermetropia (long sight), the opposite state exists—the eyeball is too short, so that a distant object can be focused only by a little accommodation of the eye, involving a certain amount of strain. Near objects cannot be focused without a

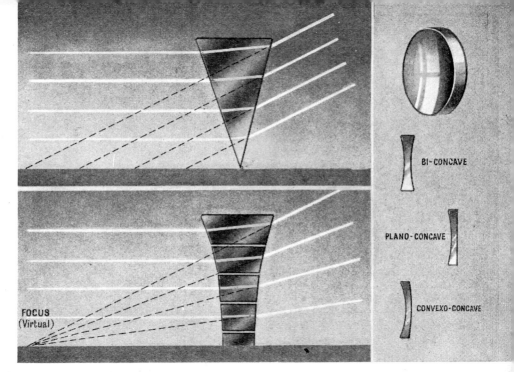

PRINCIPLE OF A CONCAVE LENS

FIG. 8. *Concave, or divergent, lenses, as illustrated here, may be considered as being made up of a series of prisms whose angles increase gradually from the centre outwards.*

tremendous amount of strain. The spectacle lens, therefore, has to be convex in order to make the lens stronger.

The accommodating power of the eye diminishes with advancing age and in very old people it is generally very limited. Near objects cannot be focused and again a convex lens is required. If the accommodating power of the eye is very limited, different lenses are required for distant and near objects respectively.

Optical Spectrum

In considering the phenomenon of refraction, we referred to the deviation of a ray of light by a prism. Now, if we look at a square piece of white paper through the prism we observe an interesting effect, which is illustrated in Fig. 9. Admittedly, the square as seen through the prism is displaced in the direction of the apex of the prism; but, in addition, the two opposite sides of the square parallel to the base are edged with colours, the colours near the apex being fringed with red and the colour

on the opposite side being fringed with blue and violet.

Now, if a very thin slit in a screen illuminated by a white light is viewed through the prism, it is found to be a broader band of coloured light almost identical with the colours of the rainbow. These colours are found to change gradually from red, through orange, yellow and green to blue and violet.

These two observations indicate that not only is light refracted by the prisms, but that the light is split up into a number of colours. Also, that these colours can only be made visible because the refraction, or deviation, varies with the colours, the refraction being a maximum for violet and a minimum for red light.

If a second identical prism is interposed between the eye and the first prism, but turned the opposite way round, that is, base of second prism corresponding to apex of first prism, the slit now appears as a thin, white line once more. This shows that white light, having been split up or analysed into these colours by the first prism, can be recomposed or synthesized back to its original state.

The fact that in our first experiment we saw a white square edged with colour, indicates that, where these colours overlap, white light is produced and it is only by having a thin slit that we can see the different colours clearly. When we view a thin, white slit through a prism, what we really see is an infinite number of differently-coloured images side by side, each slit image being deviated differently from its neighbours.

This band of coloured light is called a spectrum and the splitting up of the light into its different colours is called dispersion.

Now, if carefully controlled experiments are made with light as it is split up by a prism, some more very interesting results are obtained. It is found to be a great advantage in studying dispersion if we view

the spectrum in a slightly different way. The best method is to take a convex lens and fasten it on one end of a tube which is just as long as the focal length of the lens. Then, at the other end of the tube, a piece of metal with a very fine, straight slit is fastened. This arrangement is called a collimator.

When the slit is illuminated, the light emerging from it is a parallel beam with all the rays parallel to the axis of the collimator. If this light is allowed to fall on a prism, so that the prism edges are parallel to the slit, then all the rays will strike the surface of the prism at the same angle. When the light is dispersed by the prism, all the rays of each colour will form separate parallel beams and we shall have, emerging from the prism, parallel beams of rays at angles corresponding to the dispersion of each colour.

If a convex lens is placed to receive these beams it will produce a coloured image for

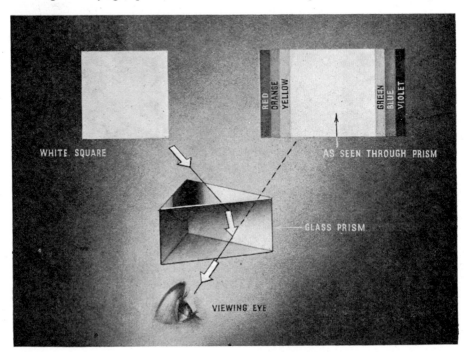

OBTAINING AN OPTICAL SPECTRUM

FIG. 9. *When a white square is viewed through a prism, it appears tinged with colour, owing to the prism producing a number of coloured images separated from each other.*

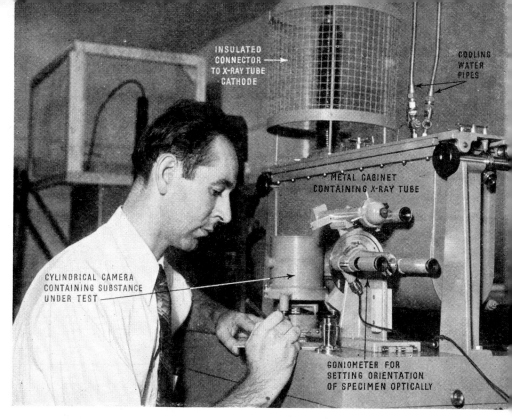

INSULATED CONNECTOR TO X-RAY TUBE CATHODE

COOLING WATER PIPES

METAL CABINET CONTAINING X-RAY TUBE

CYLINDRICAL CAMERA CONTAINING SUBSTANCE UNDER TEST

GONIOMETER FOR SETTING ORIENTATION OF SPECIMEN OPTICALLY

OPERATING AN X-RAY SPECTROSCOPE

In this photograph is seen a spectroscope which is used for investigating crystalline structures. It produces spectra by means of interference effects between X-rays reflected from successive atom planes in the crystal.

each colour, side by side at the plane containing its focus. In this way a very clear and pure spectrum is produced. This arrangement is known as a spectroscope and is shown in detail in the diagram on page 161. The spectrum can be viewed by producing it on a screen or it can be observed by looking at the light leaving the prism by means of a telescope.

Viewing Other Spectra

If, instead of white light, we illuminate the slit by other types of light, we get different types of spectra. Suppose, for example, we take a non-luminous bunsen flame and place in it a piece of wire which has been dipped in salt solution (sodium chloride). The light is yellowish, and if we look through the spectroscope we see what appears to be a single yellow line. If the spectroscope is a good one, with a very fine slit and an accurately made prism, further examination will show that the spectrum really consists of two fine lines close together.

Now, if a little strontium chloride is heated in the flame it has a pretty reddish colour, which, when examined in the spectroscope, shows a number of blue-green as well as red lines. Thus, the colour as registered by the unaided eye is only a partial guide as to the colour that will be expected to be observed in the spectroscope.

Other chemicals show different colours and each element in nature has its own series of spectral lines. As would be expected, the spectroscope can be used to identify the composition of unknown chemical substances. In the diagram on page 161 a number of spectra are shown.

Gases can be made luminous when they are introduced into an exhausted bulb and subjected to an electric discharge. Examples of this can be seen in some of the modern street lights, in the cylindrical lights used for diffused lighting and in the various coloured lights used for advertising signs. Metals can be made to give characteristic spectra by heating them in an electric arc.

Spectral Absorption Lines

If white light is allowed to illuminate the slit of a spectroscope, and if a sodium flame is interposed between the light and the slit, it is found that the spectrum has dark lines in the position of the sodium lines. Similarly, if the heated strontium chloride is interposed, dark lines appear, corresponding to the strontium lines, and for other chemical substances other dark lines appear.

These dark lines are always in the positions of the characteristic spectra. They exist because an incandescent vapour will, as well as emitting light, also absorb light corresponding to its own characteristic spectrum. They are, therefore, called absorption lines.

If the light from the sun is examined through a spectroscope, it is found to consist of a continuous spectrum crossed by a series of these absorption lines, corresponding to various chemical substances, showing some of the constitution of the sun's atmosphere. The constitution of stars has similarly been examined. The whole subject of spectrum analysis is a very fascinating one, providing conclusive evidence of a body's chemical and physical nature.

Rainbow Effects

The rainbow is an example of the way the sun's light is broken up into its different constituent colours. In this case the tiny droplets of water, in the form of rain or spray, disperse the light from the sun. It will be noticed that a rainbow is only seen when the sun is behind the observer and shining its light on rain directly in front of him.

The rain can be some considerable distance away, but the observer must always be between the sun and the rain. This shows that the sun's light is reflected from the backs of the drops as well as being dispersed by the water in the drop. How the spectrum colours are produced by the tiny droplets is diagrammatically shown on page 161. Rainbow effects can also be produced when the sun is shining on the spray from a fountain.

If light of a single colour, such as the yellow of the sodium flame, is allowed to pass along two separate paths, either by reflection at two different surfaces or by transmission through two different optical systems, and then allowed to re-combine, it can be shown that darkness results if the path difference is about three-tenths of a millionth part of a metre. Darkness also results when the path difference is an odd number of times this amount.

Wavelengths of Colours

When the path difference is an even number of times this amount, the two portions of light combine to produce brightness. When darkness occurs, this is because one of the waves is vibrating exactly oppositely to the other; the phenomenon is called "interference." It is used to determine the wavelengths of the different light colours. In the case mentioned, the wavelength is about $\frac{6}{10}$ths of a millionth of a metre. Interference occurs due to two reflecting surfaces as shown by the colours produced when there is a thin film of petrol or paraffin on water, or due to the two reflecting surfaces of a soap bubble. The colours that are observed are the complementary colours of the colours that are eliminated by interference. Thus, when interference occurs for red light, a delicate blue or purple is seen.

We judge the colour of a non-luminous object by the character of the light it reflects or transmits to the eye. If a substance scatters all the light falling on it, we get the impression of a white object. If it throws back very little light in comparison with other objects around it, it appears as a black object. If it scatters red light but absorbs other colours, it appears red.

Similarly, red glass allows red light to pass through it and absorbs other colours. When the light scattered or transmitted by a coloured object is examined by a spectro-

How SPECTRA and RAINBOWS are Formed

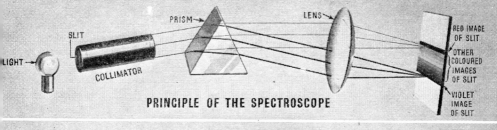

PRISM — LENS —
SLIT
LIGHT →
COLLIMATOR

RED IMAGE OF SLIT
OTHER COLOURED IMAGES OF SLIT
VIOLET IMAGE OF SLIT

PRINCIPLE OF THE SPECTROSCOPE

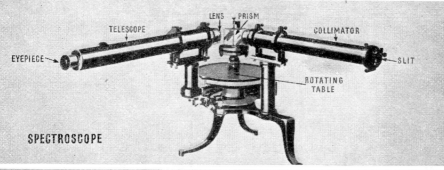

TELESCOPE
LENS PRISM
COLLIMATOR
EYEPIECE →
← SLIT
ROTATING TABLE

SPECTROSCOPE

ANALYSING THE SPECTRUM

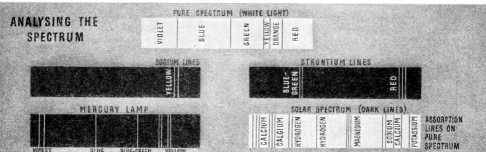

PURE SPECTRUM (WHITE LIGHT)

VIOLET | BLUE | GREEN | YELLOW ORANGE | RED

SODIUM LINES — YELLOW

STRONTIUM LINES — BLUE-GREEN — RED

MERCURY LAMP — VIOLET | BLUE | BLUE-GREEN | YELLOW

SOLAR SPECTRUM (DARK LINES)

CALCIUM | CALCIUM | HYDROGEN | HYDROGEN | MAGNESIUM | SODIUM CALCIUM | POTASSIUM

ABSORPTION LINES ON PURE SPECTRUM

FORMATION OF A RAINBOW

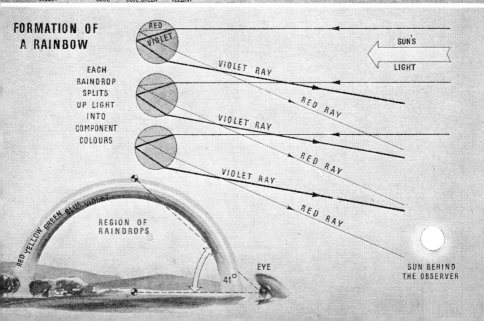

RED
VIOLET

SUN'S LIGHT

EACH RAINDROP SPLITS UP LIGHT INTO COMPONENT COLOURS

VIOLET RAY
RED RAY
VIOLET RAY
RED RAY
VIOLET RAY
RED RAY

RED YELLOW GREEN BLUE VIOLET

REGION OF RAINDROPS

EYE
41°

SUN BEHIND THE OBSERVER

scope, it is frequently found to contain other colours in addition to the main one appearing to the eye.

The eye sees colour by a mechanism which has been studied intensively by physicists, physiologists and psychologists. It is possible to discuss it only very sketchily in this short treatment. Roughly, we may say there are three sensations which give colour vision. They are often referred to as

POLISHED OPTICAL GLASS SLABS

In the manufacture of optical glass, the high standard of the material required necessitates close control and examination at every stage of manufacture. This photograph shows a table of slabs of glass at the works of Chance Brothers after having been polished.

red, green and violet sensations respectively, although each of these elements is sensitive to a range of colours.

The violet sensation is sensitive to violet-blue and green with a maximum response to blue-violet. The green sensation is sensitive to blue, green, yellow and scarlet, and the red element to all colours from blue to deep red, although it is not very sensitive to blue and blue-green.

A yellow object will affect both the green and red sensitive elements; a blue object will affect all three sensations, and a red object affects the red only. A scarlet object will affect the red sensation mainly and the green sensation only slightly.

Superimposing the Primaries

This system of three-colour vision is responsible for the many effects of producing colours by mixing of primary colours. For example, if red light and green light from separate lanterns are thrown together, the eye says the colour is yellow, although a spectrum analysis of the light would show no yellow light but only red and green. This effect can be observed when different-coloured spotlights are superimposed on the stage. When red, green and blue lights are superimposed, the eye gets the impression of white, although so many colours are absent from the white light spectrum.

This way of obtaining a colour sensation is known as an additive process, in contrast to the method of getting colour by the mixing of pigments, which is known as a subtractive process. In the subtractive process, light is seen by a series of absorptions; thus, when a yellow pigment is painted over a blue colour, which normally reflects blue, green and violet, the yellow absorbs the blue and violet so that only green is transmitted. In this way, red and yellow produce orange, blue and red produce purple, and red and yellow and blue produce brown or black.

Examples of three-colour processes occur in colour photography and coloured illustrations in books. If these are examined under a strong lens it will be found that they consist of a series of dots of three colours, but to the unaided eye the mixtures blend to give an infinite variety of colours. Coloured cinema films also are made up from a series of three-colour prints superimposed on each other.

Certain substances, after being exposed to light for some time and then being placed in a dark room, have the property of emitting light for some time. This phenomenon is called phosphorescence. Luminous paint, which consists mainly of a sulphide of calcium, is an example of this. It will shine for hours if exposed to strong sunlight for a time.

Some substances, such as lubricating oils and red ink, shine with a peculiar light when white light is thrown on them. Also, if light of a certain colour is used, the light they emit is often of a different colour. The emission entirely disappears when the exciting light is removed. This phenomenon is called fluorescence.

Owing to certain psychological and physiological effects in the manner in which the eye functions and some minor imperfections, the eye is sometimes deceived in its interpretation of visible phenomena. We call such phenomena "optical illusions," since the impression given to the eye can be proved incorrect by physical measurement.

No single explanation of all illusory phenomena is possible. One of these examples is that in which a white square on a black background appears larger than an equal black square on a white background.

Illusory Phenomena

This can be explained as follows. A luminous point produces an image on the retina which is a small circle. Thus, all the edges of a white square extend a little into the black border, making it appear larger than it really is. Also, the edges of the white surround of the black square extend a little into the black square, thus making the black square appear smaller than it really is.

Another example is that parallel lines appear to converge or diverge if these lines are crossed by acute short lines. This is because the short lines give the mental impression of coming from, or going to, a point which the eye assumes applies to the

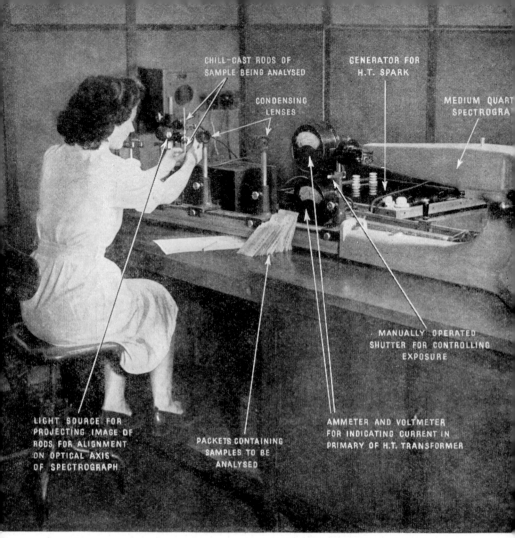

ALUMINIUM ALLOYS UNDER THE SPECTROGRAPH
Medium quartz spectrograph shown in this picture is being operated for the analysis of "Hiduminium" aluminium alloys in the laboratories of High Duty Alloys, Ltd. Between 60 and 70 per cent of the analyses required for the composition control of this company's production of aluminium alloys is now undertaken by the Spectrographic Department.

parallel lines as well. Optical illusions are of no great scientific importance, but are an ever-present reminder that the eye is capable of being deceived.

Light Has Other Effects

Light has been mentioned as an example of electromagnetic radiation and so far the eye has been the judge of its existence. Now, we have other tests of radiation apart from the eye. For example, light has a heating effect on some bodies; it can affect a

photographic plate; and we have already observed that it can make certain substances fluoresce or phosphoresce.

When these tests are made with certain special spectroscopes, it is found that heating effects occur beyond the part of the spectrum ending in the red. This is termed infra-red radiation. It is also found that photographic action as well as phosphorescent and fluorescent phenomena occur beyond the violet end of the visible spectrum. This is called ultra-violet radiation. The wavelengths of ultra-violet light are the shortest of the spectrum of a luminous body and the infra-red or heat rays are the longest.

As is now well known, ultra-violet light is a part of sunlight which is very beneficial to health. As the wavelengths of electro-magnetic waves are increased still further than the infra-red, we come to the wireless wavelengths. As the wavelengths are de-creased beyond the ultra-violet, we come to the radiations called X-rays and gamma-rays of radium, which are capable of pene-trating opaque bodies like human tissue and are very useful for medical purposes.

Why the Sky is Coloured

We have seen how bodies can reflect light waves. Generally speaking, the bodies we are accustomed to as showing reflection effects are quite large in comparison with the wavelengths of the light they reflect. We have noticed, however, that small dust particles in the path of a beam of light, such as can be seen at the cinema, scatter the light and show up its track.

Now, it is found that small particles of sizes of the same order as the wavelengths of visible light scatter the shorter wave-lengths more than the longer ones. There-fore, they scatter blue and violet more than green and red.

In the sky there are fine particles of dust as well as gas molecules which scatter the blue and violet of the sun's light more than the other spectrum colours. This accounts for the colour of the clear sky. It accounts for the colour of smoke from a chimney when you see it with your back to the sun.

A sunset is seen by transmitted light. When the sun is low, its beams traverse a greater amount of atmosphere before reach-ing us than they do earlier in the day. As a result, as the sun sinks lower and lower, more and more of the bluer light is scattered, leaving the red and other colours which give the vivid effects we see at sunset.

Test Yourself

1. At night it is difficult to see through a closed window from a lighted room, but relatively easy if the room lights are switched off. Why?

2. Explain how glasses are of assistance to anyone with defective eyesight. Can you explain why some people wear spectacles called bi-focals in which each eyepiece is made up of two lenses in one piece?

3. When you open your eyes under water in a clear swimming bath, objects on the bottom appear very blurred, whereas a diver in a diving suit sees everything clearly defined through the window of his headgear. Why is this?

4. Why can you see a sunbeam in a dusty room? Why does light appear coloured when viewed through some glass ornaments?

5. Why are lamp globes sometimes made of frosted or opalescent glass?

6. Explain how rainbows are formed. Why are rainbows sometimes seen in the spray from a garden hose?

7. How can we tell that certain chemical substances are on the sun and stars?

8. Why do colours of dress show up differently in the colours of stage lighting?

9. Explain why a person wearing glasses can sometimes see the image of an object behind him.

10. In bright sunshine, why are the small bright patches on the ground under trees circular and not the shape of the holes between the leaves?

Answers will be found at the end of the book.

EXCITER

GENERATOR

FAN FOR AIR SUP
TO GENERATOR

EJECTORS

GEAR WHEEL

TURBINE ROTC

VALVE GEAR

TRANSPORTABLE GENERATING PLANT

*Practical illustration of the advance made during recent decades in the design and construc-
tion of electrical apparatus. This 500-kW power unit, with turbine and gear-case covers
removed, is part of a transportable turbo-generator set designed by Metropolitan-Vickers
Electrical Co., Ltd., for the U.S.S.R., to the instructions of the Ministry of Supply.*

CHAPTER X

ELECTRICITY AND MAGNETISM

IN the text-books of bygone days it was customary to treat electricity and magnetism as separate and distinct subjects, with electromagnetism as a rather mysterious bridge between the two.

With the development of the Electron Theory, it came to be realized that electricity and magnetism were inseparably bound together; the electron, in fact, proved to be the missing link of Science. Investigation of its properties showed not only that electricity and magnetism were closely united, but also that inter-connections, previously unsuspected, existed between many other branches of scientific knowledge.

In Chapter V it was shown that matter of all kinds is composed of atoms and that atoms of every sort are built of the same kinds of tiny bricks, electrons and protons. Most atoms contain neutrons as well; but these do not come into the picture when we are studying the elements of electricity and magnetism.

The electron may be regarded as a minute charge of negative electricity. The proton, though very much heavier, contains a precisely equal charge of the opposite kind, a charge of positive electricity. The negative charge of one electron exactly counterbalances or cancels out the positive charge of one proton.

Structure of the Atom

In its normal condition, an atom is perfectly balanced. All of its protons are contained in the nucleus. Its electrons revolve in orbits round the nucleus. The total number of electrons is just equal to the total number of protons: every positive charge is cancelled by a negative charge, with the result that such an atom has no electric charge.

An atom may, however, lose one of its orbital electrons, temporarily at any rate. When this has happened, the atom is no longer balanced, for one proton has no corresponding electron to annul its charge.

Thus, an atom which has been deprived of one or more of its orbital electrons has a positive charge and is known as a positive ion.

This brings us to the first of the fundamental rules of electricity: an electron deficiency means a positive charge.

Similarly, an atom may gain an electron over and above its proper number. Here the position is reversed: all the positive charges are cancelled by the negative charges of the original electrons; but the newcomer has no proton to neutralize. In an atom, then, which has acquired one or more extra electrons, the protons are outnumbered, with the result that the atom itself is negatively charged.

Fundamental rule number two is that an electron surplus means a negative charge.

Nature of the Neutron

We can see now why the neutron need not be taken into account electrically; as its name implies, it is neither positive nor negative. Its presence in an atom makes, therefore, no difference to the electrical condition of that atom.

Charges of the same kind repel one another. Fig. 1 (a) shows diagrammatically that there is repulsion between electron and electron, between proton and proton, and between positive ion and positive ion. On the other hand, charges of different kinds attract one another. Thus there is attraction between electron and proton or between electron and positive ion. These attractions and repulsions are very strong indeed; their force is, in fact, vastly greater than that of gravity.

Imagine the situation that arises in Fig. 1 (b), where in the area on the left is a large number of electrons; that on the right contains an equal number of positive ions.

There is no connecting path between the two areas; nothing, therefore, can pass from the one to the other. Electrons and positive ions attract one another strongly, so there is a state of strain between the two areas.

With its assembly of electrons, the area on the left is said to have a negative charge or to be at a negative potential. The area on the right, with its concourse of positive ions, is positively charged, or at a positive potential. Between the two areas there is a difference of potential, called, in electrical parlance, a potential difference, or p.d.

Electronic Tug-of-War

Now, suppose that we provide, as shown in Fig. 1 (c), a connecting path between the two areas. Owing to the mutual attraction of electrons and positive ions there is a tug-of-war; something is going to move through the connecting path, and as the positive ions are hundreds of times heavier than the electrons, there cannot be any doubt what that something is going to be. Electrons rush through the path from the left-hand to the right-hand area.

A flow of electrons constitutes an electric current.

But a current of this kind cannot be set to do continuous work, since it endures for but an instant. After a tiny fraction of a second, all the electrons have passed from the left-hand area to the right, where each combines with and neutralizes a positive ion. Once this has happened there are no more electrons in the left-hand area and no more positive ions in the right; all the electrons have been, so to speak, mopped up by the positive ions. There is now no potential difference and no electrons are available to give rise to a current.

To produce a current capable of doing continuous useful work we must find some means of maintaining an excess of electrons in one area and an excess of positive ions in the other. In this way the potential difference between the two areas will be kept in being and it will now become a constant electromotive force (a force which makes electrons move), or e.m.f.

The expression "generation of electricity" is one often used, though it should not be. We cannot generate electricity,

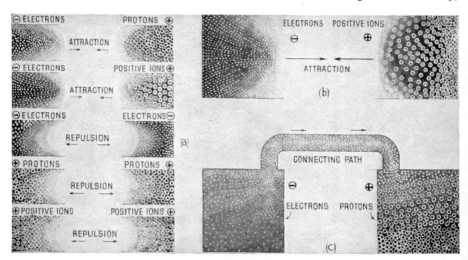

REPULSION AND ATTRACTION BETWEEN CHARGES

FIG. 1. *(a) There is attraction between unlike electric charges, and repulsion between like electric charges. (b) Showing two imaginary areas with no path between them. That on the left contains a large number of electrons, and that on the right a similar number of protons. The two assemblies attract one another and a state of tension exists between the two areas; but nothing can pass from one to the other, as there is no path between them. (c) If a connecting path is provided between the two areas, the light electrons are drawn along it by the attraction between them and the far heavier protons.*

FIG. 2. *Simple electric cell, formed by immersing zinc and carbon plates in a solution of sal ammoniac. The chlorine in the solution attacks zinc and builds up a negative charge on that plate.*

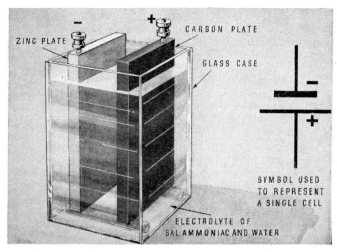

CARBON PLATE
ZINC PLATE
GLASS CASE
SYMBOL USED TO REPRESENT A SINGLE CELL
ELECTROLYTE OF SAL AMMONIAC AND WATER

for it is, in fact, everywhere and in everything; but we can find means of producing an e.m.f. and, therefore, of generating that flow of electrons which constitutes an electric current.

There are many ways in which this can be done. One of the simplest is illustrated in Fig. 2, which shows an elementary form of what is known as a primary cell. The term primary cell will be more fully explained later; for the moment it will be sufficient to say it is one kind of apparatus for producing an e.m.f. by chemical means.

The drawing shows a glass jar containing a solution of 1 oz. of sal ammoniac to a pint of water. In it are immersed two plates, or electrodes, one of zinc and the other of carbon. As soon as the plates are placed in the solution, which is called the electrolyte, things begin to happen and to happen very rapidly.

Every molecule of sal ammoniac consists of one atom of chlorine combined with one of nitrogen and four of hydrogen. The chlorine atoms attack the zinc, tearing atoms from the zinc plate. But the zinc atoms do not come out of the plate in complete form. Each leaves behind it two electrons.

Remembering what was said earlier in this chapter, you will realize that the torn-out zinc atoms enter the electrolyte as positive ions; that is, as atoms which have lost some of their orbital electrons. As each atom leaves two electrons behind it on the zinc plate, an electron surplus, which constitutes a negative charge, is soon built up on that plate. Meantime the electrolyte is acquiring more and more positive ions.

You will recall that like charges repel like; therefore, as the number of positive ions in the solution increases there is more and more opposition to the emergence of others from the zinc. Eventually—this takes some time to describe, though actually it happens very quickly indeed—the repulsion exercised by the large number of positive ions in the electrolyte is so great that no more can be torn from the zinc by chlorine atoms. The action, therefore, ceases and the cell is said to be in a state of equilibrium.

Electrical State

Now let us take stock of the position at this point. The zinc plate contains a large electron surplus and is, therefore, at a negative potential. The electrolyte, with its many positive ions, or electron deficiency, is at a positive potential. The carbon plate is not acted upon chemically. It merely serves as a contact with the electrolyte; you can fasten wires to carbon, but you cannot fasten them to a liquid!

Electrons, however, pass from the carbon plate to the electrolyte, and on the plate we thus have an electron deficiency, or a positive potential. Between the terminals fastened to the zinc and carbon plates there is now a potential difference.

In Figs. 2 and 3 are shown the symbols used in electrical diagrams to represent the apparatus seen in the drawings and the connecting paths. This practice will be followed in succeeding diagrams where appropriate, so that the reader may become gradually familiar with such symbols.

Now let us provide, as shown in Fig. 3 (a), a connecting path between the terminals of the two plates, and let us put into that path some simple piece of electrical apparatus such as a small lamp bulb. What the connecting path is and how a current travels through it will be explained in a moment. The same rush of electrons that we saw when discussing Fig. 1 now takes place. Electric current is generated and its passage through the filament of the lamp causes this to be heated and to emit light.

How e.m.f. is Maintained

Current does not cease after one wild rush of electrons. Electrons, passing via the wires, the lamp and the carbon, neutralize positive ions in the electrolyte. The repulsion which previously existed is reduced and further positive ions can be torn from the zinc. Therefore, the supply of electrons is maintained at the negative terminal and the supply of positive ions at the positive terminal; an e.m.f. is maintained and current continues to flow through the lamp.

All is not yet plain sailing, however, as anyone who cares to make up the simple cell and try out the experiment will discover. The lamp glows for a few seconds, then becomes dimmer and finally ceases to light up. What has happened?

In the chemical action between the electrolyte and the zinc plate, hydrogen is liberated from the molecules of sal ammoniac. This makes its way to the surface of the carbon plate, where it forms a coating of bubbles. These bubbles, unfortunately, clog the cell and bring its action to a stop. Some means of getting rid of them must be found. Happily, this is not difficult.

Fig. 3 (b) shows a wet Leclanché cell of the type employed a great deal in the past for ringing household bells. Here the carbon electrode takes the form of a rod, which is placed in a porous pot containing manganese dioxide and powdered carbon. Each molecule of manganese dioxide contains one atom of manganese and two of oxygen. The substance has the property of parting readily with some of its oxygen atoms.

When two hydrogen atoms approach a pair of manganese dioxide molecules, rearrangements of their constituent atoms take place and fresh molecules are formed. One of these consists of two atoms of hydrogen and one of oxygen; in other words, it is a molecule of water. Thus, the

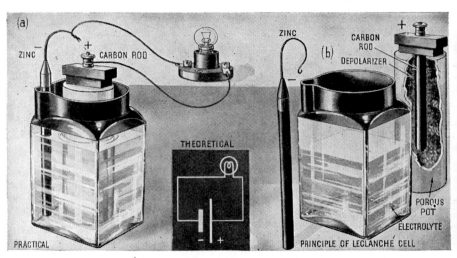

LECLANCHÉ CELL IN A SIMPLE ELECTRICAL CIRCUIT

FIG. 3. *(a) This Leclanché cell is made to do work by being connected to an electric lamp. (Inset) The theoretical circuit diagram. (b) Parts of a commercial "wet" Leclanché cell.*

PRIMARY POWER FOR A GENERATOR

Fundamental purpose of a generator is to convert mechanical power into electrical power. The mechanical power is normally obtained from a prime mover, such as an oil engine or a turbine. The above photograph illustrates an English Electric Company's water turbine which drives a generator developing 11,000 volts, in the Tarraleah Power Station.

clogging hydrogen bubbles are got rid of and the water produced serves the purpose of making good some of the natural evaporation of the electrolyte.

When a cell becomes clogged by hydrogen bubbles it is said to be polarized and the manganese dioxide is called a depolarizer. The process of depolarization is not quite perfect; but, speaking generally, the supply of electrons at the negative terminal and the supply of positive ions at the positive terminal are maintained so long as zinc is available for chlorine atoms to act upon and chlorine atoms are available to act upon the zinc. When one or other of these, or both, have ceased to be available, an e.m.f. can no longer be produced and the cell is said to be run down.

By this time some readers may have become restive about the direction in which

an electric current has been shown to flow. Older text-books and, unhappily, some that are not so old, still maintain the long-exploded idea that current flows from positive to negative in a circuit. This idea is a legacy dating back to a time long before the discovery of the electron. Most unfortunately, it was accepted as a convention that current flowed from the positive to the negative terminal.

The Electron Theory assumed that the real flow is in exactly the opposite direction, from negative to positive. This conception makes it far easier to understand appliances such as the cathode-ray tube and the thermionic valve, and the writer will adhere to it, for he sees no reason why an error should be perpetuated, no matter of how long standing it may be.

The wet Leclanché cell is not widely used

nowadays, but almost everyone employs the cell in its dry form to light flashlamps or cycle lamps, or to provide high-tension current for the wireless set. The term "dry," by the way, is only relative in its application to electric cells; if the interior of a cell were really dry it could not work. Fig. 4 (a) illustrates diagrammatically the construction of a dry Leclanché cell.

Paste Electrolyte

The container, or "can," is of zinc and forms the negative electrode. The electrolyte is not liquid; it is a stiff paste, containing sal ammoniac. Instead of a porous pot, a bag of coarse fabric is used to hold the depolarizer of powdered carbon and manganese dioxide which surrounds the central carbon rod.

The action of a dry Leclanché cell is exactly the same as that of the wet cell earlier described. Next time you are about to discard a run-down dry battery, extract

a cell from it and pull it to pieces, referring to Fig. 4 (b) as you do so and identifying each component as you come to it, as they are all very similarly constructed.

Cells in Series

Battery? Cell? What is the difference? A battery is an assembly of cells. If you remove the cardboard bottom of the case of a flashlamp or a high-tension battery, you will find that the former contains two or three zinc cans and the latter from forty to eighty. In a three-cell flashlamp battery the connections are as shown in Fig. 4 (b).

The can of the cell on the left of the drawing is connected to the carbon rod of the second cell, and the can of this cell to the carbon rod of the third. Two strips of brass serve to connect the battery with the flashlamp bulb. The shorter of these is soldered to the little brass cap of the carbon rod of cell No. 1 and this forms the positive contact of the battery. The longer, the

MAKING PRECISE ELECTRICAL MEASUREMENTS

With modern electrical instruments, very precise measurements of even extremely minute electrical quantities can be made rapidly and with comparative ease. In the above photograph a student is handling equipment in one of the laboratories attached to Oxford University.

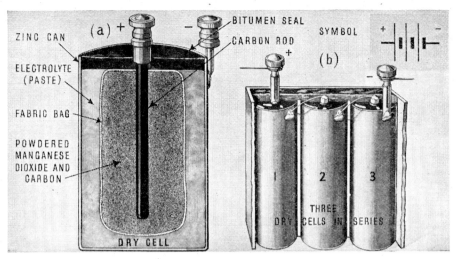

HOW "DRY" CELLS ARE CONSTRUCTED

FIG. 4. *(a) Leclanché cell, in "dry" form, drawn in section to show its component parts. (b) Cells are joined together in series to form batteries of various voltages; three in series give approximately 4½ volts. Theoretical circuit is shown in the top right-hand corner.*

negative contact, is soldered to the can of cell No. 3. This arrangement provides just three times the e.m.f. at the positive and negative brass strip terminals that any one of the three individual cells possesses.

A p.d. or an e.m.f. is an electrical pressure. Just as the pressure of steam is measured in pounds per square inch, so an electrical pressure is measured in volts. The volt is the unit of electrical pressure.

A single Leclanché cell, dry or wet, has an e.m.f. (when in first-class working order) of 1·5 volt. In Fig. 4 (b), we have three such cells wired in series. The e.m.f. between the positive and negative terminals of No. 1 is 1·5 volt, and that between the positive and negative terminals of No. 2 is the same.

But if we connect the negative of No. 1 to the positive of No. 2, the e.m.f. between the positive terminal of No. 1 and the negative terminal of No. 2 is 1·5+1·5, or 3 volts. When No. 3 cell is connected to the other two, the e.m.f. between the positive terminal of No. 1 and the negative terminal of No. 3 is 1·5+1·5+1·5, or 4·5 volts.

We have spoken several times of a flow of electric current through a wire or other connecting path; let us now see how it takes place. The atoms of certain substances, metals in particular, are ever ready to part with one or more of their orbital electrons and to receive others in exchange for them. We can picture thus what happens when a single electron, travelling at high speed, enters one end of a wire: the incoming electron collides with an atom, knocks an electron out of it and takes its place. The ejected electron collides with another atom and the process continues until an electron is driven out at the far end of the wire; for each electron that goes in at one end, an electron emerges at the other.

Unit of Resistance

All this business of colliding with atoms and driving out electrons means that work must be done. Electrons must expend energy to force their way through the wire. There is, in a word, some opposition to their progress, and in electricity that opposition is called resistance. The unit of resistance is the ohm.

Substances with readily detachable electrons offer little resistance to current and are called good conductors; those whose atoms hold on to their electrons more tightly offer higher resistance and are bad conductors; those whose orbiting electrons cannot normally be detached by electron collisions and, therefore, do not allow a current to pass, are known as non-conductors, or insulators.

Examples of good conductors are silver, copper, aluminium and carbon; examples of insulators are dry air, oils, mica and porcelain.

Actually, there are no perfect conductors or insulators. The best of conductors offers some resistance and the best of insulators permits minute leakages of current.

The number of electrons needed to produce an appreciable flow of current is immense. When you switch on a pocket flashlamp some 2,000,000,000,000,000,000 electrons are driven by the battery through its filament in every single second.

If water is driven through a pipe by a pump, the driving pressure is measured in pounds per square inch and the rate of flow in gallons per minute. Similarly, the pressure driving an electric current through a resistance is measured in volts and the rate of flow in amperes.

Volts drive amperes through ohms.

The amount of current flowing depends upon the pressure driving it and the resistance encountered. Or, as Ohm showed in his famous law of electricity, the steady current flowing in a conductor is directly proportional to the pressure and inversely proportional to the resistance.

Simple Calculating Method

Here is an easy way of memorizing and using Ohm's Law. All that you have to do is to remember the name ERIc—or you may think of Ohm as a homERIc figure in electricity. In electrical calculations and formulæ the symbol E stands for e.m.f., or voltage, R for resistance and I for current. As all are interdependent, you can find any one of them if you know the other two.

$$\frac{E}{R \times I}$$

Cover up the symbol representing what is to be found, and what is left shows you how to do it. For example, a flashlamp

bulb is rated at 3·5 volts, 0·25 ampere; what is the resistance of its filament? We have to find R, so cover up that letter in the diagram and $\frac{E}{I}$ is left: $3 \cdot 5 \div 0 \cdot 25 = 14$, and 14 ohms is the answer. How much current will 2 volts drive through 10 ohms? Covering up I, we have $\frac{E}{R}$ left; that is, $\frac{2}{10}$, or $\frac{1}{5}$th ampere.

A current of 3 amperes is passing through a resistance of 12 ohms; what pressure is driving it? With E covered up, we have $R \times I = 12 \times 3 = 36$ volts.

Points to be Noted

There are still one or two points about primary cells to be noted. There are many other types besides the Leclanché, but all work on the same general lines by producing chemically an electron surplus on the negative plate and an electron deficiency on the positive. An electric current is generated by the conversion of chemical energy into electrical energy. It is a one-way process, for a cell of this kind cannot be recharged by passing an electric current through it and converting electrical into chemical energy.

That is the essential difference between the primary cell and the secondary cell, otherwise known as a storage cell, or accumulator. In this the charging process consists in passing an electric current through the cell, where it is converted into chemical energy. During discharge, chemical energy is converted into electrical energy. Such a cell may be charged and discharged hundreds, or even thousands, of times before it wears out.

There are two chief kinds of secondary cell, the nickel-iron and the lead-acid. Readers are probably more familiar with the latter, owing to its wide use for motor-car starting, lighting and ignition and for providing the filament current of battery-operated radio sets.

To describe fully the action of a lead-acid secondary cell would need far more space than is available in this chapter; but the following brief account will demonstrate the general principles. The positive plate (Fig. 5) is coated with lead peroxide, each molecule of which contains one atom of

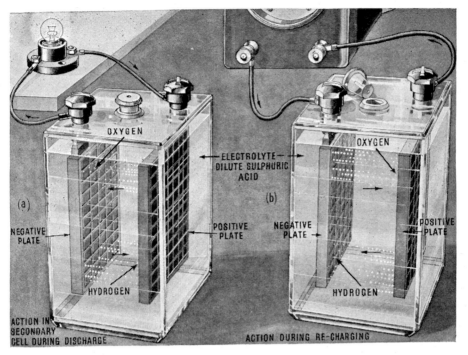

ACTION TAKING PLACE IN A SECONDARY CELL

FIG. 5. (a) During the discharge of an accumulator cell, negatively charged oxygen atoms maintain the electron surplus on the negative plate, whilst positively charged hydrogen molecules travel to the positive plate to maintain its electron deficiency. (b) Showing the re-charging of a run-down secondary cell, by passing current through the cell in reverse

lead and two of oxygen. The negative plate is of pure, spongy lead and the electrolyte is dilute sulphuric acid, the molecules of which consist each of two atoms of hydrogen, one of sulphur and four of oxygen.

Operation of a Charged Cell

When a charged secondary cell is connected to a lamp as in Fig. 5 (a), or to some other piece of apparatus, a complex chemical process begins. Some of the water molecules of the electrolyte break up into hydrogen molecules (each consisting of two hydrogen atoms) and oxygen atoms. The oxygen atoms have an extra electron apiece and travel to the negative plate, where they help to maintain the electron surplus. The hydrogen molecules are short of electrons, so that their arrival at the positive plate assists in maintaining the electron deficiency.

It is impossible here to give a complete account of the complex chemical reactions within the cell. What follows is a much simplified outline of them.

The main chemical activity is at the positive plate, where molecules of lead peroxide, sulphuric acid and hydrogen undergo a remarkable transformation, for these molecules break up and the atoms regroup themselves to form molecules of other substances.

A molecule of lead peroxide (one atom of lead and two of oxygen), a molecule of sulphuric acid (two atoms of hydrogen, one of sulphur and four of oxygen) and a molecule of hydrogen (two atoms of hydrogen) contain twelve atoms in all. Chemical action re-arranges these into a molecule of lead sulphate (one atom of lead, one of sulphur and four of oxygen) and two molecules of water (each with two hydrogen atoms and one of oxygen).

You will see that the same twelve atoms, differently assembled, form this second set of substances.

The net results of this activity—imagine billions of such re-groupings occurring each second—are (1) that the electrolyte gradually becomes weaker, for sulphur is taken from it and water added, and (2) that the positive plate gradually becomes coated with lead sulphate. In time the cell is polarized, just as we saw the primary cell was, the e.m.f. falls and the cell is run down. When the cell is discharged, the positive plates are dirty brown in colour and the negative dull grey.

Unlike the primary cell, it can be restored to its original condition ·by a reversal of the chemical action, which is done by passing current through the cell (Fig. 5 (b)) in the opposite direction. Some of the

water molecules again split up, but this time the hydrogen molecules travel to the negative plate and the oxygen to the positive. At the positive plate, molecules of lead sulphate and water together with an oxygen atom re-arrange themselves into molecules of lead peroxide and sulphuric acid. Work out, as an exercise, the grouping and re-grouping of the ten atoms involved in this action.

As the cell is re-charged, the coating of lead sulphate is removed from the positive plate and the electrolyte becomes stronger, owing to the addition to it of sulphur. When the charge is complete, the positive plates are chocolate brown in colour and the negatives slate grey.

The e.m.f. of a charged lead-acid cell is a little over 2 volts.

Secondary cells of the lead-acid type are made in several different forms. One kind is known as the mass-plate cell. Owing to

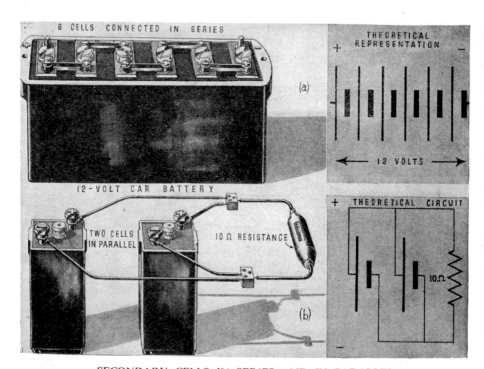

SECONDARY CELLS IN SERIES AND IN PARALLEL

FIG. 6. (a) This 12-volt motor-car battery is built up of secondary cells connected in series. (b) Two cells connected in parallel and discharging through a resistance of 10 ohms

HIGH-VOLTAGE TESTING EQUIPMENT

Trend of electrical power transmission has been steadily in the direction of higher voltages. Therefore, manufacturers of electrical apparatus find it necessary to study intensively the problems associated with these voltages, and test pressures up to 1,000,000 volts have become an industrial necessity. Here is seen the interior of a high-voltage laboratory, with an operator measuring the width of the large spark gap.

its low cost, it is popular for light work, but it is unsuitable where heavy currents are required. For heavy duty, such as the starting and lighting of motor cars, multi-plate cells are used. In these a number of positive plates, all connected together, are interleaved with a number of negative plates. Secondary cells are also made in jelly-acid, or "unspillable," and "dry" forms.

Secondary cells, like primary cells, may be connected in series to obtain a higher e.m.f. Fig. 6 (a) shows a motor-car battery of six cells in series which has an e.m.f. of 12 volts.

Cells of the same size and type, whether primary or secondary, may also be con-

nected in parallel. In Fig. 6 (b), two cells are shown so joined; it will be seen that the two positives and the two negatives are both connected to the resistance, in this instance one of 10 ohms. When cells are in parallel, the e.m.f. is the same as that of one cell, but a heavier current may be drawn from them, since each is called upon to supply only part of the total current. *Series*=more volts; *parallel*=more am-peres.

Whilst we are on the subject of series and parallel, let us see how such connections apply to resistance. A component designed to offer resistance to current is called a resistor. Two resistors, each of 10 ohms,

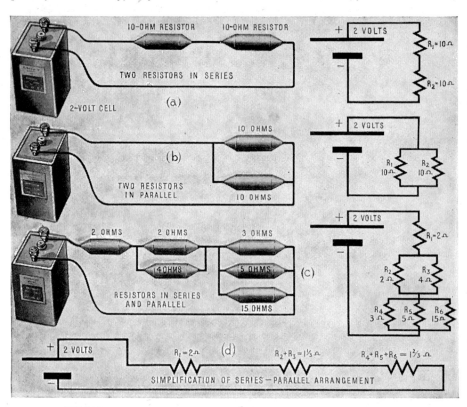

SERIES, PARALLEL, AND SERIES-PARALLEL CONNECTIONS

FIG. 7. *(a) If two 10-ohm resistors are wired in series, the total resistance is doubled. (b) When two resistors are in parallel, the total resistance is, as explained in the text, less than that of either of them. (c) More complicated network of resistors, connected in series-parallel. (d) The network of (c) is simplified and is found to be the equivalent of three single resistors in series. The total resistance in the circuit is 5 ohms.*

are shown in Fig. 7, connected in series across a 2-volt cell. What is the total resistance? If 10 yd. of piping connects a water tank to a tap, there is a definite amount of resistance in the form of friction to flow of water. Add a further 10 yd. of piping and you add as much friction again. The same is true of resistors: when they are connected in series the total resistance is the sum of their individual resistances. Hence, the total resistance is $10+10$, or 20 ohms.

If instead of one 10-yd. length of piping we connect two lengths side by side to a tank, much more water can flow, for with the two pipes in parallel there is only half the friction.

With resistors in parallel, the guiding rule is that the total resistance is less than that of any one of them. The formula (which should be memorized) for finding the exact value is:—

$$\frac{1}{R} = \frac{1}{R_1} + \frac{1}{R_2} + \frac{1}{R_3} \cdot \cdot \cdot$$

Applying this to the example in Fig. 7 (b), we have:—

$$\frac{1}{R} = \frac{1}{10} + \frac{1}{10}$$

$$\therefore \frac{1}{R} = \frac{1}{5}$$

$$\therefore R = 5 \text{ ohms.}$$

Resistors are often arranged in rather complicated "networks" (c). The secret of finding the total value is to start by simplifying each group of parallel resistors. The first group is R_2 and R_3. $\frac{1}{R} = \frac{1}{2} + \frac{1}{4} = \frac{3}{4}$ $\therefore$ $R = \frac{4}{3} = 1\frac{1}{3}$ ohms. In the second group, R_4, R_5 and R_6, $\frac{1}{R} = \frac{1}{5} + \frac{1}{3} + \frac{1}{15} = \frac{3}{5}$ $\therefore$ $R = \frac{5}{3} = 1\frac{2}{3}$ ohms.

The network is equivalent to three resistors in series and the total resistance is now seen to be:—

$$R = 2 + 1\frac{1}{3} + 1\frac{2}{3} = 5 \text{ ohms.}$$

Practical Examples

To make sure that you have mastered the application of Ohm's Law, work out the current flowing in the three circuits shown in Fig. 7.

The term circuit, which has been used more than once, must now be explained

A circuit means a journey in which there is eventually a return to the starting point, and an electric current cannot flow unless a path is provided which enables it to make such an out-and-home journey.

Such a path, often spoken of as a closed circuit, is shown in Fig. 8 (a). When the switch is closed the circuit is said to be "made" and there is a path for electrons from the negative plate through the conductors, the resistor and the switch to the positive plate, and finally through the electrolyte to their starting point.

Open Circuit

A circuit may be broken deliberately by disconnecting a wire or by opening a switch, as in Fig. 8 (b). It is then known as an open circuit. Opening a switch, or switching off, is the normal way of stopping an electric current when it is no longer required.

One of the commonest causes, however, of electrical breakdowns is the accidental open circuit or disconnection, known colloquially as a "dis," brought about by a conductor coming adrift (Fig. 8 (c)). When this happens, electrons cannot be made to light the lamp, ring the bell, turn the machine, or do whatever work they normally do, until the out-and-return circuit is made good by re-connecting the disconnected conductor.

Another cause of electrical troubles is the short circuit (Fig. 8 (d)). Electrons, like many of us humans, always prefer the easiest path and will avoid work if an opportunity of so doing is offered to them. In this diagram the two bare wires connecting the cell with the lamp have come into contact accidentally. A circuit is provided which does not go through the "work." The electrons, taking the easier path, do not traverse the filament, and the lamp does not light up.

A short circuit, or "short," is amongst the most serious of electrical faults, owing to the damage which may result from it. In the case shown in Fig. 8, the resistance of the short circuit indicated by the arrows might be only a minute fraction of an ohm. If a lead-acid secondary cell were in use it might be wrecked, owing to the tremendous chemical activity produced within it by the heavy current drain upon it.

It was explained a little earlier that when an electrical pressure (volts) is driving a current (amperes) through a resistance (ohms), work must be done in the process. It was shown, too, that there are no perfect conductors, every conductor offers some resistance to the passage of an electric current. When a current is made to do useful work it has to overcome resistance. The current flow is always in the same direction, from the negative to the positive pole of the source of supply, and so is known as direct current, or D.C.

Power is the rate of doing work and the electrical unit of power is the watt.

Power does not depend only on the rate at which current flows in a circuit. Consider a 100-candle-power household lighting bulb and a motor-car side or tail lamp; the same current (half an ampere) may be flowing through the filaments of each, but it is plain that work must be going on at a much higher rate inside the larger bulb to produce the far more brilliant light that comes from it. Watts are the units of power and are the products of the volts driving the amperes and the amperes that they drive through resistances.

Suppose that the domestic bulb is connected to 200-volt mains; then the power dissipated in heating its filament to incandescence, if the current is half an ampere,

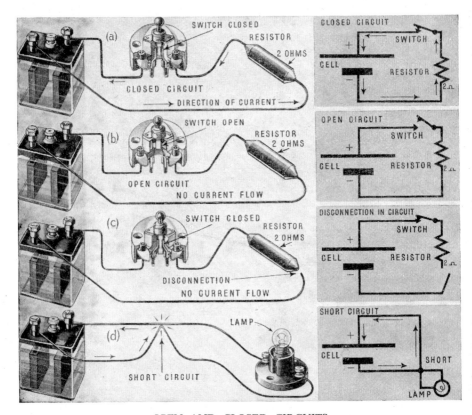

OPEN AND CLOSED CIRCUITS

FIG. 8. *(a) Out-and-home path for electrons is provided when the switch closes the circuit. (b) Circuit deliberately opened by switching off. (c) Accidental open circuit, known as a disconnection. (d) Short-circuit; current obviously does not pass through the "work."*

is $200 \times \frac{1}{2}$, or 100 watts. Similarly, if the side lamp is worked from a 12-volt battery, the power used to heat its filament is $12 \times \frac{1}{2}$, or 6 watts.

Watts = Volts × Amperes, or $W = E \times I$.

There is another way of expressing or calculating power which is often used. $W = E \times I$; but by Ohm's Law, $E = R \times I$ $\therefore W = (R \times I) \times I$, or I^2R. Let us see how this works out for the two lamps. The current in the larger is $\frac{1}{2}$ ampere and the voltage 200. The filament resistance is $200 \div \frac{1}{2} = 400$ ohms. The square of $\frac{1}{2}$ is $\frac{1}{4}$ and $\frac{1}{4} \times 400 = 100$ watts. In the case of the side lamp, the resistance is $12 \div \frac{1}{2}$, or 24 ohms, and $W = \frac{1}{2} \times \frac{1}{2} \times 24 = 6$ watts.

Practical Unit of Energy

Electricity supply authorities sell their current by the kilowatt-hour. A kilowatt is 1000 watts and a kilowatt-hour is 1000 watts for one hour. A kilowatt-hour is often called a "unit."

If you know the power consumed by any electrical appliance, it is easy to work out the cost of running it. Suppose that you have two 75-watt lamps in a sitting-room and that electricity costs 2d. per kilowatt-hour; what is the expense per week of running them for six hours a day? The lamps together consume 150 watts; hence for one hour the running cost is $\frac{150}{1000} \times 2$ pence; for a week of 7×6, or 42, hours it is, $\frac{150}{1000} \times 2 \times 42 = 12 \cdot 6$ pence.

Before we go further, we had perhaps better learn a little more about the units by which rate of flow of current, pressure and resistance are measured.

The ampere, we saw, is an electrical parallel with the gallons-per-minute by which a flow of water is measured. A gallon is a definite quantity of water, which can be measured in pints, or fluid ounces, or cubic inches. In electricity the unit of quantity is the coulomb; an ampere is a flow of 1 coulomb per second. A coulomb is a definite quantity of electrons, 6,290,000,000,000,000,000 to be more precise—six trillions in round figures!

The other units that we have come across all link up with the coulomb. The ampere is a flow of 1 coulomb per second; the volt is the pressure needed to drive 1 ampere through 1 ohm; the ohm is the resistance which requires a pressure of 1 volt to force a current of 1 ampere through it; the watt is the rate of work when 1 volt drives 1 ampere through 1 ohm. If you raise a pound weight 9 in. in 1 second, you work at about the rate of 1 watt.

Accumulator cells and batteries are usually rated in ampere-hours, the ampere-hour being 1 ampere for 1 hour. An accumulator with an ampere-hour capacity of 40 should supply, when fully charged, 1 ampere for 40 hours, or 2 amperes for 20 hours. But it will not deliver 8 amperes for 5 hours unless it is specially made for heavy discharge rates. The ampere-hour capacity of small accumulators is based usually on what is known as the "20-hour discharge rate" (the stated ampere-hour capacity of larger accumulators is based sometimes on the 10-ampere-hour and sometimes on the 5-ampere-hour discharge rate); that is, if the discharge is spread over 20 hours the ampere-hour capacity should be obtained. Thus, a 10-ampere-hour cell should supply $\frac{1}{2}$ ampere for 20 hours, a 50-ampere-hour cell $2\frac{1}{2}$ amperes for 20 hours, and so on. If these discharge rates are exceeded, the ampere-hours will be considerably less than the rated number.

It was mentioned in a preceding paragraph that a kilowatt is 1000 watts. Kilo is one of the several prefixes used to indicate multiples or fractions of the basic electrical units. Others are milli = $\frac{1}{1000}$ and micro = $\frac{1}{1,000,000}$. A table showing the units so far discussed, with prefixes in general use and their meanings, is on page 182.

It should be noted that in electrical formulæ, E, R, I and W always stand for volts, ohms, amperes and watts. When calculations involve millivolts, micro-amperes and so on, these must be expressed as fractions or decimal parts of the basic units. For example, if it is desired to find what voltage drives 25 milliamperes through a resistance of 8000 ohms, the calculation becomes:—

$$25 \text{ mA} = 0 \cdot 025 \text{ amp., or } \tfrac{1}{40} \text{ amp.}$$
$$\therefore E = 8000 \times 0 \cdot 025 \left.\right\} = 200 \text{ volts.}$$
$$\text{or, } E = 8000 \times \tfrac{1}{40} \left.\right\}$$

Unit	Symbol	Abbreviation	Meaning
Coulomb .	Q	—	A vast but definite quantity of electrons
Microcoulomb .	μQ	—	$\frac{1}{1,000,000}$ coulomb
Ampere .	A	amp	1 coulomb per second
Milliampere .	mA	milliamp	$\frac{1}{1000}$ ampere
Microampere	μA	microamp	$\frac{1}{1,000,000}$ ampere
Volt . .	V	—	Unit of electrical pressure
Millivolt .	mV	—	$\frac{1}{1000}$ volt
Microvolt .	μV	—	$\frac{1}{1,000,000}$ volt
Kilovolt .	kV	—	1000 volts
Ohm . .	Ω	—	Unit of resistance
Kilohm .	$k\Omega$	—	1000 ohms
Megohm .	$M\Omega$	—	1,000,000 ohms
Watt .	W	—	Unit of power
Kilowatt .	kW	—	1000 watts
Watt-hour .	Wh	—	1 watt for 1 hour
Kilowatt-hour . .	kWh	—	1000 watt-hours
Ampere-hour . .	Ah	—	1 ampere for 1 hour

With an e.m.f. of 10 volts the current is $5\mu A$; what is the resistance? As a decimal, $5\mu A = 0.000005$ amp., or $\frac{1}{200,000}$ amp.

$$\therefore R = 10 \div 0.000005$$
$$\text{or, } R = 10 \div \frac{1}{200,000} \Bigg\} = 2,000,000 \ \Omega,$$
$$\text{or } 2 \ M\Omega.$$

We shall come across a good many more electrical units and each will be explained as it occurs.

Suppose two metal plates are placed facing one another with a layer of air between them. Air is an excellent insulator. One plate is connected to the positive pole of a cell and the other to its negative pole.

Offhand you may be tempted to say that nothing will happen. As air is an insulator, it must surely act as a barrier to current from the cell and none can flow. It is quite true that after a very brief time current will be barred; but before that happens there is a momentary flow of current into the combination of plates and insulator which form what is called a capacitor.

When the cell is connected up it at once begins to produce an electron surplus on the plate wired to its negative pole and an electron deficiency on that wired to its positive. A flow of electrons (that is, an electric current) takes place until the two plates are at the same potentials as the corresponding poles of the cells. Current

stops as soon as it has produced the same e.m.f. between the plates of the capacitor (2 volts in this case) as there is between the plates of the cell or battery.

Fig. 9 (a) illustrates diagrammatically the position at this point. On the positive plate there is an assembly of positive ions, faced by an equal number of electrons on the negative plate. Between the two there is an attractive force. The electrons would like to pass through the insulator to the positive plate by cannoning into atoms of the insulator, knocking out electrons and taking their place. But they cannot do this, for, as we have seen, an insulator has atoms whose orbiting electrons are too tightly bound to them to be driven out by such collisions.

Charging a Capacitor

The insulator between the plates of a capacitor is called the dielectric. When a momentary flow of current has produced an electron deficiency on one plate and an electron surplus on the other, the electron orbits of the atoms of the dielectric are pulled out of shape, so to speak, owing to the state of strain which exists between the two plates. This state of strain constitutes an electric field. When it exists the capacitor is said to be charged.

If the charged capacitor is disconnected from the cell or battery, it retains its charge; provide a connecting path between positive and negative plates, and current flows until the surplus electrons on the negative plate have neutralized the positive ions in the positive.

How the charge and discharge of a capacitor may be demonstrated by means of a two-way switch and two galvanometers is also shown in Fig. 9 (b)—the galvanometer is an instrument which detects an electric current; we shall see more about it later.

When the switch is turned to the right, the right-hand galvanometer's needle gives a flick which indicates the momentary passing of current into the capacitor as it charges. Turning the switch to the left disconnects the cell and provides a conducting path between the plates; the capacitor discharges and a flick of the needle

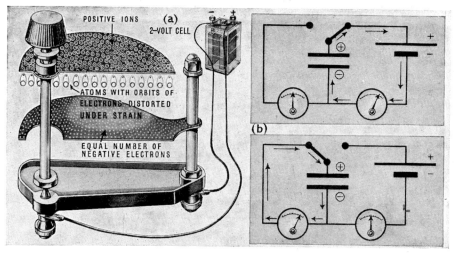

ELECTRON DISPOSITION IN A CHARGED CAPACITOR

Fig. 9. *(a) On the positive plate, positive ions are present. Opposite them, on the negative plate, is an equal number of electrons. Electrons cannot leave the atoms of the insulator between the plates, but their orbits become distorted by the strain. (b) Showing diagrammatically how a capacitor may be charged and discharged by means of a switch.*

of the left-hand galvanometer shows the passage of current for a brief instant.

No capacitor retains its charge indefinitely, for, as we have seen, there are no perfect insulators. According to the nature and quality of the dielectric, the charge leaks away in time.

Property of Capacitance

The amount of electricity which flows into a capacitor when an e.m.f. of 1 volt is applied across its plates is known as the capacitance of the capacitor (symbol: C) and the unit of capacitance is the farad (symbol: F). A capacitor has a capacitance of 1 farad when the entry of 1 coulomb of electricity into it produces an e.m.f. of 1 volt between its plates.

A capacitor of this capacitance with air dielectric would be about as big as a furniture van! Those generally used are very much smaller and for these a smaller working unit is required. This smaller unit is the microfarad, which is one-millionth of a farad (symbol: μF, though mfd is often incorrectly used). For some purposes, even the microfarad is too big; in wireless, television and radar. the micro-microfarad.

or picofarad (symbol: $\mu\mu$F or pF), which is one-billionth of a farad, is often employed. But remember that where C occurs in formulæ it stands for farads; hence, before making calculations, μF or $\mu\mu$F must be converted to decimals or fractions of a farad.

The capacitance of a capacitor depends on the surface area of its plates, the distance between the plates and the nature of the dielectric. The greater the area of the plates, the smaller the distance between them; and the higher the permittivity of the dielectric, the larger is the capacitance of the capacitor.

In older text-books, the term permittivity is often called "specific inductive capacity"; a well-known brand of insulating oil used in industrial electrical apparatus has about twice, and mica about six times the permittivity of air. Thus, a capacitor with air-spaced plates would have twice the capacitance if its plates were immersed in this oil and six times the capacitance if same thickness of mica were substituted for the air between its plates.

Under a high electric pressure, a capacitor may break down; the strain is so great that electrons are wrenched from the atoms of its dielectric. The dielectric is ruptured and current flows through it from plate to plate. An air-spaced capacitor can repair itself, for a new supply of air replaces the old; but a capacitor with mica or some other solid dielectric, such as glass or paper, is usually ruined.

Interesting Similarities

The charging of a capacitor may be likened aptly to the process of inflating the tyre of a motor car. If the working pressure of the tyre is 50 lb per sq. in., so many cubic inches of air must be driven in before that pressure is built up. So with a capacitor: so many microcoulombs of electricity must go in to build up a given voltage between its plates.

There are other interesting similarities too. When you blow up a tyre with a foot pump (Fig. 10 (a)), the work is at first easy, for there is no pressure inside the tyre to oppose the entry of air. But as you pump in more and more air, the internal pressure rises and offers growing opposition to the incoming of air

Were you to plot a curve of tyre pressure against pumping time it might look something like that shown in Fig. 10 (a). In the first two minutes the pressure rises rapidly to about 30 lb. per sq. in.; but the work is harder and the growth of pressure slower after that. It takes about twice as long to put in the last 20 lb. as the first 30 lb. per sq. in.

Fig. 10 (b), with the switch in position 1, shows the charge of a 1-microfarad capacitor from a 50-volt battery through a resistor of 1,000,000 ohms, or 1 megohm. At the

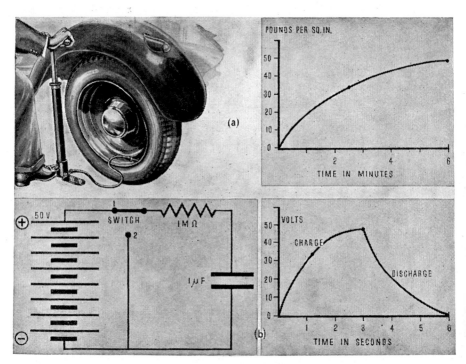

WHAT HAPPENS WHEN A CAPACITOR IS CHARGED

FIG. 10. (a) Inflating a motor-car tyre with a foot-pump bears a resemblance to the charging of a capacitor. (b) A curve plotted alongside a circuit containing a 50-volt battery, a 1,000,000-ohm resistor, and a 1-mfd. capacitor. The pressure rise tails off as when inflating the tyre. If switch were turned to position 2, discharge curve would be as shown.

FIG. 11. *When capacitors are in parallel their capacitances add together. When they are in series, the overall capacitance is less than that of any one of them.*

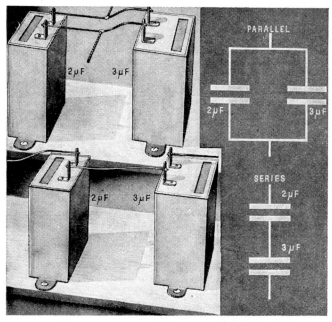

end of 1 second the pressure between the plates has risen to $31\frac{1}{2}$ volts; after 3 seconds it is $47\frac{1}{2}$ volts—you see how the rise in pressure tails off in much the same way as in inflating the motor tyre.

The reason is very similar. When the capacitor is first connected to the battery it contains atoms in a state of equilibrium and there is no pressure across its plates. When current begins to flow, an increasing electron deficiency is caused on the positive plate and an increasing surplus on the negative. Electrons on the negative plate exercise repulsion on those entering from the negative pole of the battery. This repulsion increases as their number grows and current flows in more slowly.

Charging Curve

The time in seconds taken to charge a capacitor to 63 per cent of the full voltage can be found by multiplying its capacitance in farads by the resistance in ohms through which current is flowing—there must always be some resistance, since there are no perfect conductors. In this instance, we have 1,000,000 ohms and 0·000001 farad: hence the time is 1 second. In Fig. 10 we mark in 63 per cent of 50, or $31\frac{1}{2}$ volts, at 1 second. Further measurements and plots would produce the charging curve shown, the capacitor reaching 95 per cent of its charge in 3 seconds.

The time taken by a capacitor charging through a resistor to reach 63 per cent of its full charge is called the time constant of the circuit (symbol: CR). By using high-grade components and choosing the right values, we can make a capacitor charge consistently in any desired time from a fraction of a millionth of a second upwards. Such a circuit can thus be made an accurate timekeeper for very small spaces of time. It is used for such purposes in both radar and television.

When the valve of an inflated tyre is unscrewed, air is released very rapidly at first, owing to the high pressure which is driving it out; but as more and more air is released the pressure falls and the outward rush of air tails off.

Much the same thing happens when a capacitor is discharged by the provision of a conducting path between its plates. If the switch in Fig. 10 (b) is turned to position 2, the battery is cut out and there is a conducting path through the resistor from plate to plate. The discharge curve would be like that seen in Fig. 10 (b). Readers with a mathematical bent will recognize the shapes of the charge and discharge curves as exponential.

When two capacitors are placed in

parallel (Fig. 11) their capacitances add together. These have a combined capacitance of $2+3=5$ µF. But when they are in series, the rule is:—

$$\frac{1}{C}=\frac{1}{C_1}+\frac{1}{C_2}+\frac{1}{C_3}\cdot\ \cdot\ \cdot\ \cdot$$

Thus, we have:—

$$\frac{1}{C}=\frac{1}{2}+\frac{1}{3}$$

$$\therefore\ \frac{1}{C}=\frac{5}{6}$$

$$\therefore\ C=\tfrac{6}{5}=1\tfrac{1}{5},\text{ or } 1\cdot2\ \mu F.$$

You will see that the rules for capacitors in series and parallel are exactly the opposite of those for resistors.

And now, having seen something of the way in which a one-way or direct electric current can be generated, and of some of the things into or through which it can pass, we must discuss certain of the effects produced by a flow of current. The best way of understanding and remembering these effects is to make the simple experiments which will be described, writing notes on them as you do so in order to have a record of them.

Inexpensive and Interesting

The apparatus required is quite inexpensive and the results of the experiments are so interesting that you will find the small outlay upon it most amply repaid. You will need the following:—

A $\frac{1}{4}$-lb. reel of No. 26 double-cotton-covered copper wire; 2 or 3 yd. of No. 26 Eureka enamelled resistance wire; a small compass; a bar magnet, about 4 in. long and $\frac{1}{2}$ to $\frac{3}{4}$ in. in width; a 3-in. length of cardboard tubing, about $\frac{3}{4}$ in. in diameter; a similar length of cardboard tubing, about 1 to $1\frac{1}{4}$ in. in diameter—the smaller tube must slide *easily* into the larger; 2 or 3 oz. of *soft* iron wire; a piece of white cardboard, about 10 by 8 in.; four corks of equal length; four brass drawing-pins or small copper nails; about a tablespoonful of fine iron filings; an accumulator cell. If you do not possess one, you may be able to hire one from a wireless shop. It should have an ampere-hour capacity of 20.

Begin by making up the little table illustrated in Fig. 12—just the four corks, acting as "legs," fixed near the corners of

the cardboard by brass drawing-pins or short copper nails.

We are ready now to make the first experiment. Pierce two holes in the table top. Cut off a yard of the copper wire, connect one bared end to the negative pole of an accumulator cell and pass the wire through the holes, as shown in the sketch, bending it so that it stands rather less than $\frac{1}{2}$ in. above the table. Twist together the far end of the copper wire and one end of a 30-in. length of the Eureka (both ends must, of course, be bared). Do not yet connect the other end of the Eureka to the positive pole of the cell.

Place the compass in the middle of the table and under the copper wire. Turn the table until the needle of the compass, pointing north and south, is directly in line with the wire.

Connect the free end of the Eureka to the positive terminal of the cell, watching the compass as you do so. Its needle is suddenly deflected to the left—it points now west of north.

Next, change over the connections to the cell; that is, connect the copper wire to its positive and the Eureka to its negative terminal. Current now flows from south to north through the wire above the compass and its needle is deflected eastwards, or to the right.

Now arrange the copper wire so that it lies flat on the table and place the compass on top of it, propping it level with two slips of cardboard. You will find that a current moving from south to north *under* the compass produces the same deflection of the needle as one passing from north to south *above* it.

Wind about thirty turns of wire on to a rectangular "former," such as a matchbox or a medicine bottle, moulding the turns of wire to the shape of the former with the fingers. Slide the coil of wire off the former and connect it as shown in bottom sketch (Fig. 12), placing the compass inside it.

Home-made Galvanometer

When the cell is connected to the coil as shown, current flows from south to north in the turns under the compass and from north to south in the turns above it. Each

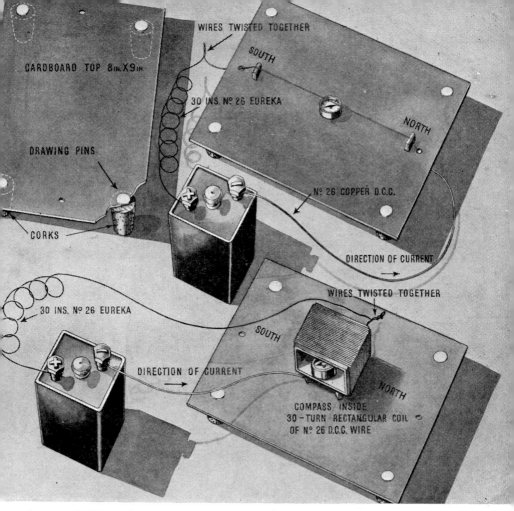

CONSTRUCTING A SIMPLE FORM OF GALVANOMETER

FIG. 12. *First make the little experimenting table shown at top (left), which is a sheet of white cardboard supported on four corks. Experiment as described in the text, and note direction of current flow. When the 30-turn coil of No. 26 D.C.C. wire is connected as shown (bottom, right), with the compass inside it, we shall have made a simple galvanometer.*

turn, therefore, doubles the deflecting effect produced by a single wire lying above or below the compass, which is strongly deflected to the west. The effect is greatly increased by using thirty turns. You have, in fact, made a simple form of galvanometer, an instrument capable of detecting quite small currents.

External Effect

In these experiments, by the way, the current taken from the 2-volt cell is about 1 ampere, for 30 in. of No. 26 Eureka wire

have a resistance of about 2 ohms—the resistance of the small amount of copper wire used is negligible.

Clearly, the flow of current in the wire produces some effect *outside* the wire, since it can cause the compass needle to err and stray in this way.

A length of canvas fire hose is lying flat on the ground. We connect one end of it to a hydrant and turn on the water. Water does not immediately issue from the nozzle at the far end. Before a flow of water can take place, the pressure driving it must round out the flat walls of the pipe. The water pressure exerts energy in doing this; but what happens if the water is turned off at the hydrant? Water does not immediately cease to flow from the nozzle; it does not, in fact, do so until the walls of the pipe have fallen together and become flat again.

Energy is on Loan

In other words, the energy which rounds out the pipe is not spent: it is only on loan. When the water is turned off at the hydrant this loaned energy is repaid, for the collapsing walls of the pipe now supply energy which keeps the water flowing until the collapse is complete and the loan entirely repaid.

When an e.m.f. is applied to a conductor such as a wire, it cannot immediately cause current to flow. Before it can do so it must build up a magnetic field, which surrounds the wire like an invisible sleeve (see Fig. 13 (a), page 190). Only when the magnetic field is fully developed does current reach the value laid down by Ohm's Law. It is as though an applied e.m.f. were met at first by an e.m.f. of equal value but opposite in direction. Not until the applied e.m.f. has overcome this "back-e.m.f." can current flow freely.

When the battery is disconnected or switched off, current does not immediately cease to flow. The magnetic field collapses; falling, so to speak, back into the conductor. In doing so it repays the energy which was borrowed during its formation; it sets up a forward e.m.f. which causes current

PRACTICAL DEVELOPMENT OF THE PRINCIPLES

Even this large English Electric generating plant in a London power station is merely a practical development of the principles of electromagnetism which are explained in the accompanying text. The alternator is an alternating-current generator with an output of 32,000 kilowatts at 33,000 volts. It is installed at the Willesden generating station.

TRANSFORMING ELECTRICAL INTO MECHANICAL POWER

An electric motor is a device for transforming electrical power into mechanical power. Above is seen one of those manufactured by the British Thomson-Houston Co., Ltd., for driving metal-rolling machinery. It is of the reversing type and develops 3000 horse-power.

to keep on flowing until the field has entirely fallen in. ·

It must not be imagined that a long time is needed for the production or the collapse of the magnetic field. It may actually build up and decay millions of times in a single second. But an event cannot occur in no time at all; some time must elapse whilst it is taking place, and modern science is quite used to measuring time in *fractions* of millionths of seconds!

Important Conclusions

From the experiments already made, certain important facts about the magnetic field may be inferred.

(1) It represents a force—the compass needle is deflected; (2) it has a definite direction—the same conditions will always produce the same deflection of the needle;

(3) the direction of the field depends upon the direction in which current flows in the conductor surrounded by the field—if the direction of the current is reversed, the deflection of the needle is reversed.

When the erroneous idea of an electric current flowing from positive to negative was accepted, all sorts of queer rules were invented about the direction and effects of a magnetic field; the student was asked to arrange his fingers in odd ways, to imagine that he was swimming in the current and so on.

Such things are not needed when we have the true conception of a current flowing from negative to positive.

The hands of a clock, the head of a screw that is being tightened, both rotate in the same direction. We call this direction "clockwise" and it seems to us the normal direction of circular motion, for it suggests advancing or moving towards completion.

Now look at Fig. 13 (a) again. If your eye is at the right-hand end of the conductor, current is moving towards you. In that case the direction of the magnetic field is *clockwise* round the conductor. The simple rule then is: if a current is flowing towards you as you look along a conductor, the magnetic field has a clockwise direction.

Now for another experiment. Place the rectangular coil on the little table and connect up as shown in Fig. 13 (b). The coil is arranged so that its long sides lie north and south and the compass is placed to the east, just outside the coil. If you stand east of the coil and look at its end, current is flowing clockwise round it. Now look at the compass needle; it has been deflected so violently that it now lies east and west, with its south-seeking end pointing towards the coil.

The compass needle is a magnet and the basic rule of magnetism is the same as one of the basic rules of electricity. Just as like charges repel like and attract unlike, so like magnetic poles repel like and attract unlike. The north-seeking and south-seeking ends of the needle are usually known as its north and south poles respectively.

As the south pole of the needle is strongly attracted by the end of the coil at which you are looking, that end must be a north pole. From this we can formulate the simple rule that if current is flowing clockwise in the turns of wire at the end of a coil at which you are looking, that end is a north pole. Clockwise, north; counter-clockwise, south.

Verify by moving round to the west end of the coil. With the cell connected as in Fig. 13 (b), current flows counter-clockwise when you look at that end of the coil: that end is a south pole. With the Fig. 13 (c) connections that end is a north pole. Verify with the compass.

Stop the flow of current at any point in your experiments by disconnecting the cell. The coil at once ceases to have any effect on the compass needle. In a word, the coil is a magnet, with one end of it a north pole and the other a south, so long—but only so long—as current is flowing round it.

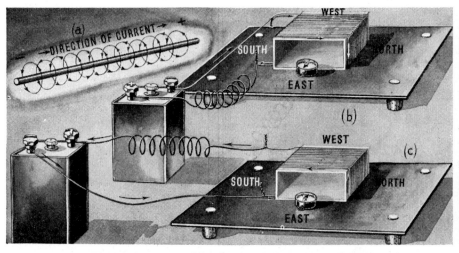

FINDING THE DIRECTION OF CURRENT FLOW

FIG. 13. *(a) Magnetic field surrounding a current-carrying conductor is like an invisible sleeve. (b) Compass is placed just outside one end of the rectangular coil, resting on experimental table. With current flowing in a clockwise direction in the end of the coil at which you are looking, the south-seeking end of the compass needle is attracted to that end.*
(c) Counter-clockwise flow causes north-seeking end of needle to be attracted.

FIG. 14. *Iron filings show the shape of the magnetic field of a bar magnet. They do not show the direction of the field (indicated by arrows), but this can be easily verified with a compass.*

We shall see presently that the same is true also of the piece of steel which forms the compass needle.

For our next experiment we require the bar magnet and a small quantity of the iron filings. Lay the magnet on the cardboard table (Fig. 14), take a pinch of filings and let them fall thinly, tapping the table gently as you do so. Add more when they have arranged themselves. You may not succeed at first in producing the neatly ordered arrangement of filings shown in the drawing, either because the filings are scattered rather too densely or because your table-tapping is a little too hard. Try again and the picture of the field will be built up at last.

The filings indicate that there are "lines of force" linking the two poles; they do not, however, show the direction of the field. This can be found by sketching in lightly with a pencil one or two of the lines of filings between the poles, shaking the filings off the table and then moving the compass slowly along the lines. The north end of the compass needle points in the direction of the field, which will be found to be from the north to the south pole of the bar magnet.

Magnetized by Induction

From the behaviour of the filings we deduce that a magnet attracts iron. Verify by picking up a piece of soft iron with the magnet. Whilst the soft iron is suspended in this way, bring one or two small nails into contact with it. They are attracted and held; the iron is magnetized, but it is only a temporary magnetism. It disappears and

the nails fall as soon as the iron is detached from the magnet. The soft iron is said to have been magnetized by induction during its contact with the bar magnet.

Next take a piece of steel (a screwdriver or an old chisel will do well) and rub its end for some little time on one end of the bar magnet. You will find that the steel has become magnetized, but this time its magnetism does not disappear when it is detached from the bar magnet.

Soft iron, then, can be magnetized only temporarily, whilst steel, if hard, can be magnetized permanently.

Making the Coil

Now wind a coil of about 60 turns of the D.C.C. (double-cotton-covered) copper wire on the smaller cardboard tube, putting the turns on closely, tightly and evenly.

Mark out on the cardboard table a rectangle of the same length as the tube and with a width equal to the tube's diameter. Cut out the rectangle with an old razor blade. Fit the coil into the slot in the table so that it is half above and half below the surface—prop below with a book if it is too loose a fit to stay in position. Connect to the 2-volt cell, as shown in Fig. 15 (a).

Scatter iron filings as you did with the bar magnet and a similar magnetic field will be shown to exist by the pattern that they form. The coil has become a magnet. Verify with the compass that its north pole is that end round which, as you face it, current is flowing clockwise. Verify also with the compass that the coil ceases to be a magnet as soon as current is switched off.

Cut the soft iron wire into 3-in. lengths and make these into a bundle, tied tightly with thin string, which will just fit nicely into the tube round which the coil is formed. Slip the bundle into the tube to form a core to the coil and repeat the experiment with the iron filings. It will be found that the filings now indicate a far denser magnetic field. The compass, too, is deflected at a much greater distance from the coil when the core is inserted than when it is withdrawn. The coil with its soft iron core is an electromagnet so long as current is flowing.

Single-layer Helical Coil

Fig. 15 (b) indicates diagrammatically how the field of a single-layer helical coil is built up. Each turn has its own field when current is flowing. The fields of adjacent turns have the same direction and their combined effect is the production of larger fields.

When an iron core is inserted into the coil, a denser field can be built up, for the iron offers less opposition to it than air. Iron is said to have greater permeability than air.

It will be seen that permeability in the magnetic field of a coil is analogous to permittivity in the electric field of a capacitor.

All kinds of matter have some magnetic qualities and there are several which display properties similar to those possessed by iron and steel. In this necessarily brief survey of magnetism, however, we need concern ourselves with iron and steel alone.

How does a piece of either of these metals become magnetized? Why does steel, once magnetized, retain its magnetism, whereas soft iron is demagnetized as soon as the magnetizing source is removed?

The answers to these questions are provided in Fig. 15 (c). In an unmagnetized piece of either metal, the atoms are arranged higgledy-piggledy, with their orbiting electrons travelling in all sorts of directions.

Place a piece of iron inside a helical coil through the turns of which an electric current is flowing and the magnetic field of the coil lines up the iron atoms as shown diagrammatically.

You will see that the one-way movement of electrons shown is equivalent to a steady flow of electric current round the metal bar. So long as this flow is maintained, a magnetic field is produced and the bar is magnetized. The flow is clockwise, hence that end is the north pole of the magnetized bar.

The atoms of soft iron are easily pulled into line by a magnetic field, but when the field is removed they return at once to their normal random arrangement. With its readiness to be magnetized, soft iron is said to have low reluctance; as it parts with its magnetism quickly, it has poor retentivity.

The harder the iron, the more difficult it is to magnetize and the slower it is to become demagnetized when the field is removed; hardness increases both reluctance and retentivity.

Hard steel has less permeability than soft iron and much greater reluctance. But once its atoms have been forced into line they stay there for good. Hard steel, therefore, has high retentivity and permanent magnets can be made from it.

To say that the atoms of magnetized steel retain their arrangement for good is, perhaps, an overstatement. "Permanent" should mean everlasting; but permanent magnets, like permanent waves, do deteriorate with time. Vibration and heat both tend to allow the steel atoms to resume their original haphazard arrangement. Hammer a permanent magnet hard, or bring it to white heat and allow it to cool, and little, if any, of its magnetism remains; the atoms cease to be aligned in orderly formation and an electric current no longer flows around the steel.

It is true, then, to say that steel magnets and electromagnets *are* magnets only if an electron current is flowing round them. This is equally true of iron, whether magnetized by induction or by being used as the core of a coil.

The strength of the field of an electromagnet depends upon the number of turns

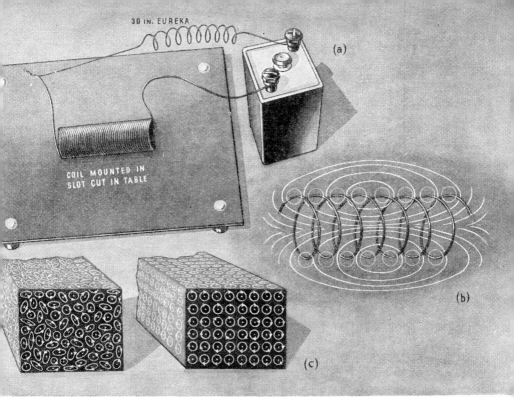

EFFECT OF MAGNETISM ON ELECTRON ORBITS

FIG. 15. *(a) Coil is mounted in its slot in the home-made table. (b) Diagrammatic representation of the field of a single-layer coil. (c) In an unmagnetized piece of iron or steel the orbits of the electrons lie higgledy-piggledy. When the metal is magnetized, the orbits of the electrons are, so to speak, pulled into line, as shown on the right.*

of wire surrounding its core and the current driven through them. Magnetism is produced by magnetomotive force (m.m.f.) and the unit of this is the ampere-turn (At). Multiply the turns of an electromagnet by the current flowing through them and you have the ampere-turns of m.m.f.

Thus, when 1 ampere flows through your 60-turn coil, the m.m.f. is $1 \times 60 = 60$ ampere-turns. If 7 milliamps flow through 5000 turns, the m.m.f. is $0.007 \times 5000 = 35$ At.

How important a discovery was the electromagnet we shall see in the next chapter.

We saw earlier that the e.m.f. which drives a current through a conductor causes a magnetic field to come into being; we saw, too, that when current is switched off, the collapsing magnetic field gives rise to an e.m.f. which causes current to flow

in the conductor until the collapse is complete. Our next experiment (Fig. 16 (a)) shows that if a magnetic field is made to "cut" the conducting turns of a coil, a current is caused to flow in them.

Orienting the Coils

The connexions of the cylindrical and rectangular coils need no description. The latter must be oriented, so that the long sides of its turns point north and south. Push the bar magnet quickly into the 60-turn coil, watching the compass needle as you do so. If the bar magnet is a strong one and the compass sensitive, the needle will give a momentary flick to one side. Withdraw the magnet quickly and a flick in the opposite direction takes place. Should the flick not be seen, the compass is probably too sluggish. In that case, borrow or hire a good galvanometer or a small milliammeter (an instrument which measures milliamperes) and there should be no doubt about successful results.

When the magnet is inserted, the lines of force of its field cut, or pass through, the turns of the coil in one direction. An e.m.f. is set up during the process and drives a spurt of current through the coil. Withdrawing the magnet causes the field to cut the turns in the opposite direction: there is another e.m.f. driving current the opposite way.

Exactly the same effects are produced if the process is reversed by making the turns cut the magnetic field. Try this by propping up the magnet vertically and moving the coil up and down so as to cover and uncover it. The needle can be kept continually flicking by moving the coil rapidly up and down.

Current produced by these means is said to be induced.

The direction of an induced current is always such that its magnetic field opposes any change in the inducing field, or any movement of the inducing agent. In Fig. 16 (b) the north pole of a bar magnet is about to enter a coil. To oppose the magnet's movement the induced current must be such as to make the end of the coil entered a north pole, for like repels like; that is, current must flow clockwise at this end. Hence, whether current flows downwards through the coil as in Fig. 16 (b) or upwards as in (c) depends upon the direction in which the windings have been made.

Direction of Current Reversed

Fig. 16 (c) illustrates what occurs when the magnet is withdrawn. The end of the coil nearest the north pole of the magnet now becomes a south pole, attracting the nearest end of the magnet and trying, so to speak, to prevent its withdrawal; current must, therefore, flow anti-clockwise at this end. As before, the direction of the windings determines whether current flows upwards or downwards through the coil.

Induction by the movement of a magnetic field through a coil or the movement of a coil through a magnetic field provides a means of generating and maintaining vastly greater electric currents than is economically possible with any kind of battery.

The induction method converts mechanical energy into electrical energy, which is a far cheaper business than the conversion of chemical energy, which we discussed when studying electric cells.

A medium-sized dry cell, costing, say, 2s. 6d., might provide 0·25 ampere of current, with an average e.m.f. of 1·1 volt, intermittently for a total "working life" of 60 hours. Its total output in watt-hours is, therefore, 0·25 × 1·1 × 60, or 16·5 watt-hours, and running costs work out at approximately 1·8d. per watt-hour. That is about a thousand times as much as the average amount paid for domestic electricity supplies from the mains.

Direct-current Generator

Fig. 17 (a, b, c, d, e), pages 196-7, shows the principle of the D.C. generator, or dynamo. A single rectangular coil of wire is seen revolving in the field between the north and south magnet poles. The ends of the coil are connected to different halves of a split metal ring, the halves being insulated from one another and from the spindle. The ring rotates between two spring-loaded metal contacts called brushes, which collect the current generated and deliver it through leads or cables to the work. The split-ring is known as the commutator.

The induction of the e.m.f. which gives rise to current is dependent upon the rate at which the lines of force of the field are being cut by the turns of the coil. To simplify the explanations which follow, one half of the coil is shown white and the other black.

With the coil in the position shown at (a), no lines are being cut and there is no current in the windings. At (b) the coil has turned through 45 deg.; lines of force are being cut at a rapid rate and induced current is flowing. Lines of force are cut at a somewhat increasing rate until the coil reaches the horizontal position; the rate decreases rather slowly during the next 45 deg. of rotation and then more rapidly until the vertical position is reached again.

In (b) and (c) the coil is shown rotating

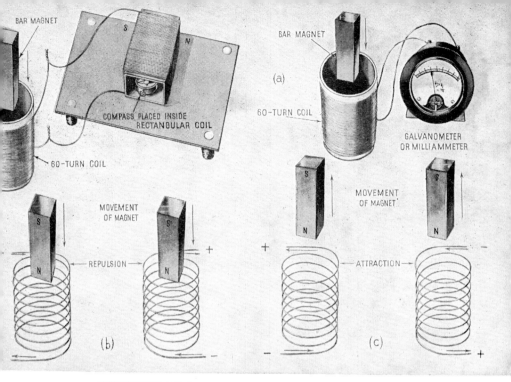

DIRECTION OF FLOW OF INDUCED CURRENT

Fig. 16. *Deflection of the needle when a bar magnet is inserted into the coil, and then withdrawn from it, indicates that a current of electricity is flowing. (b) When a magnet is inserted, north pole first, into a coil, the end of the coil at which it enters becomes a north pole. Current must, therefore, flow clockwise round that end. Which is the positive and which the negative ends of the winding depend on the direction in which it is wound on the former. (c) When the magnet is withdrawn, the direction of the induced current is reversed. The north pole of the magnet is attracted and its withdrawal is opposed.*

clockwise; it is simple to remember that with this direction of rotation, current in the turns of the coil nearest the north pole of the magnet flows towards you. Reverse *either* the rotation of the coil *or* the positions of the magnet poles and current in the coil is reversed.

In (b) current flows towards you in the upper (black) half of the coil which is connected to the half of the commutator now in contact with the left-hand brush. Induced current, therefore, leaves the coil by way of the left-hand brush, goes through the work and returns to the right-hand brush.

Half a revolution later (c), the other (white) portion of the coil is uppermost. Current is again moving towards you in this portion and, owing to the rotation of the commutator, the left-hand brush once more picks up current that is leaving the coil.

Thus, by means of the commutator, current flowing always in the same direction is delivered to the work. It would, however, not be a steady current, for it would rise to peaks when the coil was horizontal and fall to zero when it was vertical; (d) shows what the output would be like from a machine built on these lines with its armature, or rotor, as the revolving part is called, making fifty revolutions a second.

By making use of a symmetrically arranged combination of four coils with a commutator divided into eight segments, the much more even output illustrated in (e) could be obtained. By employing what

HOW A GENERATOR WORKS

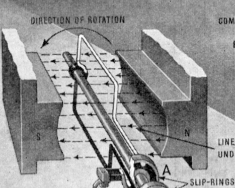

MAGNETIC POLES

DIRECTION OF ROTATION

COIL OF WIRE (ARMATURE)

SOUTH

NORTH

BRUSH

MAGNETIC LINES OF FORCE UNDISTURBED

COMMUTATOR

BRUSH

LAMP

(a) PRINCIPLE OF D.C. GENERATOR

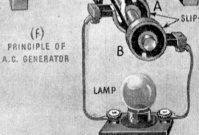

DIRECTION OF ROTATION

S

N

LINES OF FORCE UNDISTURBED

A

SLIP-RINGS

B

(f) PRINCIPLE OF A.C. GENERATOR

LAMP

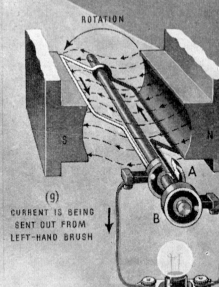

ROTATION

S

N

A

B

(g) CURRENT IS BEING SENT OUT FROM LEFT-HAND BRUSH

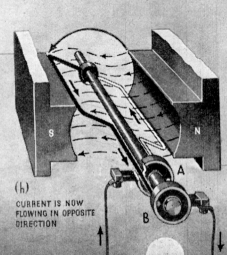

S

N

A

B

(h) CURRENT IS NOW FLOWING IN OPPOSITE DIRECTION

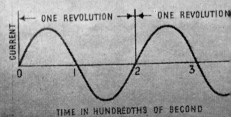

ONE REVOLUTION

ONE REVOLUTION

CURRENT

0   1   2   3

TIME IN HUNDREDTHS OF SECOND

(i) FORM OF CURRENT PRODUCED BY A.C. GENERA

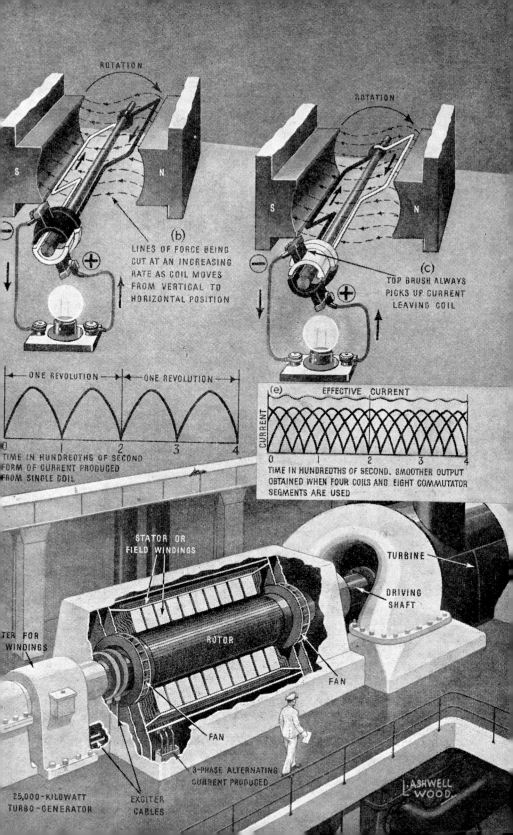

ROTATION

(b)

LINES OF FORCE BEING
CUT AT AN INCREASING
RATE AS COIL MOVES
FROM VERTICAL TO
HORIZONTAL POSITION

S

N

ROTATION

(c)

TOP BRUSH ALWAYS
PICKS UP CURRENT
LEAVING COIL

S

N

←— ONE REVOLUTION —→←— ONE REVOLUTION —→

0   1   2   3   4

TIME IN HUNDREDTHS OF SECOND
FORM OF CURRENT PRODUCED
FROM SINGLE COIL

(e) EFFECTIVE CURRENT

CURRENT

0   1   2   3   4

TIME IN HUNDREDTHS OF SECOND. SMOOTHER OUTPUT
OBTAINED WHEN FOUR COILS AND EIGHT COMMUTATOR
SEGMENTS ARE USED

STATOR OR
FIELD WINDINGS

TURBINE

DRIVING
SHAFT

TER FOR
WINDINGS

ROTOR

FAN

FAN

3-PHASE ALTERNATING
CURRENT PRODUCED

25,000-KILOWATT
TURBO-GENERATOR

EXCITER
CABLES

L. ASHWELL
WOOD.

are known as smoothing circuits, the "ripple" can be suppressed.

In the next chapter we shall see more about D.C. generators and about another kind of machine which converts mechanical energy into electrical energy. This latter is the alternator, or A.C. generator, to the basic principles of which we now come.

Connected to Slip-rings

In Fig. 17 (f, g, h), page 196, we see a single-turn coil rotating, like that of (a), (b), (c), between the poles of a magnet. The

Testing an insulator. When a difference of electrical pressure of 400,000 volts was applied to this insulator, the electric current, unable to find a path through the device, produced a spectacular arc.

coil in (f), (g) and (h) is seen rotating anti-clockwise, though it could equally be shown revolving in the opposite direction. There is, however, one important difference between the two sets of drawings: instead of being taken to a commutator, the ends of the coil which forms a rudimentary alternator armature are connected to separate slip-rings, each with its own collecting brush.

In (g) the coil has turned about 45 deg., cutting the lines of force, and, as the rotation is anti-clockwise as you look at the apparatus, the induced current is flowing away from you in the part of the coil (black) nearest the north pole. Current leaves the coil via slip-ring A and its brush, passes through the filament of the lamp and returns by way of slip-ring B. The lamp, by the way, is merely symbolic, for no generator with a single-turn armature could generate sufficient current to light even the smallest lamp.

Half a revolution later (h), current is flowing away from you in the white portion of the coil and towards you in the black. It now leaves the coil through slip-ring B, and after passing through the work returns through slip-ring A.

Each half-revolution of the coil the current changes direction, or alternates.

Cutting the Lines of Force

Starting from the position shown in (f), in which no lines of force are being cut and there is no induced current, the coil cuts a rapidly increasing number of lines of force until it reaches the (g) position. Then, though it continues to cut lines of force, the increase in their number tails off until the maximum number of lines is being cut when the coil is horizontal between the magnet poles. The coil, continuing its rotation, cuts a rather slowly decreasing number of lines of force until it has travelled through a further 45 deg. From then until it has completed half a revolution from the starting point, the decrease in the number of lines cut is rapid.

During the next half-revolution the process is repeated, but the current delivered to the slip-rings is in the opposite direction.

The strength of the induced current

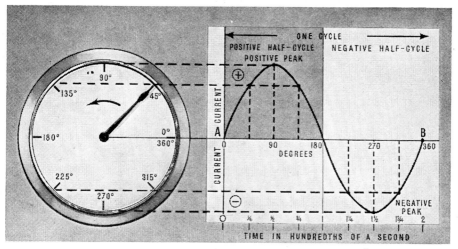

PURPOSE OF A SINE CURVE

FIG. 18. *Sine curve on the right shows how current from an A.C. generator rises and falls. The pointer on left indicates the relative positions of the armature as it rotates.*

depends on the rate at which lines of force are cut and we can see what is taking place at any instant in the way shown in Fig. 18, where the radius moving anti-clockwise represents the armature. It is conventional, by the way, to make the starting point of the radius "three o'clock" and its movement anti-clockwise.

Equal divisions on the horizontal straight line AB represent the number of degrees through which the radius rotates. At the intersection of a vertical line from the 45-deg. mark on AB and a horizontal line from the 45-deg. mark on the circle, a dot is made. The same is done for the 90-deg. and 135-deg. marks, and so on round the circle. The dots are then linked up by the curved lines shown in the diagram. We have made plots only at each 45 deg.; the greater the number of plots, the more accurately do the curves represent the rate at which current rises and falls.

In each complete revolution of the armature the train of events is:—

First quarter revolution. (0 deg. to 90 deg.) Current rises to maximum in what we may call a positive direction.

Second quarter revolution. (90 deg. to 180 deg.) Current falls from maximum positive to zero.

Third quarter revolution. (180 deg. to 270 deg.) Current rises to maximum in a negative direction.

Fourth quarter revolution. (270 deg. to 360 deg.) Current falls from maximum negative to zero.

This complete train, illustrated in Fig. 18, is called a cycle. The "shape" of the current in a cycle forms what is known as a sine curve.

Besides a horizontal scale of degrees in Fig. 18, we may also insert a time scale. If the coil is rotating fifty times a second, the positive half-cycle occupies $\frac{1}{100}$th second, the negative half-cycle $\frac{1}{100}$th and the whole cycle $\frac{1}{50}$th second.

The number of cycles occurring each second is called the frequency.

As we have seen, the induced current is produced by the induced e.m.f. The voltage cycles are also sine curves and are similar to those of current.

The standard frequency for domestic A.C. supplies in this country is 50 cycles a second (abbreviation 50 c/s), though this has not yet been attained everywhere. The standard A.C. voltage will eventually be 240.

Some readers may be wondering how current such as 50-cycle A.C., which changes direction one hundred times a second, and reaches a value of zero one hundred times a second, can be made to light lamps or work machines. For the moment the following analogies may serve to clear up the difficulty.

Relevant Analogies

(1) If you want to warm chilly fingers you rub them. The hand doing the rubbing moves in one direction, stops, changes direction, stops, changes direction . . . the electrons whose flow heats a filament to incandescence do the same. Heat is produced in both cases.

(2) The piston of a steam engine turns a wheel by means of a connecting rod and a crank. For each revolution of the wheel the piston moves in one direction, stops, moves in the opposite direction, stops . . . think of the positive and negative half-cycles as pushes and pulls like the to-and-fro movements of a piston. Once we have a source of pushes and pulls, we can make wheels go round.

Alternating voltages and currents are not measured by their "peak" values. Suppose that the positive and negative peaks in Fig. 18 each reach 10 amperes. That amount of current flows only for a brief instant in each half-cycle. Over the whole cycle current is varying between 10 amperes and nothing at all.

The only way of obtaining a satisfactory effective value for the whole cycle is to set A.C. and D.C. a task (such as heating an electric fire), which both can do equally well, to measure the peak alternating current needed and to discover what amount of steady direct current is required to produce the same temperature.

Root Mean Square

It can be proved that the equivalent D.C. is always $\frac{1}{\sqrt{2}}$, or 0·707 of the peak A.C. value. The net value of A.C. over a whole cycle is, therefore, 0·707 of the peak value. This is known as the Root Mean Square, or R.M.S. value. Alternating voltages are measured in the same way. Most A.C. measuring instruments are designed to record R.M.S. values.

If, therefore, the peak current in Fig. 18

were 10 amperes, an ammeter would read 10 × 0·707, or 7·07 amperes.

Knowing the R.M.S. value, you can find the peak value by multiplying it by $\sqrt{2}$, or 1·414. Thus, if you have 200-volt A.C. mains, the peak of each half-cycle reaches 282·8 volts.

Remember that E and I in A.C. formulæ are R.M.S. volts and amperes, unless it is expressly stated otherwise.

We have seen that current cannot flow until the e.m.f. has built up a magnetic field round a conductor. Once a steady direct current is flowing, the field exerts no opposing force; but when current is switched off, the collapsing field produces an e.m.f. which keeps it flowing until the collapse is complete. A little thought will show that the field will oppose any change in the rate of flow: if the driving e.m.f. is raised, increased current cannot pass until the field has been extended; similarly, reduction of e.m.f. cannot bring about a decrease in the flow of current until a corresponding falling in of the field allows this to take place.

Owing to the magnetic field, all conductors possess the quality of opposing a change in the rate of flow of current. If the conductor is wound into a coil, the opposition is increased because of the much denser field (see Fig. 15). The opposition is much greater when the insertion of an iron core into the coil produces a still denser field.

This quality is known as self-inductance (symbol: L). The unit of inductance is the henry (symbol: H). The corresponding sub-units are the millihenry (mH, $\frac{1}{1,000}$ henry), and the microhenry (μH, $\frac{1}{1,000,000}$ henry).

A conductor has an inductance of 1 henry if a current in it changing by 1 ampere per second induces an e.m.f. of 1 volt.

It will be clear that inductance must have important effects where A.C. is concerned. A current of 6 amperes R.M.S. from 50-cycle mains, for instance, changes in $\frac{1}{50}$th second from zero to 8·48 amp., from 8·48 to zero, from zero to 8·48 amp. in the other direction, and from 8·48 amp. to zero.

The opposition which a coil of wire offers to the continual changes of A.C. is consider-

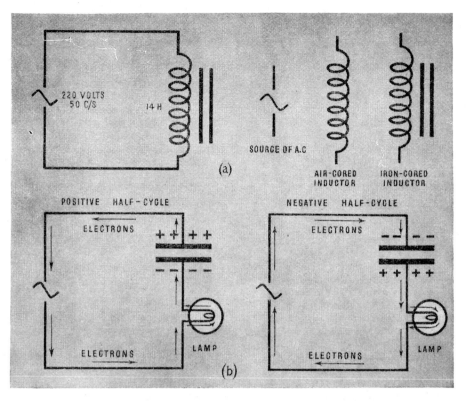

POSITIVE HALF-CYCLE

NEGATIVE HALF-CYCLE

EFFECT OF A.C. ON DIFFERING CIRCUITS

FIG. 19. (a) A.C. at 220 volts is applied to an inductor of 14 henries, presumed to have zero resistance. Note symbols for source of A.C. and inductors. (b) A lamp is connected to a source of A.C. through a capacitor. During the positive half-cycle, electrons flow through the filament in one direction; in other direction during the negative half-cycle.

able. Though a coil offers no opposition, save that due to the resistance of its wire, to a flow of D.C., once that flow has reached its normal rate, it is always opposing the fluctuations of A.C. That opposition to the passage of A.C. is called reactance (symbol: X). Reactance is measured in ohms.

The A.C. flowing through an imaginary inductor containing no resistance$=\frac{E}{X}$, just as either A.C. or D.C. flowing through a resistor$=\frac{E}{R}$.

The reactance of a conductor$=2\pi fL$, where:

π is a constant, equal, for practical purposes, to $\frac{22}{7}$;

f is the frequency of the A.C.;

L is the inductance in henries.

Thus if, as in Fig. 19 (a), 50-cycle, 220-volt A.C. is applied to an inductor of 14 henries (imagining the inductor to have negligible resistance; in comparison with its reactance, the resistance of an inductor is often so small as to be negligible),

$$X = 2 \times \tfrac{22}{7} \times 50 \times 14$$
$$= 4400 \text{ ohms}$$
$$I = \tfrac{220}{4400}$$
$$= \tfrac{1}{20} \text{ A}$$
$$= 50 \text{ mA}.$$

As we have seen, a capacitor completely bars a flow of D.C. once current has flowed in and charged it fully. Matters are very different with A.C. Fig. 19 (b) shows diagrammatically what would happen if a lamp were connected through a capacitor to a source of A.C.

During the positive half-cycle, electrons are drawn from the upper plate of the capacitor to create an electron deficiency (positive charge), and electrons are supplied to the lower plate to produce an electron surplus (negative charge). The latter must pass through the filament of the lamp. The process is reversed during the negative half-cycle, electrons streaming from the lower plate through the filament. Thus, in each half-cycle current traverses the filament.

You will see that A.C. does not in reality pass through a capacitor, though the net effect is precisely as if it did. In practice, A.C. is always regarded as passing through capacitors, for this leads to considerable simplification and no harm is done so long as we know what really does occur.

Like an inductor, a capacitor has reactance. The reactance of an inductor is usually written X_L and that of a capacitor X_C. $X_C = \frac{1}{2\pi fC}$, where C is its capacitance in farads and the other factors are as before.

Suppose that the capacitor in Fig. 19 (b) has a capacitance of $1\,\mu F$; what is its reactance?

$$X_C = \frac{1}{2 \times \frac{22}{7} \times 50 \times \frac{1}{1,000,000}}$$
$$= \frac{7,000,000}{2200}$$
$$= 3185\,\Omega \text{ approx.}$$

Now comes a very important point. When either A.C. or D.C. flows through a resistor, work is done at a certain rate and power is expended in producing heat. The power in watts $= I^2R$. But this is not the major effect when A.C. flows through an inductor or a capacitor.

The energy lent when the magnetic field is built up in the one case and the electric field in the other is repaid when those fields collapse—as they do when A.C. falls to zero at the end of a half-cycle. The work done in producing the field is exactly undone when it collapses. We may put it in the following way:

Work done = work undone;
∴ Work done − work undone = 0;
∴ Rate of work = 0;
∴ Power = 0.

Every conductor, whether a straight wire, a coil or the plates of a capacitor, must have both inductance and capacitance. The opposition to A.C. in a circuit (Fig. 20) containing inductance, capacitance and resistance in series is a combination of these three qualities. The combination is called impedance (symbol: Z), which is measured in ohms.

$$Z = \sqrt{R^2 + (X_L - X_C)^2}.$$

That expression may seem rather formidable, but it is not quite so bad as it looks. Let us see what current would flow in the circuit seen in Fig. 20. We have already worked out X_L (4400 Ω) and X_C (3185 Ω) in previous examples. $R^2 = 4,000,000\,\Omega$.

$$Z = \sqrt{4,000,000 + (4400 - 3185)^2}$$
$$= \sqrt{4,000,000 + 1215^2}$$
$$= \sqrt{4,000,000 + 1,476,225}$$
$$= \sqrt{5,476,225}$$
$$= 2340\,\Omega, \text{ approx.}$$
$$I = \frac{E}{Z}$$
$$= \frac{200}{2340}$$
$$= 0.0855\,\text{A} \Big\}\,\text{approx.}$$
$$= 85.5\,\text{mA}$$

Power Factor

This brings us to a seeming anomaly found in A.C. circuits. As $E = 200$ and $I = 0.0855$ amp., the power apparently dissipated in the circuit is $E \times I$, or 17·1 watts. But we have seen that the actual power is $I^2R = (0.0855)^2 \times 2000 = 0.00073 \times 2000 = 14.6$ watts. We shall see in a moment how this discrepancy comes about; meantime it should be noted that the ratio of real watts to apparent watts forms what is known as the power factor of the circuit. The power factor is also the ratio of resistance to impedance.

In the Fig. 20 circuit the power factor is:

$$\frac{14.6}{17.1} = 0.85$$
$$\text{or, } \frac{2000}{2340} = 0.85.$$

An ammeter inserted into this circuit would read 0·0855 amp., and a voltmeter would read 200 volts. These readings multiplied together give the apparent watts; multiply

GANTRY ENABLING LID
TO BE REMOVED FOR
INSERTION OF CHARGE

FURNACE

FURNACE "ROCKS" ON
THESE TRUNNIONS

AND THE MOLTEN STEEL
EMERGES FROM HERE

PRACTICAL APPLICATION OF HEATING EFFECT

One of the most useful applications of electricity is in the development of heat. In this English Electric steel furnace a temperature of 5000 deg. F. is produced by means of an arc.

apparent watts by the power factor of the circuit and the real watts are obtained.

The apparent watts may be measured in volt-amperes (VA) or kilovolt-amperes (kVA).

Not only must the e.m.f. build up the magnetic field before current can flow through an inductor, but it must also cause increases or decreases in the field before there can be any change in the current. It follows that if there is an inductor in a circuit where the voltage is continually changing, the changing current must always lag behind the e.m.f.

It does not lag in such a circuit by 90 deg. as in that of Fig. 21 (a); if capacitance and resistance are negligible in a circuit, any change in current occurs a quarter of a cycle after the change in e.m.f. which causes it.

A capacitor behaves in exactly the opposite way. Here current must flow in (remember the analogy of pumping up a tire) and build up the electric field before there can be a pressure, or e.m.f. Apply A.C. to a capacitor in a circuit where inductance and resistance are negligible and e.m.f. lags 90 deg. behind the current (Fig. 21 (b)).

If A.C. is applied to a resistor (inductance and capacitance being so small as to be negligible), e.m.f. and current rise and fall together and are said to be in phase (Fig. 21 (c)). In the top two diagrams of Fig. 21 they are 90 deg. out of phase.

Only when E and I are in phase does $E \times I = I^2 R$.

In a circuit containing, as in Fig. 20, resistance, inductance and capacitance, the inductive element makes current lag, whilst the capacitative element makes it lead. Look again at the impedance formula and you will see that X_L (the inductive reactance) and X_C (the capacitive reactance) tend to cancel one another, for the net reactance in a circuit is the difference between them. Whether current leads or lags depends, therefore, on whether the net reactance is capacitative or inductive. The amount of this net reactance determines the angle of lead or lag.

The power factor is actually the cosine of this angle (don't bother about this if you have forgotten your trigonometry, or if it is a book still to be opened to you). In the calculations we made on the Fig. 20 circuit we saw that the power factor was 0·85. From a cosine table we find that this corresponds to an angle of 31 deg. 47 min. As X_L predominates in the circuit, the current lags behind the voltage and 31 deg. 47 min. is the angle of lag.

In household circuits, current is chiefly

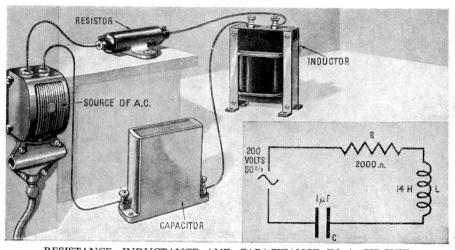

RESISTANCE, INDUCTANCE AND CAPACITANCE IN A CIRCUIT

FIG. 20. *These properties exist, to some extent, in all circuits. This diagram, however, shows components employed to contribute to a circuit a required amount of each property.*

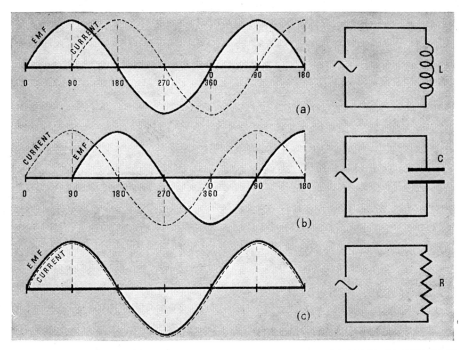

EFFECT WHEN A.C. IS APPLIED TO INDUCTANCE, CAPACITANCE, RESISTANCE

FIG. 21. *(a) When alternating current is applied to a pure inductance, the current lags 90 deg. behind the voltage across the inductance. (b) Exactly the opposite effect occurs when A.C. is applied to a pure capacitance: the e.m.f. lags 90 deg. behind the current. (c) E.m.f. and current are in phase when A.C. is applied to a pure resistance.*

used for producing heat in the filaments of lamps or the heaters of electric fires, irons, kettles, and so on, by overcoming resistance. In electrical parlance, the load is mainly resistive and the power factor is as near unity as makes no great matter; the real watts and the apparent watts are to all intents and purposes the same. There is no angle of lag. Cos 0 deg. $=1$; $E \times I = I^2 R$.

Factories and other installations using electrically driven machinery may, however, have a poor power factor that would be serious if correcting devices were not used; more current would be needed to supply a given amount of power and this would mean heavier (and, therefore, more expensive) cables.

Referring again to the impedance formula, you will see that the net reactance is zero and the power factor 1 if $X_L = X_C$. It is by evening up X_L and X_C to reduce the

angle of lead or lag that such corrections are made. You make X_C equal to X_L and produce a power factor of 1 every time you tune in a station by turning the knobs of a radio receiver.

For the last of our experiments you will need to wind a coil of about thirty turns of No. 26 D.C.C. wire on the larger cardboard tube. This done, wire up the arrangement shown pictorially and in diagram form in Fig. 22.

Watching the compass, touch the free wire ("free," electrically, means not connected into any circuit) from the inside coil against the metal part of the positive terminal of the cell. The needle records a momentary "whiff" of current. Break the circuit by removing the wire from contact with the terminal; again there is a flick of the needle. Note the directions of the flicks; then reverse the connexions to the cell and make the experiment again. The flicks are also reversed in direction.

At first sight it may seem uncanny that an e.m.f. due to the cell can produce a current in a circuit to which it has no means of access: the turns of the two cylindrical coils are well insulated from one another. But is there really any mystery? Before reading further, run over in your mind what you have learnt about magnetic fields and see whether you can puzzle out what is happening.

Done that? Well, now see whether your explanation was the right one.

Momentary Current Flow

When contact is made with the cell, a magnetic field begins to build up round the turns of the inner coil. As the field expands, it cuts the turns of the outer coil and induces in them an e.m.f. which causes a current to flow. The current is but momentary, for the induced e.m.f. dies out as soon as the magnetic field of the inner coil stops expanding and ceases to cut turns as it moves outwards.

On your breaking contact with the cell, the magnetic field of the inner coil collapses and cuts the turns of the outer on its way in, again setting up an e.m.f. and a spurt of current in the outer coil.

Now what will happen if, instead of switching direct current on and off, we apply A.C. to the inner coil (L_1) as in Fig. 23 (a)? Do *not*, by the way, try this by connecting the coil to A.C. mains—R is only about $1\frac{1}{2}$ ohms, X_L is very small and I would be enormous.

As A.C. is always changing in strength and reaches zero (equivalent to switching off) twice in every cycle, the magnetic field of L_1 moves outwards as each positive half-cycle rises from zero to maximum e.m.f., falls in as the e.m.f. drops to zero, moves outwards (but with changed direction) as the e.m.f. rises towards maximum negative and collapses as the e.m.f. falls to zero again. You will readily see that an alternating e.m.f., giving rise to an alternating current, is induced in L_2.

L_1 and L_2 are said to be coupled. The coupling is tightest when all the lines of force of L_1 cut all the turns of L_2, as they do in the position illustrated in Fig. 23 (a). Fig. 23 (b) shows somewhat looser coupling; it is looser still at (c) and zero at (d),

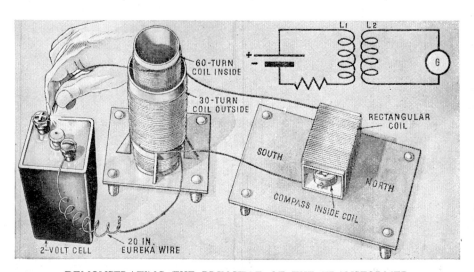

DEMONSTRATING THE PRINCIPLE OF THE TRANSFORMER

FIG. 22. *Whenever the free end of the windings of the inner coil makes connexion with the cell, the compass indicates a momentary flow of current in the outer coil and the rectangular coil. Current again flows, but only for an instant, when the contact is broken.*

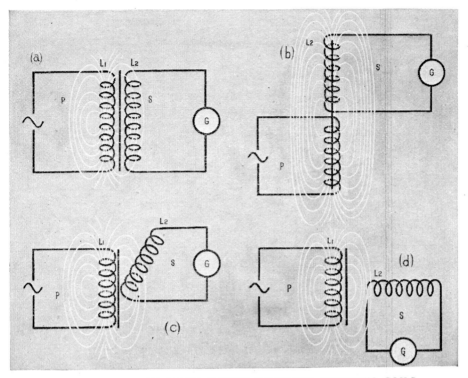

DEGREES OF ELECTROMAGNETIC COUPLING BETWEEN COILS

FIG. 23. *When one coil, the primary, is coupled to another, the secondary, A.C. applied to the primary induces a current in the secondary. These examples show that at (a) and (b) the coupling is tight; at (c) it is much looser, and at (d) the coupling is zero.*

where none of the lines of force of the field of L_1 cut the turns of L_2.

Take the sixty-turn coil out of the thirty-turn coil, lay the two on a table top and make and break the connexion to the cell with the two coils in positions such as those shown in Fig. 23. You will find that the deflections of the compass needle decrease in magnitude as the coupling is loosened, and that there are none at all when the zero position is reached.

Repeat the Fig. 22 experiment and those outlined in the preceding paragraph, with the bundle of iron wire inserted as a core into L_1. The deflections will be much larger, owing to the denser field of the coil.

The arrangement of coupled coils shown in Figs. 22 and 23 is called a transformer. The coil of a transformer in which the

inducing current flows is the primary and that in which the induced current flows, the secondary.

Suppose that we have 250-volt A.C. mains and need a very high voltage—say, 10,000—to operate some particular device. The e.m.f. in the secondary of a transformer has the same relation to the primary e.m.f. as the number of secondary turns has to the number of primary turns: 10,000 is 40 times 250; therefore, if we make the secondary turns 40 times as numerous as the primary, the secondary e.m.f. will be 40×250, or 10,000 volts.

There is no such method of stepping up the voltage of direct current. The only practical method of obtaining 10,000 volts from 250-volt D.C. mains is to use the mains current to drive a motor and to make

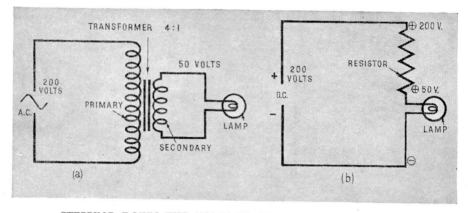

STEPPING DOWN THE VOLTAGE OF A.C. AND D.C. MAINS

FIG. 24. *(a) By means of a transformer, a 50-volt lamp can be run from 200-volt alternating-current mains with very little loss. The only way of doing this from D.C. mains is shown at (b), where 75 per cent of the original power is wasted by inclusion of the resistor.*

the motor turn a 10,000-volt D.C. generator or alternator—a far more expensive business than employing a transformer with A.C.

A.C. can also be stepped down in the same way with very little loss. If we wish to light a 50-volt lamp drawing 0·5 amp. of current from A.C. mains, a 4:1 transformer will serve admirably (Fig. 24 (a)). But if the mains carry D.C., the only reasonable way of lighting the single lamp from them is by using a resistor as at (b).

Voltage Dropping

As the lamp passes 0·5 amp. at 50 volts, the resistance of its filament is $50 \div 0\cdot5 = 100$ ohms. The applied e.m.f. is 200 volts. To make I in the circuit 0·5 amp., the total resistance must be $\frac{200}{0\cdot5} = 400$ ohms. Therefore, R must have a value of $400 - 100 = 300$ ohms. We can check this, if we feel at all doubtful, by another calculation from Ohm's Law. We want to apply 50 volts to the filament of the lamp; therefore, the resistor must "mop up" or drop 150 volts. The current in the whole circuit is 0·5 amp. Hence, by Ohm's Law, the volts dropped in the resistor are $300 \times 0\cdot5 = 150$ volts.

The lamp itself consumes $50 \times 0\cdot5 = 25$ watts; the resistor consumes $150 \times 0\cdot5 = 75$ watts; 75 per cent of the power is

wasted in the resistor and 100 watts are needed from the mains.

There is no such waste with A.C., for the transformer should be at least 80 per cent efficient (large transformers may be over 95 per cent efficient), so that any loss there may be is small. Assuming 80 per cent efficiency, only $\frac{5}{4} \times 25$ watts = 31·25 watts are needed from the mains, against the 100 watts with D.C.

But, some readers may cry, are we not doing even better than that with A.C.? The transformer primary is an inductor; we have learned that no power is expended by A.C. in overcoming pure inductance. If the resistance of the primary is small enough to be negligible, we require no watts at all from the mains and can light the lamp at no cost!

Alas! In electricity, as in most other things, you cannot get anything for nothing; when the secondary of a transformer has a resistive load, this resistance reflects, so to speak, back into the primary. The amount of reflected or transferred resistance is the secondary resistance multiplied by the square of the ratio of primary to secondary turns.

In the present instance, the secondary resistance is $50 \div 0\cdot5 = 100$ ohms and the primary to secondary ratio is $\frac{4}{1}$. Hence, the resistance transferred to the primary is

$(\frac{4}{1})^2 \times 100 = 16 \times 100 = 1600$ ohms. This makes the primary current $\frac{200}{1600}$, or $\frac{1}{8}$ amp., and the primary watts due to transferred resistance are $I^2R = \frac{1}{64} \times 1600 = 25$ watts. Adding 6·25 watts, owing to the fact that the transformer is only 80 per cent efficient, we have a grand total of 31·25 primary watts required to produce 25 watts in the secondary. Compare this with the 100 watts consumed when the 25-watt lamp is lighted from D.C. mains.

One of the most valuable qualities of A.C. is that it can be transformed. Not only does it lend itself readily to all manner of uses in the home, the factory and elsewhere, but the fact that the kilowatts of power can be transformed into large E and small I means that power can be conveyed economically over great distances.

Any cable must have some resistance and the power used in overcoming that resistance is I^2R, all of which is wasted. Therefore, the smaller the current and the higher the volts, the less will the losses be when power is sent from place to place through a network of cables like that of the Grid system.

But do not think that D.C. is entirely overshadowed by A.C. For some purposes, direct current is essential.

So ends our brief survey of the vast science of electricity, of which space has allowed us to touch only the fringes. If, as the writer hopes, your interest has been stimulated, you will wish to go more deeply into the subject. Guidance about books that will help is to be found in the Study Guide at the end of this volume.

In the following chapters we shall see some of the wonderful ways in which electricity has been harnessed to the service of man.

Test Yourself

1. What constitutes (a) a positive and (b) a negative charge?
2. What is an e.m.f.?
3. Briefly describe the way in which a Leclanché cell works.
4. What constitutes an electric current? In which direction does it flow through a circuit?
5. If the direct current in a circuit and the resistance through which it is flowing are known, how can the e.m.f. be calculated?
6. Give the rules for calculating (a) the resistance of resistors and (b) the capacitance of capacitors (condensers) arranged in series and in parallel.
7. What is meant by permittivity, permeability, reactance, impedance?
8. What is power factor?
9. Briefly explain the functions of the commutator of a D.C. generator and the slip-rings of an alternator.
10. In the end of a coil nearest your eye the direction of the electron current is anti-clockwise. Would this end attract or repel the north-seeking end of a compass needle?
11. What is (a) a permanent magnet; (b) an electromagnet?
12. You have 200-volt A.C. mains and require an e.m.f. of 1000 volts to work a certain piece of apparatus; how can the 1000 volts be obtained?
13. How could an e.m.f. of 1000 volts be obtained from 200-volt D.C. mains?
14. Explain briefly how a secondary battery, or accumulator, differs from a primary battery.
15. Explain why a capacitor blocks the passage of D.C., but allows A.C. to pass.
16. What is a milliampere? A megohm? A kilocycle? A microvolt?

Answers will be found at the end of the book.

ROTOR

WINDINGS IN SLOTS
IN LAMINATED
IRON STAMPINGS

STATOR

USING NATURAL SOURCES OF POWER

Millions of kilowatts of electrical power are developed by the big hydro-electric power stations. Here, for example, can be seen an enormous generator in the process of being assembled at the Grand Coulee Dam in America. The rotor is being lowered into its position inside the stator. The rotor consists of a number of poles, each pair of which forms a powerful electromagnet whose lines of force sweep the fixed conductors in the stator.

CHAPTER XI

APPLICATIONS OF ELECTRICITY

So vast a department of human knowledge is electricity today, so many and so wide its branches, that no one man could master the whole of its theory and practice. A hundred years ago, fifty years ago (perhaps even less), such a thing was possible; nowadays it is not. A physicist or an engineer may be thoroughly conversant with the general theory of electricity and of the theoretical and practical details of one or possibly two or three of its applications; but to cover the whole huge field completely and to keep pace with the advances that are continually being made would be a task that no human being could accomplish.

Importance of the Electromagnet

It is no exaggeration to say that the development of electricity from an interesting, but more or less useless, laboratory curiosity into one of the most potent factors in human well-being and comfort is due entirely to the discovery of the electromagnet.

Had that discovery not been made, practical electricity could not have advanced far beyond the lighting of small lamps from batteries; the pocket flashlamp might represent the summit of its achievements!

The generation of electric current on a large scale and at reasonable cost would be impossible without the electromagnet, for no permanent magnets could provide sufficiently strong fields for suitable alternators or generators. The electromagnet is an essential part of all but toy electric motors.

Without the electromagnet, then, houses and towns could not be lighted by electricity. There could be no heaters, cookers, fans nor refrigerators in the home. There could be no electric trains (and, therefore, no tube railways), electric trams, nor trolley-buses. Without electric ignition, which requires the electromagnet whether it is operated by magneto or by coil and

battery, the development of motor vehicles would have been slow until the advent of the Diesel engine, and man might still be unable to fly. The telegraph and television services, wireless, television and radar all depend upon the electromagnet . . . the list could be continued almost indefinitely.

There are few people, in a word, living in any civilized country of the world whose daily lives are not in some way made happier or more comfortable by electricity, which could confer very few indeed of its benefits without the aid of the electromagnet.

The telephone is one of the most striking of electrical devices which have become part and parcel of our everyday life. The telephone is available to probably nine people out of ten in this country today; for if it is not installed in their homes or offices, they live within reach of a public call-box.

When you speak into the microphone of a telephone the sounds of your voice are converted into electrical impulses, which travel at almost incredible speed over the wires to the receiver at your correspondent's ear. The receiver re-converts the electrical impulses into sounds and communication is as easy as if you were both in the same room. Let us see briefly how the telephone does its work.

Sound Waves

When you speak, air from the lungs brushes past the edges of the taut vocal cords and causes them to vibrate, that is, to move rapidly to and fro. Each outward movement of the cords compresses the air lying above them in the throat; each inward movement has just the opposite effect, causing a rarefaction of the air. Think of each outward movement of the cords as a push given to the surrounding air and of each inward movement as a pull. Try in your bath the effect on water of gentle pushes and pulls made with the palm of your hand. The push causes a miniature wave to rise to a crest; the pull provides a trough.

The pushes and pulls of the vocal cords set up similar waves in air, as shown in Fig. 1 (a). The shape of these waves may remind you of the cycles of A.C., which we discussed in the last chapter. Sound waves are also sine waves or combinations of sine waves; they have cycles and their frequency is the number of cycles that occurs in a second. When middle C is sung or played on any instrument, 256 vibrations a second take place and the frequency is 256 cycles per second.

Telephone Transmitter

The working parts of the microphone are shown in simplified form in Fig. 1 (b). A metal case is closed at its large end by a thin disk of carbon. Between the disk and a conducting block within the case lie carbon "shot" or granules. The conducting block is insulated from the case. One terminal of a battery (sometimes a single cell is used) is connected to the case and the diaphragm, the other to a metal rod coming from the conducting block.

When the switch is closed (usually this is done automatically when the telephone is picked up) a small current flows through the instrument, for carbon is a fairly good conductor. You speak. A sound-wave crest presses the diaphragm inwards, packing the shot more tightly against one another and so making better electrical contact between them. The resistance is reduced and the battery drives more current through the microphone.

Next instant a trough pulls the diaphragm outwards, the granules make poorer contact, the resistance rises and current falls. Thus the pressure half-cycle of sound produces an electrical half-cycle of

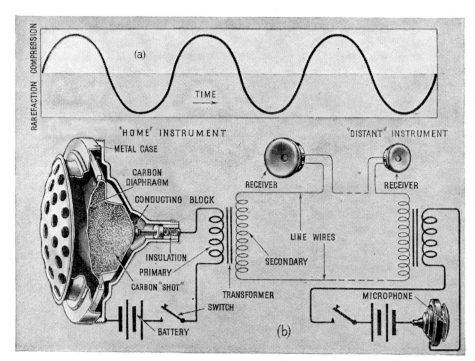

PICTORIAL DIAGRAM OF A SIMPLE TELEPHONE CIRCUIT

FIG. 1. *(a) Sound waves in air are generated by the pushes and pulls of the vibrating vocal cords. (b) Showing the working parts of a microphone, with circuit route to distant instrument.*

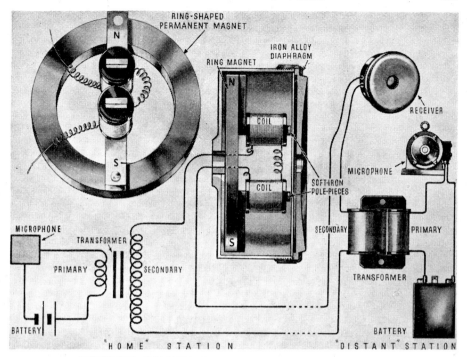

WORKING PRINCIPLES OF A TELEPHONE RECEIVER

FIG. 2. *Simple telephone circuit similar to that shown at (b) in Fig. 1, but this time with the addition of a receiver, sectionalized to show its principles of operation.*

increased current and the rarefaction half-cycle an electrical half-cycle of decreased current. The current wave is an electrical copy of the sound wave.

The current wave passes through the primary of a step-up transformer and produces in its secondary a similar wave with a much higher e.m.f. As the small amount of power generated in the microphone has to be sent a long way over the wires, which may have considerable resistance, losses must be reduced to a minimum (remember I^2R) by keeping the volts high and the current low.

The two receivers, the "home" and the "distant," and the two transformer secondaries are in series, with the line wires connecting them. This is clearly illustrated in Fig. 2 above.

The receiver consists of a metal case, closed by a thin iron or alloy diaphragm with a protecting cap over it. To the

bottom of the case is fixed a ring-shaped permanent magnet, to which are attached L-shaped north and south pole pieces of soft iron. Each pole piece carries a coil of fine wire wound on a bobbin, the turns of the coils being in opposite directions. The diaphragm, as you will see from Fig. 2, lies a short distance from the ends of the pole pieces.

At the Receiving End

Now let us see what happens when a current wave, whose generation in the microphone circuit was described just now, reaches the receiver.

Before its arrival the diaphragm is bent slightly inwards by the attraction of the pole pieces, which are magnetized by induction from the ring magnet. Suppose that the first half of the incoming cycle causes current to flow clockwise round the coil attached to the north pole piece and

RECORDING THE BEHAVIOUR OF ELECTRICAL CURRENTS

Above is a Duddell Oscillograph, by which variations in an electric current and voltage can be recorded photographically. Current passes through a fine wire coil situated in an electromagnetic field. As current changes, this coil vibrates, a mirror reflecting light on to the film.

counter-clockwise round the other. Then electromagnetism is added to induced magnetism and the diaphragm is drawn inwards.

The next half-cycle causes a flow of current in the opposite direction. Electromagnetism partly cancels induced magnetism and the diaphragm springs outwards.

Thus the push of a sound wave pressing the diaphragm of the microphone inwards causes the diaphragm of the receiver also to move inwards, whilst the pull allows both diaphragms to spring outwards. The receiver diaphragm copies the movements of the microphone diaphragm. As the receiver diaphragm moves to and fro, it compresses and rarefies the air adjacent to it, producing sound waves which are copies of those reaching the microphone. These sound waves strike the eardrums of your correspondent and he hears the sounds of your voice.

Automatic telephone exchanges are now in operation in many towns and villages and their use is likely to be much extended in the near future. The general principles of the automatic exchange system are fairly simple, though the actual circuits used are rather complicated. Suppose that your own exchange is RABbitwarren and that you dial STOatsnest 5246. Lifting the hand set, containing the microphone and receiver, off its cradle allows a plunger to rise which operates two switches. One admits current to your microphone; the other connects you to a travelling contact, or selector, the movements of which are controlled by the contacts on the dial.

Why Exchange Letters are Used

When you turn successively to S, T and O, you are really dialling not the letters but the numbers to which they correspond —the first three letters of the exchange you want are far easier to remember than three figures: STO5246 is much simpler than 7805246.

The combination STO (780) causes the selector to travel to the contact which connects your line to the STOatsnest exchange. At that exchange, further selectors pick out the fifth thousand, the second hundred, the fourth ten and the sixth unit.

That done, the selector may find the contact 5246 free, in which case it connects you to it and at the same time switches on an automatic ringer. Should 5246 be already occupied, another automatic device is brought into play and you hear the "number engaged" signal. If all is well and connexion is made, your correspondent lifts off his hand-set; the plunger rises, switching off the ringer and admitting current to his microphone.

Dialling Big Cities Direct

Already the London Trunk Exchange dials numbers in Birmingham and other large towns direct and the exchanges of some of these towns dial London numbers direct. This system is being extended as rapidly as possible. In a few years time it is quite likely that a telephone subscriber living in any part of this country will be able to dial the distant number that he requires without having to ask for Toll or Trunks.

When the telephone was young, any conversation over a distance of more than some twenty-five miles entailed shouting into the microphone and listening with all one's ears to the faint sounds that came from the receiver. Today communication by telephone is possible over immense distances with no strain on voice or ears.

Every twenty-five miles, on the average, in trunk telephone lines a device called a repeater is installed. This contains valves such as we use in our wireless sets, and its function is to restore to their original strength by magnifying them the electrical impulses which have become weakened by their journey over miles of wire.

Four wires were once required for each long-distance conversation. Nowadays, one pair of wires can carry, simultaneously and without the least mutual interference, a large number of conversations. The principle is akin to that of wireless. Each conversation takes place on a particular wavelength and they are separated from one another by filter circuits which act in much the same way as the tuning arrangements of our wireless sets. The tuning-in is done automatically at the trunk exchanges.

Very remarkable devices with almost

SAFETY USE OF PHOTO-ELECTRIC CELL IN INDUSTRY

FIG. 3. *At (a) is shown a photo-cell which is connected to a battery and micro-ammeter. When light falls on the cathode, electrons are released and a minute current flows. A practical use for a photo-cell is illustrated at (b). Should the operator's hand interrupt the light beam, the paper-cutting machine is at once automatically stopped, thus avoiding injury.*

innumerable uses are the family of electrical apparatus known as vacuum tubes, of which the thermionic valve, used in wireless sets, is probably the most familiar example. Broadly speaking, the essential parts of a vacuum tube are a glass bulb from which every possible trace of air has been removed and within it a cathode (or source of an electron stream) and an anode (the point or area to which the electron stream is drawn by the presence upon it of an electron deficiency).

Surrounded by Ejected Electrons

When a piece of metal is brought to a sufficiently high temperature in a vacuum the activity of its orbiting electrons becomes so intense that some of them are actually ejected from it. Normally, these return after making short journeys. Some metals, tungsten, for instance, emit electrons much more readily than others; the tungsten filament of an electric lamp is surrounded by a whirling cloud of ejected electrons. Emission can be made to take place at much lower temperatures if the tungsten is treated with a substance such as thoria, as it is in the dull-emitter radio valve.

Heated Filaments

The filament, or cathode, may be heated by passing an electric current through it; but this is not essential. In many valves and other vacuum tubes, current passes through a heater which is insulated from the cathode. The heater brings the cathode up to the necessary temperature and emission takes place. Full details of radio valves and cathode-ray tubes are given in the next chapter.

Another most interesting example of the vacuum tube is the photo-electric cell. The cathodes of the thermionic valve and of the cathode-ray tube emit electrons under the influence of heat. If a cathode coated with one of the alkali metals, such as lithium or cæsium, and an anode are placed in an evacuated bulb, the cathode emits electrons when light falls upon it. Make the anode positive, as shown in Fig. 3 (a), and a stream of electrons flows across the vacuum when light impinges on the cathode and excites emission. The current flowing through a photo-cell is usually minute, being measured in microamperes, or millionths of amperes.

Nowadays, it does not much matter how small a voltage or current may be to start with. The thermionic valve has given us a means of amplifying tiny currents or e.m.f.s until they reach such magnitudes that they can be used for controlling large amounts of power.

Fig. 3 (b) shows how a photo-cell may be so used. No current passes through the cell until light reaches its cathode. When this happens the feeble output of the cell is passed to a valve amplifier. If the operator's hand intercepts the light, the current ceases. This operates a relay actuating switchgear which stops the machine and so prevents an accident.

The Photo-cell in Industry

The applications of the photo-cell in industry are legion. It may, for example, be used for counting manufactured articles passing rapidly on a conveyer belt. A beam of light is focused across the belt on to a photo-cell. So long as the light is uninterrupted, current flows steadily through the cell and the relay to which it is connected is not actuated. But as soon as the belt begins to convey articles, each of these passes in its turn between the source of light and the photo-cell, cutting off the light from the cell as it does so. Each brief "black out" actuates a relay which operates a counting device.

Or the cell may be used to reject manufactured articles which are either too large or too small. One of correct size cuts off what we may term a normal amount of light when passing in front of the cell; but if it is over size, it cuts off more light, and less light if it is under size. Appropriate relays are operated, articles of standard size being passed on to the collecting bin, whilst those too large or too small are directed into "too-small" or "too-large" bins.

Space permits but a mention of the uses of the photo-cell for colour matching, for the grading of things, such as beans or cigars, according to colour, for the detection of black smoke from factory chimneys, for the regulation of humidity in workshops, for burglar alarms in conjunction with an invisible beam of infra-red light and for making the sound tracks of talking films.

Regulating Air Condition

Excessive humidity is guarded against by focusing a light beam on to a photo-cell through one of the window panes of the factory. Excessive humidity causes the pane to "fog," thus cutting off some of the light and making the cell actuate a relay which brings air-drying machinery into operation.

It is impossible in the space available to deal with all of the many types of vacuum tube, each with a host of useful applications. Only a few can be mentioned; we will take as our last example the X-ray tube. The principle of this is that electrons emitted from a hot cathode are made to acquire very high speeds by a large positive voltage on the anode. In mid-career they are brought up short by striking a "target." The result of this high-speed collision is that ether waves far shorter than those of visible light are generated.

These waves penetrate solid bodies, which are, in fact, transparent to them. The shorter the waves the greater is their penetrating power; very short X-rays are used today, for example, in detecting flaws in large castings, and for many other industrial purposes when it is necessary to discover hidden faults that do not appear on the surface.

The use of X-rays for medical purposes is so common nowadays that a large proportion of readers will have had practical experience of their wonderful work.

Detected by Fluorescence

X-rays are invisible to the eye, but they affect photographic plates. The images due to them can also be seen by the use of fluorescent screens similar to that of the cathode-ray tube.

The electric lighting and heating of our homes on the scale that we know today is possible because the D.C. generator and the alternator provide means of converting mechanical energy cheaply into electrical energy. In the last chapter we saw very briefly what were the elementary principles of these machines.

Coils of Many Turns

No D.C. generator or alternator could produce useful amounts of current if its armature consisted of the single turn of wire whose movements between permanent-magnet poles we discussed in the last chapter.

All practical generators, A.C. or D.C., use coils of many turns in their armatures and the armature itself forms an iron core to the coils.

This core serves to concentrate the lines of force between the magnet poles, owing to its high permeability.

As the armature turns, the lines of force are, so to speak, slightly bent. Then the turns of the coil cut through them at a rapid rate and the resulting e.m.f. causes a large current to flow.

Permanent magnets do not produce a strong enough field for the generation of heavy currents. In all but miniature and toy generators, the field magnets are electro-magnets. D.C. generators use part of the generated direct current to energize their own field magnets. In alternators there is usually a small exciter, driven off the same shaft, which supplies the necessary D.C. for the field magnets.

In most generators there are many coils on the armature and many pairs of field magnet poles.

Alternator as Motor

An alternator or D.C. generator will work as a motor if current is made to flow *into* it by way of the brushes and the slip-rings or the commutator, as the case may be. Fig. 4 (a) illustrates the basic principle of the A.C. motor; you will see that it

ELECTRIC POWER IN A STEEL WORKS

This powerful electric motor is coupled up to a mill for rolling steel plates. Work of this kind requires considerable driving power, and the motor in this case is capable of developing a maximum of 17,000 horse-power.

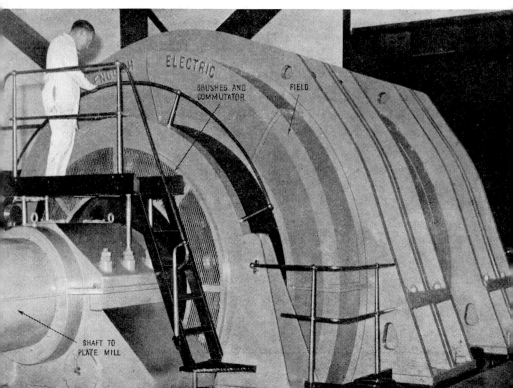

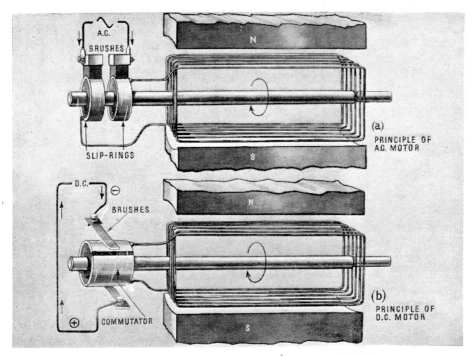

A.C. BRUSHES

SLIP-RINGS

(a)
PRINCIPLE OF
A.C. MOTOR

D.C.

BRUSHES

COMMUTATOR

(b)
PRINCIPLE OF
D.C. MOTOR

BASIC PRINCIPLES OF A.C. AND D.C. MOTORS

FIG. 4. *All electric motors operate in accordance with the basic electromagnetic principles that unlike magnetic poles attract, and like ones repel, each other. Current flowing through an armature coil sets up a magnetic field, the polarity depending upon direction of current flow.*

would work as an alternator if the coil were driven round between the magnet poles.

Suppose the A.C. is fed into the coil from a source of electric power. During the first half-cycle an electron current flows, let us take it, clockwise in the end of the coil seen. This end thus becomes a north pole. It is attracted by the south pole of the magnet, whilst the opposite end of the coil is attracted by the north pole. The coil starts to rotate; but by the time it has arrived with one end facing the south pole and the other end the north pole of the magnet, current has fallen to zero at the end of the half-cycle.

At this moment neither end of the coil is attracted by the magnet poles and it continues to move owing to the momentum that it has acquired. Then the next half-cycle begins; current flows in the opposite direc-

tion through the coil and the polarity of its ends is reversed. The ends of the coil are now repelled by the magnet poles to which they are near. The coil continues to move until it has described half a revolution from the position in Fig. 4. Owing to the changed direction of current in the second half-cycle, the end now nearest the eye is a north pole and the rotary movement continues.

Motor Principle

Remembering what was said about the commutator in the last chapter, you will have no difficulty in working out with the aid of Fig. 4 (b) how the coil representing the armature is caused to revolve when D.C. is supplied to it through a commutator.

Like generators, all practical motors have electromagnets. Their coils, too, contain many turns and have iron cores. Some types are very complex affairs, but all rely for

DIESEL ENGINES AS PRIME MOVERS

Generating plant in which the two generators are driven by Diesel engines. The plant is used to provide emergency supplies for a B.B.C. transmitting station. The engines can quickly be started by means of compressed air, stored in metal bottles, one of which is indicated.

their operation on the same principle: the mutual attraction of unlike poles and the mutual repulsion of like poles.

The electric motor is one of man's most useful servants. Miniature motors work domestic appliances such as the electric clock, the rotary fan, the radiogram turntable, the food mixer, the vacuum cleaner.

Varied Uses of Motors

Motors of larger size provide power in other surroundings for organ-blowers, garage tire pumps, coffee-grinders and single pieces of light machinery such as lathes, polishers and drilling machines. Motors rated at many horse-power drive trams and electric trains. Very large motors supply the power for huge factories and workshops.

The electric lighting of our homes is likely to see many improvements in the near future as the new fluorescent lamps become more readily available. In these certain gases are used which glow brightly under the influence of an electron stream.

"Daylight" tubes of this kind provide a white light so like that of day that colour-matching can be done by it. These tubes give much more light than filament lamps for the same consumption of electricity.

Electric heating is making great strides. Its advantages over all other kinds are that it is efficient (all of the heat comes into the room instead of largely going up the chimney), that it is clean and labour saving and, if properly installed, it is perfectly safe.

Besides the glowing "electric fire," other types of electric heating are being developed. Two of these may be mentioned, both of which run at comparatively low temperature and contain no brightly glowing radiants. The first of these is the tubular heater, which contains coils of resistance wire enclosed in a steel tube.

The tubes, about 2 in. in diameter, can be fixed to skirting boards and they provide a very pleasant form of heat; the temperature tending to be uniform, if they are properly arranged, in all parts of the room.

Next, there is the convection type of heater, which by means of a low-speed rotary fan draws cold air in at one opening, passes it over heater elements and delivers a gentle stream of warm air from a second opening.

Some use was made before the war in certain industrial processes of high-frequency heating and during the war enormous strides were made in this most interesting branch. The principle is that if alternating fields of very high frequency are applied to conducting materials, such as metals, currents are induced in them which can give rise to high temperatures. Further, the heat can be applied to the surface of the material without greatly raising the temperature of its interior, or to its interior and not to the surface.

Non-conductors can be heated in the same way by using them as the dielectric between metal plates. The possibilities of the high-frequency process are enormous, for there are many kinds of work which can be done better with its help than in any other way.

We have surveyed briefly some of the chief ways in which electricity is helping to make the world a better and more comfortable place for mankind. To write of all would require many volumes the size of this! Indeed, the task could never be completed, for existing apparatus is undergoing continual improvement, whilst new inventions appear in such numbers that no one could possibly keep pace with all the developments of all the branches of electricity.

Test Yourself

1. How does the microphone produce an electrical copy of sound waves reaching its diaphragm?

2. Briefly explain how the telephone receiver converts electric impulses into sound waves.

3. Why is it desirable to keep the voltage high and the current low in telephone circuits?

4. What is a repeater?

5. Mention six appliances in which the electric motor is used.

6. What is a photo-electric cell? For what purposes can it be used?

7. How can X-rays be produced?

8. What is an exciter?

9. Why is electric heating more efficient than open fires?

10. What is high-frequency heating?

Answers will be found at the end of the book.

WATER-
COOLED
FILAMENT
LEADS

ANNULAR
GRID SEAL

WATER-COOLED
ANODE JACKET

HYDRAULIC
TUNING
CONTROL

MAIN TUNING
CAPACITOR

TRANSMITTING
VALVE

TRUCK FOR
INSERTION OF VALVE

VALVE REPLACEMENT—B.B.C. STYLE

Wireless valves range in size from receiving types little larger than pea lamps to big transmitting ones requiring trolleys to transport them. Above is the final R.F. amplifier of a broadcasting transmitter, the last link between transmitter and aerial.

CHAPTER XII

PRINCIPLES OF WIRELESS AND TELEVISION

THESE subjects are branches of electrical engineering. Therefore, if you have read the previous two chapters carefully, you will be in a position to extend your knowledge in specialized applications of electricity.

First of all, what are wireless waves? They are not currents of electricity, but vibrations caused by them.

When a stone is thrown into a pond of still water, waves are produced on the surface which travel outwards from the point of disturbance in circular form as shown in Fig. 1 (a). A cork, or other floating object, placed at some distance from the disturbance, would presently be reached by the waves and would bob up and down as each wave or ripple passed under it, but it would not travel across the surface with the wave. Meanwhile, the waves travel on and would affect in the same way every other object or particle floating on the water.

In a similar way, an aerial connected to a radio transmitting station is capable of causing waves: these are electromagnetic in nature and travel through a medium called the ether. This medium exists everywhere, although it cannot be seen or otherwise detected by the senses. It permeates all space, even the spaces in the atom itself. The radio waves so produced travel outwards in all directions from the transmitting aerial, as indicated in Fig. 1 (b), and are capable of affecting any number of receiving aerials placed in their path.

Velocity of Radio Waves

The waves travel through the ether with the same velocity as that with which light is transmitted from the sun or any other luminous source. This velocity is 186,000 miles per second, so that a radio wave can travel once round the earth, a distance of approximately 25,000 miles, in one-seventh of a second. This can be regarded as practically instantaneous for ordinary pur-

poses; we shall see, later, however, that for special purposes, such as radar, the time is taken into account and used as a measure of distance.

Every wave has two important properties, namely, length and frequency. The wavelength is the distance measured from the crest of one wave to the crest of the next and is usually measured in metres. The frequency is the rate at which the successive wave crests reach a given point every second; this may be expressed in cycles per second, or, more practically, in terms of millions of cycles, i.e. in megacycles per second.

Wavelength and Frequency

The product of the wavelength in metres and the frequency in megacycles per second is 300. Thus a frequency of 10 megacycles per second corresponds to a wavelength of 30 metres, while a wavelength of 200 metres corresponds to a frequency of 1·5 megacycles per second; this is sometimes expressed as 1500 kilocycles per second.

Although the energy radiated from a radio transmitter is quite large, it will be appreciated that this energy is normally broadcast in all directions and only a very small amount can be received in any one aerial. The voltage obtained in a receiving aerial is usually regarded as a measure of the strength of the received signal; if this is one-thousandth of the voltage of an ordinary torch battery, the signal is a strong one; but it may be very much weaker than this, so that the need for some form of amplification of the received signal is evident.

The device employed for performing this function is the thermionic valve, although it is important to realize that this is only one of many uses of the valve.

The thermionic valve in its simplest form comprises a glass bulb from which all the air has been pumped; inside the bulb or envelope is a filament of wire, which is heated by passing through it an electric current, just as in the case of an incandescent lamp. This heated filament may act as a cathode, or it may be employed to heat a metal tube surrounding it which then acts as a cathode. The cathode of a thermionic valve is an element which, when heated, gives off electrons; an electron is a particle having a negative charge of electricity. A stream of such electrons flowing in a circuit constitutes an electric current in the same way as a stream of water particles constitutes a current of water.

Function of the Anode

Now, if a metal plate is introduced into the valve and is given a positive charge by being connected to the positive terminal of a battery (Fig. 2 (b), page 226), the electrons emitted from the cathode are attracted to this plate, since unlike charges attract each other. They continue their course through the meter and battery, returning to the cathode to complete the circuit. This flow of electrons constitutes an electric current which is indicated by a reading on the meter. The metal plate is called the anode and is normally connected to the positive battery terminal.

The two principal elements of the valve are the cathode and the anode, and such a device is called a two-electrode valve, or simply a diode.

Reason for the Name " Valve "

If the anode of the valve is connected to the negative battery terminal as at (c), page 227, the electrons given off by the cathode do not pass to the anode but are repelled by it, since like charges repel. Thus there is no current in the anode circuit and the meter shows a zero reading. It is not possible for electrons to flow through the valve in the reverse direction. In this way the diode acts as a one-way device, allowing current to flow in one direction only; it was for this reason that the word "valve" was first adopted by analogy with an air or steam or other valve which opens to allow a flow in one direction only. The construction of a diode is shown on page 226.

The conducting properties of a two-

electrode valve may be represented by a characteristic curve as shown in Fig. 3 (a), in which a vertical distance such as PX represents the current corresponding to the voltage denoted by the horizontal distance PY. With zero anode voltage there is a small anode current OA; this is due to those electrons which are projected from the cathode with sufficient velocity to enable them to reach the anode without the aid of an attractive force.

As the anode voltage increases the anode current rises, slowly at first, then rapidly at P and again slowly at B. Beyond this point, the curve tends to become horizontal, in which condition a large increase in anode voltage produces little or no increase in anode current. The valve is then said to be "saturated," since all the electrons emitted by the cathode are attracted to the anode; the anode current cannot increase beyond this, whatever the value of the anode voltage, unless the temperature of the cathode is raised.

Rectifying Valve

Such a valve is used in a modified form in every radio receiver supplied from alternating-current mains; it is called a rectifying valve and its purpose is to convert the alternating-current supply to a unidirectional- or direct-current supply for the other valves in the set. These other valves are more complicated in construction than the diode and may have any number of electrodes from three up to eight; they are known by the terms triode, tetrode, pentode, hexode, heptode and octode, respectively.

The action of a rectifying valve may be understood by reference to Fig. 3 (b) and (c), in which half-wave and full-wave rectifying systems are shown. In the half-wave rectifier (b), the transformer primary is connected to the supply to be rectified, while the secondary is connected to the diode in series with the load.

For each half-cycle during which the anode is positive to the cathode, current flows through the valve and the load, as shown by the half-waves; during the alternate half-cycles no current flows in the circuit, since the valve is non-conducting

(a)

LENGTH OF WAVE

CORK MOVES UP AND DOWN, NOT ALONG

TTING AERIAL

ELECTROMAGNETIC WAVES

(b)

RECEIVING AERIAL

TRANSMISSION AND RECEPTION OF ELECTROMAGNETIC WAVES

FIG. 1. *(a) Disturbance at one point on an otherwise smooth surface causes waves to spread outwards in circular formation. A cork on the surface moves up and down, and not along the surface, as the wave passes under it. (b) Similarly, electromagnetic waves travel outwards from a transmitting aerial and create electrical oscillations in a receiving aerial.*

when the anode is negative with respect to the cathode; thus only one half of each voltage wave is used.

In the full-wave rectifier (c), two diodes may be used, or these may be combined in one valve having two anodes and a common

cathode; the transformer secondary is centre-tapped and this point forms one terminal of the D.C. output, while the other is common with the cathode. When the upper secondary terminal is positive, diode D_1 conducts, while when the lower

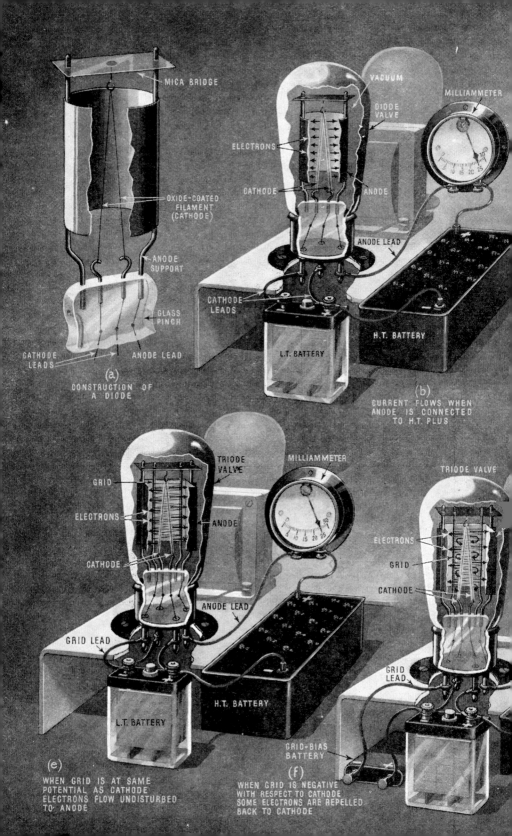

MICA BRIDGE

OXIDE-COATED
FILAMENT
(CATHODE)

ANODE
SUPPORT

GLASS
PINCH

CATHODE
LEADS

ANODE LEAD

(a)
CONSTRUCTION OF
A DIODE

VACUUM

DIODE
VALVE

MILLIAMMETER

ELECTRONS

CATHODE

ANODE

ANODE LEAD

CATHODE
LEADS

H.T. BATTERY

L.T. BATTERY

(b)
CURRENT FLOWS WHEN
ANODE IS CONNECTED
TO H.T. PLUS

TRIODE
VALVE

MILLIAMMETER

GRID

ELECTRONS

ANODE

CATHODE

ANODE LEAD

GRID LEAD

H.T. BATTERY

L.T. BATTERY

(e)
WHEN GRID IS AT SAME
POTENTIAL AS CATHODE
ELECTRONS FLOW UNDISTURBED
TO ANODE

TRIODE VALVE

ELECTRONS

GRID

CATHODE

GRID
LEAD

GRID-BIAS
BATTERY

(f)
WHEN GRID IS NEGATIVE
WITH RESPECT TO CATHODE
SOME ELECTRONS ARE REPELLED
BACK TO CATHODE

DIODE VALVE

MILLIAMMETER

MICA BRIDGE

GRID

NICKEL ANODE

ANODE

ANODE SUPPORT

CATHODE

CATHODE

GLASS PINCH

GRID LEAD

ANODE LEAD

ANODE LEAD

(d)
CONSTRUCTION OF A TRIODE

(c)
NO CURRENT FLOWS WHEN ANODE IS CONNECTED TO H.T. MINUS

DIAPHRAGM

MAGNET

MILLIAMMETER

VALVE RECTIFYING IMPULSES FROM AERIAL VIA COIL

TRIODE VALVES

GRID

CATHODE

ANODE

MOVING-COIL VIBRATING DIAPHRAGM

COIL

AERIAL

EARTH

VARIABLE CAPACITOR

L.T. BATTERY

SWITCH

CAPACITOR

GRID-BIAS BATTERY

OUTPUT TRANSFORMER

VERY SIMPLE WIRELESS SET WITH TWO TRIODE VALVES

(9)

H.T. BATTERY

ASHWELL WOOD

secondary terminal is positive, diode D_2 allows current to pass; in each case the electron flow through the load resistance is from left to right, so that the right-hand terminal is positive.

In this way, both halves of the voltage wave are used, as shown in the right-hand diagram, and twice the rectified voltage output is available; to secure this, the transformer secondary must be wound for twice the voltage of the secondary in the half-wave rectifier.

In practice, the current output obtained from the systems described is not a steady D.C., but contains a ripple, the frequency of which is that of the alternating-current supply in the half-wave rectifier and double this value in the full-wave circuit. In order to smooth out such ripples, it is necessary to employ filters, which may be constructed

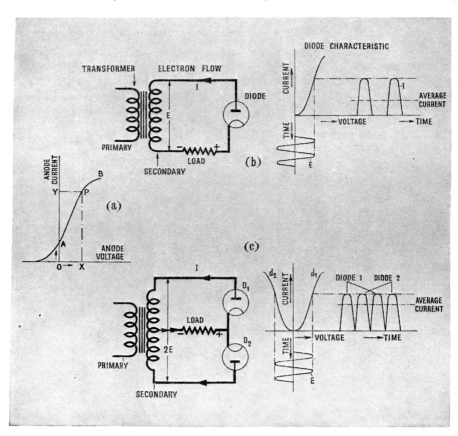

HOW A DIODE CAN BE USED AS RECTIFIER

FIG. 3. *(a) Characteristic curve of a diode, showing how the anode current increases with the anode voltage, at first rapidly and then more slowly as the valve tends to saturate. At zero anode voltage there is a very small current OA, much exaggerated in the diagram, representing the electrons which reach the anode by virtue of the velocity with which they are projected from the cathode. (b) Half-wave rectifier in which the diode conducts on each positive half-cycle and the current through the load is the average value reckoned over a complete cycle. (c) Full-wave rectifier in which, if the transformer secondary is centre-tapped, each diode conducts alternately under the same conditions as the diode in (b), with the result that the rectified current and the output voltage are doubled.*

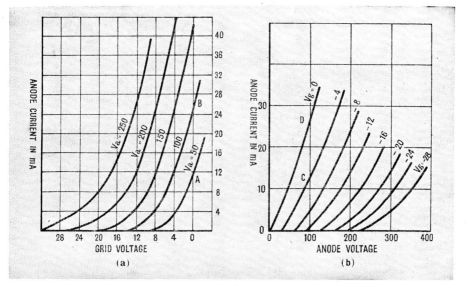

CHARACTERISTICS OF A TRIODE

Fig. 4. *These curves tell you how various voltages affect a valve. (a) At zero grid voltage the anode current is increased from 12 to 26 milliamps by increasing the anode potential by 50 volts. (b) With the anode potential at 100, the same increase in anode current is produced by changing the grid potential from — 4 volts to zero.*

of suitable combinations of coils and capacitors.

In the triode, the construction of which is shown at (d), page 227, the additional electrode is called the grid and it takes the form of a spiral or mesh of wire surrounding the cathode. It is much nearer the latter than is the anode and so it is in a more favourable position than the anode for controlling the electron flow. Moreover, since the grid is of an open construction it is possible for the electrons to pass through it and on to the anode without being intercepted by the grid.

Function of Grid

In order to ensure this, the third electrode is usually made negative in potential with respect to the cathode, so that it repels rather than attracts the electrons; the value of this negative potential is called the grid bias. Thus the function of the grid is not to collect electrons itself but to control the number which flow to the anode. It may be likened to a traffic signal in a one-way street along which the flow of traffic is thereby controlled.

Hence, if the grid is at the same potential as the cathode, as shown at (e), page 226, it has no influence on the flow of electrons to the anode. When the grid is negative, as at (f), page 226, some of the electrons are returned to the cathode; a smaller number reach the anode and the reading of the meter decreases.

As in the case of the diode, the properties of a triode may be represented by means of characteristic curves; since, however, there are three electrodes, complete representation can be obtained only by a series or family of such curves. Fig. 4 (a) shows a family of mutual characteristics; each curve shows the change in the anode current with variation of grid voltage for a fixed value of anode voltage. Any number of such lines may be drawn, each corresponding to a particular fixed value of anode voltage.

Another set of curves, called the anode characteristics, may be drawn as indicated in Fig. 4 (b); in this case, each curve shows how the anode current changes with variation in anode voltage for a fixed value of grid voltage. The similarity in the shape of these curves with the diode characteristic should be noticed.

From Fig. 4 (a) it may be observed by comparing points A and B that an increase in anode voltage from 50 to 100 causes an increase of 14 mA, i.e. from 12 to 26 mA in anode current. By comparing the points C and D in Fig. 4 (b) it will be seen that approximately the same increase in anode current is produced by a change of 4 volts in grid potential.

Amplification

The important point about this third electrode is that a small change in voltage on the grid produces a certain change in anode current, while to produce the same change in anode current a much larger change in anode voltage would be necessary. This is due to the fact that the grid is much nearer to the cathode than is the anode. The effect of this is that if a weak signal is applied to the grid, a much stronger signal is produced in the anode circuit; this amplified signal may be applied to the grid of another similar valve, in which case still further amplification is obtained.

Valves used in this way are known as amplifiers and they enable a weak signal received in the aerial to be magnified to such a strength that it is capable eventually of operating a loudspeaker or producing a picture.

For amplification at high frequencies, the triode has the disadvantage that its action is unstable; this is owing to the presence of a small capacitance between anode and grid which causes the anode circuit and the grid circuit to be coupled together, quite apart from the electronic action. Thus, referring to Fig. 5 (a), a voltage applied between grid and cathode causes a current to flow through this interelectrode capacitor C and anode impedance Z, so producing a voltage at the anode; similarly, a voltage in the anode circuit gives rise to a voltage at the grid. This causes the valve to generate oscillations

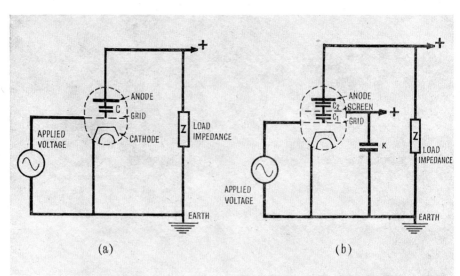

(a)   (b)

PURPOSE OF THE SCREEN GRID

Fig. 5. *(a) Voltage between grid and cathode sends a current through* C *and* Z *and produces a potential at the anode, which causes instability in the triode. In (b), a similar voltage produces a current through* C_1 *and* K, *but if* K *is large, very little current flows through* C_2 *and* Z; *therefore, a very small potential is produced at the anode and stability achieved.*

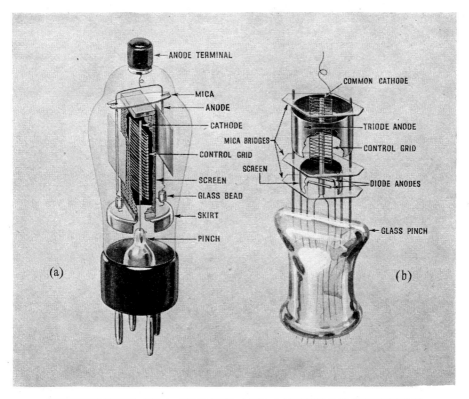

ANODE TERMINAL
MICA
ANODE
CATHODE
MICA BRIDGES
CONTROL GRID
SCREEN
SCREEN
GLASS BEAD
SKIRT
PINCH
(a)

COMMON CATHODE
TRIODE ANODE
CONTROL GRID
DIODE ANODES
GLASS PINCH
(b)

CONSTRUCTION OF A TETRODE AND A DOUBLE-DIODE-TRIODE

FIG. 6. *(a) In the tetrode (screen-grid valve), the control grid is a wire helix surrounding the cathode, while the screen grid is formed of close-meshed wire gauze. The anode consists of two parallel metal plates connected to a terminal at the top of the valve. (b) In the double-diode-triode, the upper portion is a triode consisting of a cathode, helical control grid and cylindrical anode. The same cathode serves the double-diode portion, which consists of two small anodes mounted near the lower end. A metallic screen shields the triode from the diode*

which may be manifested by "rushing" noises and whistles in the receiver.

This may be overcome by the employment of a tetrode, in which an additional grid, called the screen grid, is introduced between the anode and control grid. This electrode is connected to a steady positive voltage, less than that of the anode, in order not to impede the flow of electrons to the latter.

In addition, the screen grid, as shown in Fig. 5 (b), is connected through a relatively large capacitor K to earth; the control grid and anode have capacitances, C_1 and C_2 respectively, to the screen grid. The control

grid circuit is thus from grid through C_1 to screen, through K to earth and back to grid, while the anode circuit is from anode through C_2 to screen, through K to earth and back to anode through the load impedance Z.

The only component common to both circuits is the capacitor K and, by making this sufficiently large, the voltage introduced in either circuit by a current in the other may be made negligibly small. As a result, there is no tendency for the valve to generate oscillations and stable amplification is obtained.

The construction of a screen-grid valve

800 kW OUTPUT
FEEDER WALL
LEAD-OUT
INSULATOR

R.F. CONTACTORS
SWITCHING 200 kW
TRANSMITTER FEEDER

CONTACTORS SELECTING
INDUCTANCE TAP

COPPER TUBE
TRANSMITTER
PARALLELING
STRUCTURE

ONE OF THE
COMBINING CIRCUIT
INDUCTORS

COMBINING
CIRCUIT
CAPACITORS

COMBINING THE OUTPUTS OF TWO OR MORE TRANSMITTERS

Top floor of the central combining house in a B.B.C. transmitting station. In the foreground is the central paralleling structure where the long-wave outputs of up to four 200-kW transmitters can be combined to give a total output power of 800 kW. In the right background is an incoming 200-kW feeder, and in the left background the outgoing 800-kW feeder.

is shown in Fig. 6 (a). The screen grid itself is made of a close-mesh wire gauze, or from sheet metal with apertures covered by very fine mesh opposite the grid-cathode system. It is usually provided with one or more skirts which extend to the walls of the bulb so that the screening can be completed outside the valve.

Other Effects

The presence of the screen grid in a valve has another effect, namely, that the anode is less sensitive in its control of the electron flow than in a triode, since the screen itself exerts an important influence and is nearer to the cathode than is the anode. This has the effect of increasing the anode slope resistance of the valve and also of increasing the amplification factor; the latter is a measure of the maximum increase in signal strength which the valve and its associated circuit is capable of producing.

One disadvantage of the tetrode is the tendency of the anode to emit secondary electrons. This is owing to the fact that the rapidly moving electrons on reaching the anode dislodge other electrons from its surface; in a triode, such electrons are attracted back to the anode, but in a tetrode many are attracted to the screen grid, which is at a positive potential commensurate with that of the anode.

The effect of this is to produce a "kink" in the anode characteristic, which causes distortion and instability in the valve if the anode voltage swing is sufficient to carry the operating point on to this kink.

To overcome this, the pentode or five-

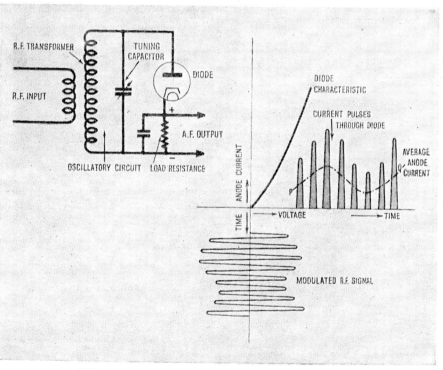

EXPLAINING HOW A DIODE DETECTOR WORKS

Fig. 7. *Modulated wave is applied from the tuned secondary of an R.F. transformer to the diode in series with the load resistance. The characteristic of the diode is such that the current pulses pass through it in one direction only; the average anode current so obtained produces across the load resistance an A.F. voltage which is fed to the following valve.*

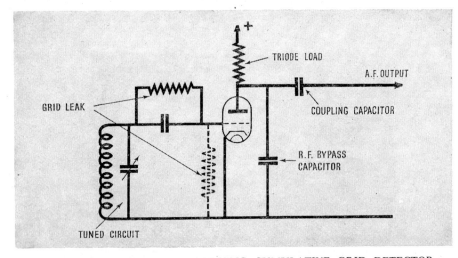

DIAGRAM OF CIRCUIT EMBODYING CUMULATIVE GRID DETECTOR

FIG. 8. *The cumulative grid detector is a combination of the diode detector and the anode-bend detector. An alternative position for the grid leak is that shown dotted.*

electrode valve was developed by introducing another grid called the suppressor grid between the screen grid and anode. This grid is usually connected internally to the cathode and its purpose is to suppress the emission of secondary electrons; such a valve is capable of dealing with large signals at the anode.

An alternative method of preventing the flow of secondary electrons to the screen grid is to increase the distance between this electrode and the anode; other modifications of the electrode structure may be adopted for the same purpose and such a valve is called a "kinkless tetrode" or beam valve. It is capable of handling large anode signal voltages and it is used mainly for audio-frequency output stages.

Multiple-electrode valves, some containing as many as eight electrodes, are widely used as frequency changers or frequency converters. In such valves the incoming radio-frequency signal is combined with a locally generated signal of somewhat higher frequency, with the result that the output obtained from the anode circuit has a frequency equal to the difference of those of the combined signals.

Multiple valves are also commonly used in radio receivers; such a valve contains in one envelope two or more groups of electrodes associated with independent electron streams. Apart from the economy in the heater-cathode system, there is the obvious advantage of using only one envelope and base for the combination, while directly connected electrodes may be either common or joined internally.

Examples of such valves are the double-diode, the double-triode, the diode-triode, the double-diode-triode, the triode-hexode, etc. The electrode assembly of a double-diode-triode is illustrated in Fig. 6 (b). It will be observed that the diode anodes, which require only a small total emission, are mounted at the end of the cathode near the glass pinch. A metallic shield is employed to screen the triode from the diode anodes, while the grid lead is taken to a cap at the end of the envelope remote from the diode leads.

The action of the diode in converting an alternating-current to a direct-current supply has already been described; this type of valve is also widely used to rectify or demodulate a signal, i.e. to extract the audio-frequency component from it.

A simple circuit for effecting this and showing its action is illustrated in Fig. 7. No current flows through the diode when the anode is negative with respect to the cathode, but during the part cycles when the anode is positive, current flows in pulses as shown shaded in the diagram. The average height of this curve is shown by the line *PQ*, which represents a unidirectional current pulsating at an audio frequency.

In passing through the load resistance, this current develops across it a D.C. voltage on which is superposed an audio-frequency voltage corresponding to the

ions are shown in Fig. 8. From this diagram it will be observed that the grid-cathode circuit is almost identical with the diode circuit just discussed. The action is similar, but the variations in potential of the grid so obtained are amplified by the triode action and fed to the grid of the next valve through a coupling capacitor. The R.F. bypass capacitor is necessary to provide a ready path for the radio-frequency component of the rectified signal; there is no further use for this component

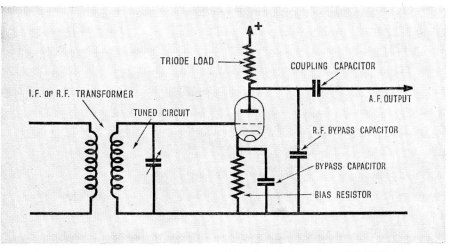

ANODE-BEND METHOD OF USING A TRIODE AS A DETECTOR

FIG. 9. *Showing how in the anode-bend detector the signal is applied to the grid, while the current pulses are produced in the anode circuit. The audio-frequency voltage produced across the load is fed to the following stage by the coupling capacitor, which prevents the flow of direct current. The R.F. component is bypassed by the capacitor shown in circuit.*

modulating signal. The latter is passed on to the grid of the first low-frequency amplifying valve and, when suitably magnified, operates the loudspeaker. The D.C. component of the voltage across the load resistance may be used for the automatic control of the gain of the receiver, as described later. The diode is usually employed as a detector in modern superheterodyne receivers and it has the advantage of being able to accommodate large signals with relatively little distortion.

The triode can also be used as a detector; in one form, known as the cumulative grid or leaky-grid detector, the connex-

and it must be diverted from the subsequent circuits.

It will be noticed that an alternative connexion, shown dotted, for the grid leak is indicated; this connexion is useful when it is necessary to connect the grid to the positive terminal of the low-tension supply or, if a potential divider is employed, to a point of any potential intermediate between the negative and positive terminals of the low-tension supply. The cumulative-grid detector is more sensitive than the diode detector, but it cannot accommodate so large a signal.

Another method of using a triode as a

detector is the anode-bend method. In this case, the connexion diagram of which is given in Fig. 9, no grid capacitor or leak is employed, but instead a bias resistor is connected in the cathode lead. The value of this resistance is chosen so that the steady anode current through it produces a potential difference sufficient to bias the grid to the point of maximum curvature near the foot of the mutual characteristic.

With this adjustment, the increase of anode current due to the positive half of the incoming signal is greater than the decrease due to the negative half, so that demodulation is obtained. It is necessary to connect a bypass capacitor across the bias resistor in order to divert from the latter the alternating component of current which would otherwise flow through it.

Valve Amplification

We have discussed the use of a valve as rectifier and detector and another important use is as an amplifier; we have already seen that a small change in potential on the grid of a triode is equivalent to a much larger change in potential at the anode. For example, an increase in grid potential of 1 volt may produce as great a change in anode current as a corresponding change of 30 volts at the anode. In this case, the amplification factor of the valve would be

30; the gain of the valve and its associated circuit would be less than this, but can be brought near this figure by a suitable circuit design.

Amplification of a signal may be carried out before or after detection; if it is before the signal is detected, the process is called radio-frequency (R.F.) amplification, or intermediate-frequency (I.F.) amplification, while if carried out after detection it is called audio-frequency (A.F.) amplification, since the process is performed at frequencies which are audible.

Tuned-anode Circuit

Almost all R.F. and I.F. amplifiers employ the tuned-anode circuit; a typical arrangement is given in Fig. 10. The input is applied to the primary of a radio-frequency transformer, the secondary of which is tuned to the frequency of the incoming signal; the magnified voltage obtained by tuning is applied to the grid of a suitable pentode or tetrode, the bias of which is set to the correct value by the cathode resistor. The anode is connected to the positive high-tension terminal through a circuit, which is also tuned to the signal frequency. Amplified signals appear at the anode terminal and are passed on to the grid of the next valve by means of the coupling capacitor. Since the

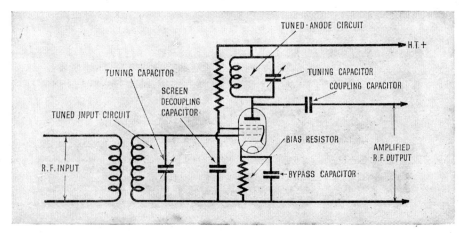

TYPICAL R.F. AMPLIFIER EMPLOYING A PENTODE

FIG. 10. *The anode load is a circuit tuned to the frequency of the incoming signal. The circuit amplifies signals having a frequency that is equal or nearly equal to this value.*

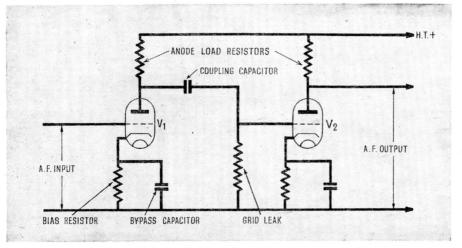

ANODE LOAD RESISTORS

COUPLING CAPACITOR

H.T.+

V_1

V_2

A.F. OUTPUT

A.F. INPUT

BIAS RESISTOR   BYPASS CAPACITOR   GRID LEAK

TWO-STAGE RESISTANCE-CAPACITANCE-COUPLED AMPLIFIER

FIG. 11. *Two-stage amplifier with the second valve coupled to the first by a capacitor connected between the grid of the second valve and the anode of the first.*

resonant circuits are tuned to the same frequency, the tuning capacitors may be ganged, i.e. the rotating plates of both capacitors are mounted on a common spindle so that the tuning of both circuits may be performed on one control.

Resistance-capacitance-coupled Amplifier

In audio-frequency amplifiers there is no tuned circuit, since the amplification is required to be the same at all audio frequencies. The simplest form of A.F. amplifier is that which employs a resistance as the anode load and a capacitance as the coupling component to the next valve; this is the so-called resistance-capacitance-coupled amplifier, a diagram of connexions for which is shown in Fig. 11.

The audio-frequency signal is applied to the grid of the first valve V_1, the bias on which is determined by the bias resistor; the corresponding variations in anode current produce fluctuations in potential difference across the anode load resistance; this gives rise to variations in anode potential, which are applied to the grid of the next valve V_2 through a coupling capacitor; the latter is necessary to prevent the high steady anode potential of V_1 from reaching the grid of V_2. Any charge which

tends to build up on the latter is allowed to leak away through the grid leak.

The same action is repeated in valve V_2, so that the output is a much magnified reproduction of the input. For example, if the incoming signal is 0·2 volt and the gain of each stage is 10, the output is $0·2 \times 10 \times 10 = 20$ volts. The great advantage of this type of amplifier is that the gain may be rendered practically uniform at all audio frequencies.

In Fig. 12 is shown a two-stage amplifier with a transformer coupling between the two valves; this gives a greater overall amplification, since the transformer provides an additional gain equal to its step-up turns ratio.

Matching Valve to Loudspeaker

In all the amplifiers we have previously discussed, the signal is required to do no work, except in supplying the losses in the tuned circuit, but merely to control the anode currents in the successive valves. Since, however, the signal has to do work in the last stage by operating the diaphragm of the loudspeaker, the output stage is of different design from that of the preceding circuits. The valve employed, which may be a triode, tetrode or pentode, should

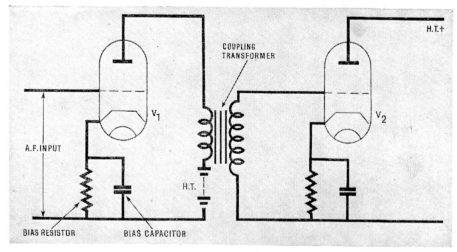

TWO-STAGE TRANSFORMER-COUPLED A.F. AMPLIFIER

FIG. 12. *Variations of potential on the grid of valve* v_1 *cause variations of current in the transformer primary. The secondary induced voltage impressed on the grid of valve* v_2 *produces a magnified A.F. current in its anode circuit.*

have a high anode current and should be matched to the loudspeaker; this is done by means of a matching transformer which enables the maximum output to be obtained consistent with minimum distortion of the signal.

A typical output circuit is shown in Fig. 13; the output from the preceding stage is applied to the pentode control grid, while in the anode circuit the primary

of the matching or output transformer is connected; the secondary of this transformer is joined directly to the speech coil of the loudspeaker. Across the valve is connected a tone-correcting circuit, which consists of a capacitor in series with a variable resistor. As the resistance is reduced, the upper frequencies become weaker, with the result that a bass response is obtained. We have seen that the valve may be used as a rectifier or as an amplifier; it may also

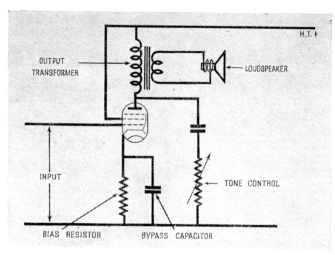

FIG. 13. *Here is a typical pentode output stage, embodying a tone control. The latter consists of a variable resistor in series with a capacitor. When the resistance is adjusted to a low value, the high audio-frequencies are attenuated and a bass response is obtained.*

be employed to generate oscillations. Such a valve is known as an oscillator and is used in every receiver of the super-heterodyne type. It is also used to generate oscillations, which, when supplied to the aerial of a transmitter, produce electromagnetic waves in space. This is known as a transmitting valve and it is, of course, very much larger than a receiving valve. While the latter has to deal with a power of about 5 watts—approximately that used in an ordinary torch bulb—transmitting valves may have

the valve with its associated tuned circuit. It will be noticed that only one coil is used and this is connected between anode and grid, while a tapping is connected to the cathode.

In Fig. 14 (b), a grid leak and capacitor are added to provide automatic grid bias, while the high-tension source is connected in the lead joining the cathode to the tapping point on the coil. In this arrangement, the valve, the tuned circuit and the high-tension are all in series. In Fig. 14 (c), the

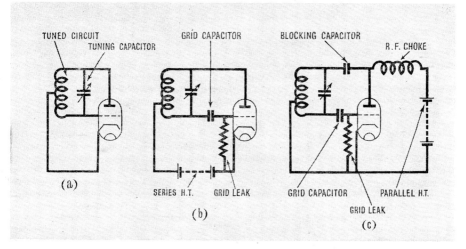

USING THE VALVE AS AN OSCILLATOR

Fig. 14. *Here are three theoretical diagrams of the Hartley oscillator. (a) The basic circuit. (b) The series-fed arrangement and (c) the parallel-fed Hartley oscillator.*

to dissipate as much as 500 kilowatts or half a million watts.

One of the problems in a transmitting valve is to keep the anode cool, so that the larger types of this valve differ from the receiving valve not only in size but also in construction. The anode is often made part of the envelope of the valve and is kept cool by circulating water or oil around it or by providing the anode with fins to facilitate cooling.

There are many circuits in which the valve may be employed as an oscillator; one of the most common of these is the Hartley oscillator, diagrams of connexions for which are shown in Fig. 14. The first of these gives the skeleton diagram showing

shunt-fed Hartley circuit is shown; the valve and H.T. are in parallel and it is necessary to include a blocking capacitor and R.F. choke as indicated.

Modulation

The transmitter generates a radio-frequency wave which is transmitted through the ether as already explained. Such a wave by itself is not capable of providing communication from one point to another, any more than a blank telegram or newspaper can do so. Something must be written or printed on the paper and, similarly, something must be impressed or superposed on the radio wave to make it intelligible.

This process is called modulation, which

implies a modification of the amplitude or frequency of the radio wave in accordance with the information to be carried by it. It is for this reason that the radio wave itself is usually referred to as the carrier wave, or simply the carrier.

The sounds, in the form of speech or music, which have to be conveyed to the listener are allowed to impinge on a microphone; this produces electrical fluctuations of audio frequency which are amplified by means of valves. The resulting voltage is used to vary either the magnitude or the frequency of the carrier wave.

Amplitude Modulation

It has been the usual practice in Great Britain to vary the amplitude of the carrier, and this process is known as amplitude modulation. In this system, the amplitude of the wave is varied by an amount proportional to the loudness of the original sound, while the rate at which these changes occur depends upon the frequency or pitch of the sound. Such a wave is illustrated in Fig. 15.

A type of microphone frequently used for broadcasting purposes is the ribbon microphone. This consists of a thin corrugated strip of aluminium supported at each end between the poles of a permanent magnet. This is enclosed for protective purposes between two perforated metal covers, as shown in Fig. 16. The microphone is mounted in a bracket, which can be supported on a stand or attached to an overhead suspension in such a way that the instrument can be set at any desired angle. Sound waves striking the ribbon cause it to vibrate between the poles of the magnet so that an audio-frequency voltage is produced in the ribbon, the ends of which are connected to a suitable transformer.

We can now form an impression of the process which takes place at the transmitting end of a radio communication system, for which reference should be made to Fig. 17. The announcer in the studio speaks into a microphone, which then generates a small electrical voltage of audio frequency. This voltage is amplified and is then supplied to a device called the modulator.

At the same time a radio-frequency oscillator generates a small high-frequency

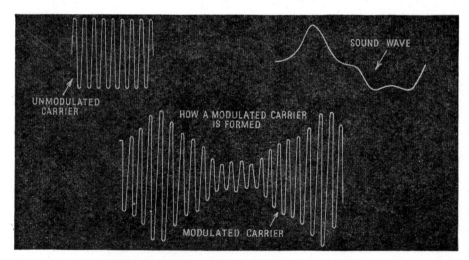

HOW A MODULATED CARRIER IS FORMED

FIG. 15. *The unmodulated carrier is represented by a pure sine wave of radio frequency and of constant amplitude; the sound wave has a complex shape and is of audio frequency. The modulated carrier is of radio frequency, but its amplitude varies in accordance with the sound wave, so that the latter has the same shape as the envelope of the carrier.*

FIG. 16. *Showing a microphone of the ribbon type. Sound waves strike the corrugated aluminium ribbon, causing it to vibrate between the poles of the magnet so that an audio-frequency voltage is produced in the circuit, the ends of which are connected to a suitable transformer and so into a transmitter.*

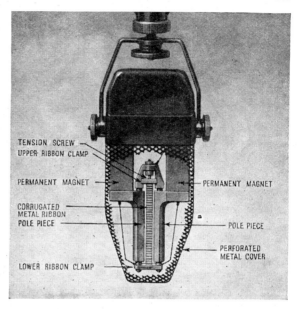

voltage which is magnified by a radio-frequency amplifier. The output of this is supplied to the modulator in which the amplified speech voltage is superposed on the radio-frequency voltage. The resulting complex voltage, which has a definite radio frequency and an amplitude which varies in accordance with the speech wave, is fed to the transmitting aerial.

Electromagnetic waves are radiated into space and under suitable conditions a distant receiving aerial may be excited with a small voltage which is a miniature replica of that fed to the transmitting aerial. We shall see later how the receiver extracts from this complex voltage the information imparted by the announcer.

The simplest type of receiver is the crystal set; this employs headphones but no valves and thus requires no electrical supplies. A crystal detector is used to change the high-frequency alternating current to the unidirectional current needed to work the headphones. But a crystal set provides no amplification of the very weak currents and is, therefore, greatly limited in its sensitivity. It can normally receive only strong signals, and even then cannot operate a loudspeaker. Valves are necessary for providing the required extension of range and volume.

Since the majority of valve receivers used at the present time operate on the super-heterodyne principle, the following description of the working of a receiver is based on this type.

To receive a signal on any radio set it is necessary to tune the receiver to the frequency of the incoming signal. Everyone knows what is meant by tuning a piano: the tension of each string is adjusted so that when struck it produces a note of correct pitch. This may be performed entirely by ear, or by comparing the note on the piano with that of a standard tuning fork. In the latter case, the fork and the piano string in question are said to be in tune. If this note is struck when the tuning fork is near, then on damping the piano string, or preventing it from vibrating, it will be found that the tuning fork is vibrating feebly at the same frequency. This will not happen when another note on the piano is sounded, unless the tuning fork is replaced by one which is in tune with the new note. The piano string and tuning fork are said to be in tune with each other or in resonance.

Tuning an Electrical Circuit

In a similar way, an electrical circuit can be brought into tune with a wireless wave by adjusting one or both of its two fundamental properties, namely, inductance and capacitance. Inductance is a property possessed by a coil of wire; two adjacent insulated conductors possess capacitance. Signals on different wavebands

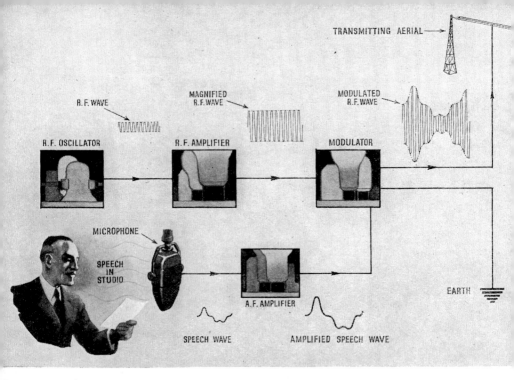

FIG. 17. *At a transmitting station, sound waves are converted by the microphone into electrical variations which are amplified by an audio-frequency amplifier and then fed to the modulator. There they are combined with the amplified output of a radio-frequency oscillator and the resulting modulated R.F. wave is supplied to the transmitting aerial; when the microphone is not actuated, this wave is of uniform magnitude and is called the*

are accommodated by changing coils, while a signal on a given waveband is tuned by adjusting a variable air capacitor. Fig. 18 (b) shows a simple arrangement illustrating the tuning of an electrical circuit.

The lead-in from the aerial is connected to one end of the aerial coil, the other terminal of which is connected to earth; this may be a copper plate or tube buried in the soil, or a water pipe which has a short run to the earth. A second (tuning) coil, wound close to and on the same former as the aerial coil, is connected to the tuning capacitor.

Operating the Tuning Control

To tune the set to an incoming signal, the plates of the capacitor are rotated by the tuning control until the correct capacitance is obtained. This is indicated aurally by maximum volume or visually by means of

a tuning indicator, or "magic eye" as it is sometimes called.

Visual Tuning Indicator

One form of tuning indicator consists of a glass bulb, exhausted of air, in which a cathode is mounted in a vertical position, as shown in Fig. 18 (a). Surrounding this is a funnel-shaped anode, the inner surface of which is coated with a chemical which glows when struck by a stream of electrons. Thus, in the absence of any other influence, a green ring-shaped glow is seen when the anode is connected. Between the cathode and the anode, however, is a third electrode, or deflector plate, consisting of a thin vertical rod.

If this electrode is less positive than the anode, it will tend to repel electrons and so produce a dark sector-shaped patch on the anode. The connexion to this electrode is such that the "eye" opens and closes in

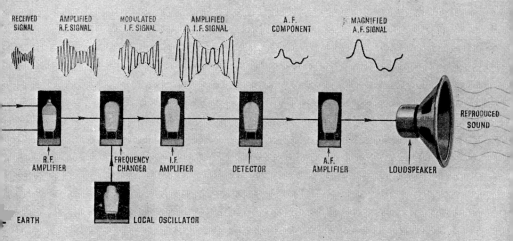

RECEIVING AERIAL

RECEIVED SIGNAL | AMPLIFIED R.F. SIGNAL | MODULATED I.F. SIGNAL | AMPLIFIED I.F. SIGNAL | A.F. COMPONENT | MAGNIFIED A.F. SIGNAL

R.F. AMPLIFIER | FREQUENCY CHANGER | I.F. AMPLIFIER | DETECTOR | A.F. AMPLIFIER | LOUDSPEAKER

REPRODUCED SOUND

EARTH | LOCAL OSCILLATOR

AND RECEIVED BY MEANS OF RADIO

carrier. At the receiver, the incoming modulated R.F. signal is first amplified and then fed to the frequency changer. There it is combined with the output of a local oscillator so that the resulting signal possesses the original modulation, but its frequency is changed to a lower value called the intermediate frequency. The modulated I.F. signal is amplified and passed to a detector, the output of which contains only the audio-frequency component.

accordance with the tuning of the receiver. The dark sector or shadow angle is smallest when the receiver is in tune.

The use of press buttons avoids the need for manual tuning, which is not always correctly performed by the listener. When a button is pressed, a switch is operated, which, in one system, connects a small fixed capacitor to the coil; this capacitor has been pre-set to tune the receiver to the required station.

When the signal is received in the tuned circuit, it is fed either directly or through a high-frequency amplifying valve to another valve called the frequency changer. Here the signal is combined with the voltage generated by an oscillator in such a way that the resulting voltage has a lower frequency than that of the signal but the modulation remains as before. This is a big advantage, since greater amplification can be obtained at this frequency, called the

intermediate frequency, than at the incoming signal frequency. This intermediate-frequency signal is fed through an intermediate-frequency (I.F.) transformer to one or more I.F. amplifying valves and thence to a final I.F. transformer.

Demodulated Signal

The magnified signal is then fed to another valve, usually a form of diode, in which the signal is demodulated. As the name indicates, the process performed by this valve and its circuit is opposite to that of modulation. In other words, instead of combining the audio-frequency voltage with the high-frequency voltage, they are separated from each other. The audio-frequency component is passed on to one or two valves which amplify the signal and finally supply it to the loudspeaker.

A schematic diagram is shown in Fig. 17 which illustrates the progress of the signal from the receiving aerial to the loudspeaker and which, when considered in conjunction with the transmitting part of the same diagram, indicates the complete chain of processes involved in communicating, for example, speech from a broadcasting studio to a distant speaker.

Receiving End of the System

Summarizing the action at the receiver with reference to Fig. 17, it is seen that the modulated radio-frequency signal received in the aerial is amplified and passed to the frequency changer, where it is combined with the output of the local oscillator. This produces a modulated intermediate-frequency signal which is amplified and fed to the detector, which converts this to an audio-frequency voltage. The latter is amplified and used to operate the loudspeaker which reproduces the original sound.

In the early days of broadcast reception, difficulty was often experienced on account of the fading of signals. This is the effect of interference between waves from the transmitter which travel along the ground and those which travel through the upper atmosphere. This made listening difficult at some distance from the transmitter.

Modern receivers incorporate a system known as automatic gain control (or automatic volume control), by means of which this tendency is almost completely overcome. Incoming signals may still fade, but weak signals automatically cause the receiver to be more sensitive, so that the sound output remains approximately

POWER SUPPLY APPARATUS FOR BROADCASTING

This picture reveals something of the extent and complexity of the apparatus used in broadcast transmission. For it forms only part of the power supply equipment, and is the rectifying equipment at London's Broadcasting House.

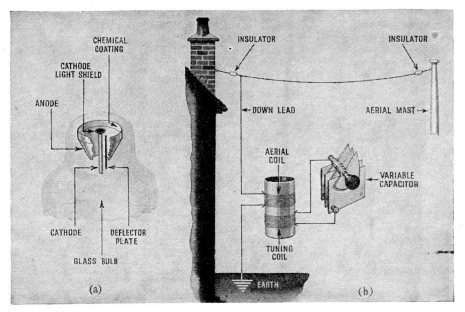

CHEMICAL COATING

CATHODE LIGHT SHIELD

ANODE

INSULATOR

INSULATOR

← DOWN LEAD

AERIAL MAST →

AERIAL COIL

VARIABLE CAPACITOR

CATHODE

DEFLECTOR PLATE

GLASS BULB

TUNING COIL

EARTH

(a)

(b)

SOME PRACTICAL ASPECTS OF TUNING

FIG. 18. *(a) In the form of tuning indicator shown, the deflector plate causes a dark sector-shaped patch on the anode, which elsewhere exhibits a green glow, owing to the impact of electrons on the chemical coating. The dark sector is narrowest when the oscillatory circuit is correctly tuned to the incoming frequency. (b) Currents induced in the receiving aerial pass through the aerial coil to earth; those currents induce corresponding oscillations in the tuning coil, which is connected to a variable capacitor.*

constant for a given setting of the manual volume control; this, of course, does not apply to signals which are so weak as to be outside the effective range of the receiver.

Using a Diode for A.V.C.

A method of obtaining this control is illustrated in Fig. 19. The valve action of the diode produces across its load circuit a D.C. voltage on which is superposed the A.F. signal voltage; the latter is fed forward to the low-frequency amplifiers. The D.C. voltage is fed back to the grids of one or more of the preceding valves, the amplification factors of which decrease as the negative grid bias increases. In this way, as the incoming signal increases, so does the D.C. bias, which reduces the gain of the receiver so that the output remains practically constant in spite of variations in input.

Practically all modern receivers are fitted with the moving-coil type of loudspeaker.

The moving-coil loudspeaker, illustrated in Fig. 20, consists of a circular magnet having a central pole so shaped that between the extremity of the latter and the outer pole a narrow annular air-gap is formed. Fixed to the magnet is a metal housing, on the outer circumference of which the speaker diaphragm is flexibly mounted.

The diaphragm is made of paper, buckram or similar material, and may be conical or elliptical in shape. Attached to the narrow end is a thin Bakelite tube or former, on which is wound a coil consisting of a few turns of fine copper wire. This coil, called the moving coil or speech coil, is free to move to and fro in the narrow annular air-gap.

Attached also to the coil former is a spider of thin elastic material which ensures that the coil moves centrally in the gap

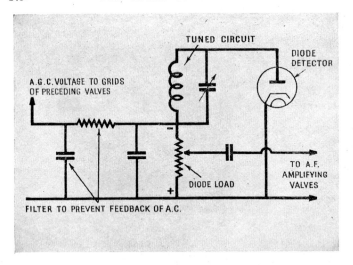

without touching the pole pieces, but is not restricted in its axial movement.

The magnet may be either a permanent magnet or an electromagnet. In the latter case, the magnetizing coil is wound on the central pole and the speaker is said to be of the energized type. The speech coil is connected to one winding of the output transformer, the primary of which is connected in the anode circuit of the output valve.

Oscillating in the Air-gap

Thus the amplified audio-frequency current flows through the moving coil, which, therefore, oscillates to and fro in the air-gap. This, in turn, causes the diaphragm

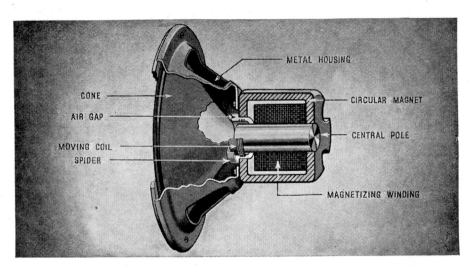

CONSTRUCTIONAL DETAILS OF A MOVING-COIL LOUDSPEAKER

FIG. 20. *Amplified audio-frequency currents flow through the moving coil, which is caused to vibrate axially in the narrow air gap formed between the central and outer poles of the circular magnet. The coil former is attached to the narrow end of a conical diaphragm, the outer end of which is flexibly supported from the metal housing of the loudspeaker*

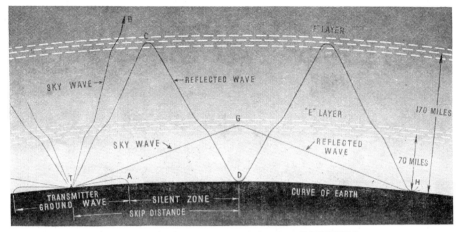

CAUSE OF FADING IN RADIO RECEPTION

FIG. 21. *Some of the waves radiated from a transmitter travel along the earth's surface and are called ground waves; others, called ionospheric, or sky waves, travel upwards. Some pass through the E and F layers, some are reflected at the upper layer, whilst others are reflected from the lower layer. If two or more waves, having travelled along different paths, arrive simultaneously at a receiver, they interfere and cause fading.*

to move backwards and forwards, so setting in motion a column of air in front of it, which in turn produces the sound corresponding to that in the studio.

Layers in the Atmosphere

When radio waves are emitted from a transmitting aerial, they are broadcast in all directions. A wave which travels along the ground is called a ground wave: such waves weaken rapidly with increasing distance from the transmitter. Waves which are radiated upwards are not necessarily lost, however, as far as receivers situated on the ground are concerned. Above the surface of the earth are two (or more) fairly well-defined layers in the atmosphere, which are capable of reflecting radio waves in much the same way as light can be reflected.

These layers, called the E and F layers, are situated at average heights of about 70 miles and 170 miles respectively above the earth; these distances, however, vary considerably, particularly with the time of day and night and with the seasons of the year.

Referring to Fig. 21, a wave such as TA is called a ground wave: TB is a sky wave and is projected so steeply that it passes through the E and F layers and is merely displaced somewhat in the process. A wave such as TC is reflected at the F layer and may be received at the point D; the same wave may suffer further reflections before becoming too weak to be received satisfactorily.

Waves are also reflected from the E layer as illustrated by the wave AG, which, when reflected, arrives at the ground level at point H. If the maximum distance for effectively receiving the ground ray is TA, then the space beyond A up to D is called the silent zone; D is the first point at which a sky wave can be received and the distance TD is called the skip distance.

Sky Waves versus Ground Waves

Since the sky wave weakens much less with distance than the ground wave, it will be appreciated that reception can be obtained at much greater distances with the former; on the other hand, however, the reception is not reliable, since the height of the layer is variable.

It will be evident from the diagram that at certain points waves may arrive after travelling along different paths. At H, for example, one wave may arrive after one reflection from the F layer, while another may arrive at the same point after, say, three reflections from the E layer. These waves may assist or oppose each other, depending upon the heights of the layers and other factors. Thus, as conditions change, so will the reception vary and fading of the signal occur. It is to overcome this effect that automatic gain control is employed in most modern receivers in order to make the sound output approximately constant.

World-wide Communication

The first station to provide regular telegraphic communication with the Empire was the Post Office Radio Station at Rugby, which was completed in 1925. This station employs a power of 1000 kilowatts and operates on long waves of 20,000 to 30,000 metres; it is capable of communication with any part of the globe and is used for transmitting British official and other news, commercial intelligence, meteorological reports, Greenwich time signals and for transmitting radio-telegrams to ships at sea.

While this station was being constructed, Marconi was experimenting with short waves and in 1926 constructed a beam station at Bodmin, Cornwall, for communication with Canada. This station operated on short waves with a power of 20 kilowatts and cost very much less than a corresponding long-wave station. In April, July and September of 1927, beam services were opened to Australia, South Africa and India respectively.

Transmitting Aerials

A beam station differs from a broadcast station in the arrangement of its aerials. A single vertical aerial wire transmits equally in all directions; this may be represented diagrammatically by a circle with the aerial at its centre (Fig. 22 (a), opposite); the distance measured from the aerial to the circle in any given direction represents the strength of the signal transmitted in that direction. If two similar vertical aerials are arranged so that the distance between them is half the length of the wave, the transmission is not uniform in all directions. The transmission diagram, or polar diagram as it is called, takes the form of a "figure of eight," with the height of the "eight" at right angles to the line joining the aerials as indicated in Fig. 22 (b). This shows that no transmission takes place along the line of the aerials, but maximum signals occur in a direction at right angles to this.

If this process is taken a stage further by the employment of four similar aerials in a straight line, the diagram shown in Fig. 22 (c) is obtained. This shows that a four-aerial array produces a considerable concentration of signal strength in a direction broadside to the array, but in other directions the transmitted signal is weak and is actually zero in some directions. It will be noticed, incidentally, that there are four small "tails" in the polar diagram.

This is the principle of beam transmission, but it will be observed that in such a system equal amounts of energy are transmitted in the forward and in the reverse directions. To avoid this, a second line of aerials is erected behind the original array; this group is called the reflector, since in effect it reflects the signals received by it, so that most of the energy is radiated in one direction, namely, that remote from the reflector. Such an arrangement constitutes a true beam aerial: the longer the array, that is, the greater the number of elements in it, the more concentrated is the main loop and the greater is the number of "tails" (Fig. 22 (d)).

Tiered Aerial

In practice, aerial arrays are built up vertically, since this also produces a concentration of energy in the vertical plane; such a system is known as a "tiered" aerial. A sketch of an eight-element aerial array having three tiers is shown in Fig. 22 (e); one half of the diagram shows the aerials only, while the other half shows the reflectors.

The wavelengths in use by the B.B.C. short-wave stations range from 13·9 to 49·6 metres, according to the part of the Empire being served. Eight high-power transmitters are employed, feeding twenty-five aerials, all of which are directional. Most of the aerials have four elements and four tiers

DIRECTIONAL AERIAL SYSTEMS

(a) AERIAL — EQUAL RADIATION IN ALL DIRECTIONS — SINGLE AERIAL

(b) AERIALS — MAXIMUM RADIATION — TWO AERIALS — MAXIMUM RADIATION

(c) MAXIMUM RADIATION — AERIAL ARRAY — ARRAY OF FOUR AERIALS

(d) MAXIMUM RADIATION — AERIALS — REFLECTORS — FOUR-AERIAL BEAM ARRAY WITH REFLECTOR

(e) MAST — AERIALS — REFLECTORS — EIGHT-ELEMENT "TIERED" BEAM AERIAL ARRAY

(f) SPREADERS — 325 FT. MAST — AERIALS — TYPICAL FOUR-TIERED AERIAL and the majority are also provided with reflectors. In some cases, reversible reflectors are provided: this means that arrangements are made for reversing the functions of aerial and reflector so that transmission may be made, say, from west to east or from east to west.

In yet other cases, the direction of transmission may be "slewed" by about ten degrees, not by mechanically rotating the aerials, but by electrically slewing the polar diagram. A typical aerial is shown in Fig. 22 (f), page 249. The masts vary in height from 150 ft. to 350 ft., according to the aerials which they support.

Cathode-ray Tube

In order to understand the subjects of radar and television, it is necessary to consider the construction and action of the cathode-ray tube. This consists of a long glass tube, one end of which is sealed, while the other forms the narrow end of a conical extension; the large extremity of the latter is closed by a glass end-piece which is made as flat as possible consistent with mechanical strength.

The inside of the large end is coated with a thin layer of a chemical material which has the property of fluorescence; this means that the material glows or becomes luminous at any point which is struck by a stream of electrons. The colour of the glow depends upon the chemical material used and may be white, blue, green, or red, according to the purpose which the tube is intended to serve. This chemical coating is called the screen, the diameter of which may have any value from 3 to 16 in., depending upon the use to which the tube is to be put. The length of the tube is usually two to three times the screen diameter.

Defining a "Soft" Tube

The tube has as much air as possible pumped from it; the more thorough the pumping process, the "harder" the vacuum is said to be. Most modern tubes are hard tubes, but in earlier types it was found desirable to introduce a small amount of gas for focusing purposes: such a tube is described as a "soft" tube.

In the narrow end of the tube remote from the screen is mounted the "gun"; this consists of an assembly of electrodes and is so called because its purpose is to shoot a narrow beam of electrons towards the screen. The electrons are provided by the cathode; as in the thermionic valve, the cathode is heated either by the passage of an electric current through it or by radiation from a filament which itself is heated by an electric current. The cathode is one of the gun electrodes, the others of which are the grid and the accelerator. The grid, or shield, is not like the grid of a valve in shape, but takes the form of a metal cup with a small hole in the bottom, or it may be a simple metal cylinder.

The anode of a soft tube is usually in the form of a disk with a hole in the middle, as shown in Fig. 23 (a). When the tube is in use, the anode is maintained at a positive potential of some 300 volts with respect to the cathode; when the latter is heated and emits electrons, these are attracted to the anode and travel towards it at high speed.

Concentrated Electron Stream

The shape and potential of the shield are such that, with the assistance of the small trace of gas in the tube, the stream of electrons is formed into a narrow pencil which passes through the central hole in the anode. The velocity of the electrons is such that they sweep down the length of the tube and eventually strike the screen at the end. This produces a luminous glow which, if the focusing adjustment is correct, is seen as a bright fluorescent spot when the screen is viewed from the outside.

Thus there is produced in the tube a beam of electrons which appears to behave like a ray of light. In fact, if a soft tube is viewed in a dark room, the path of the beam is visible as a ray of light; this is because the impact of the electrons with the molecules of gas is so great that the gas itself is made to glow in the vicinity of the electron beam, the position of which is thereby disclosed. It is easy to realize from this explanation why the name cathode-ray tube was adopted for this device.

Since in a hard tube there is no gas to

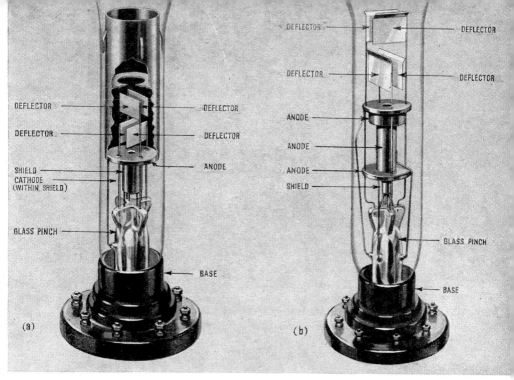

Labels in figure (a), from left and top:
DEFLECTOR — DEFLECTOR
DEFLECTOR — DEFLECTOR
SHIELD
CATHODE
(WITHIN SHIELD)
ANODE
GLASS PINCH
BASE
(a)

Labels in figure (b):
DEFLECTOR — DEFLECTOR
DEFLECTOR — DEFLECTOR
ANODE
ANODE
ANODE
SHIELD
GLASS PINCH
BASE
(b)

ELECTRODE ASSEMBLIES IN CATHODE-RAY TUBES

Fig. 23. *(a) Gas-focused tube in which anode is a metal disk with a central perforation for the passage of electrons; presence of gas within tube enables the beam to be focused. (b) A hard or high-vacuum tube has three anodes which accelerate electrons and focus the beam.*

assist in the focusing action, the anode is made in two or three parts, each of which is connected to a suitable positive potential (Fig. 23 (b)). The last part is usually at the highest potential, which may be as much as 5000 volts or more. This anode system, with correctly adjusted potentials, causes the electron beam to be brought to a sharp focus at the screen, as in the soft tube.

Tracing Pattern on Screen

We now have a glass tube on the end of which a bright spot of light is produced by the impact of a beam or jet of electrons. This may be likened to the splash which would be produced on a window pane by a jet of water directed on to it from a hose outside the window. If the hose is moved about in a definite manner, a crude sort of pattern may be traced out on the window. Similarly, if the cathode ray could be moved about, the spot would trace a pattern on the screen and if this could be repeated regularly at a high speed the

pattern would appear permanently on the screen in a fixed position.

One method of producing a simple trace on the screen is to employ a pair of parallel deflecting plates. If one plate of this pair is connected to the anode it will have little or no influence on the electron stream, which continues to travel along the axis of the tube. If the other deflecting plate is made positive, as shown in Fig. 24, the beam would be attracted towards it, while if it were made negative the beam would be repelled from it. Thus, if the upper plate in Fig. 24 were made alternately positive and negative, the spot would move up and down, and if the potential variations were sufficiently rapid, the spot would move up and down so quickly that a single vertical line of light would be observed on the screen.

Such a line of light is of very limited use in practice, so a second pair of deflector plates is added. This pair of plates is arranged to be at right angles to the former, and if one plate of this pair is connected to the anode, while the other is subjected to an alternating potential, the spot will be caused to move horizontally to and fro across the screen.

If one of the horizontal plates and one of the vertical plates are simultaneously excited with regularly varying potentials, the spot will trace out a pattern on the screen. The size and shape of this pattern depends upon the magnitude of each potential and the nature of its fluctuation. If the pattern is very closely woven, a picture is formed, to which light and shade may be imparted by applying varying potentials to control grid.

Electromagnetic Method

The method just described for obtaining deflection of the spot is called the electro-static method; the feature of this, so far as the tube itself is concerned, is the presence of two pairs of deflecting plates inside the tube. Another system is that in which the deflection is obtained electromagnetically and this involves the use of coils outside the neck of the tube; such an arrangement makes the internal structure of the tube simpler than in the electrostatic case, since deflecting plates are not required.

To produce a vertical deflection, a pair of coils may be arranged as in Fig. 25 (a); to produce a horizontal deflection, another pair may be used at right angles to this. In practice, however, to economize in space, the coils are bent around the neck of the tube as shown in Fig. 25 (b). It is very important to realize that the pattern produced on the screen is traced by the cathode ray; the latter may be likened to a pointer with the essential difference that any mechanical pointer, however light in weight, can move at only relatively low speeds. The cathode ray, on the other hand, is capable of moving at extremely high speeds.

In many applications of the cathode-ray tube, the movement of the spot in one direction, usually the horizontal direction, is required to be proportional to time. This means that if the spot moves a certain distance horizontally across the screen in one second, then it would move twice that distance horizontally in two seconds. This sounds simple, but its accomplishment requires special equipment.

The apparatus used to achieve this is called a linear time base; by employing this device, the base line of any picture or

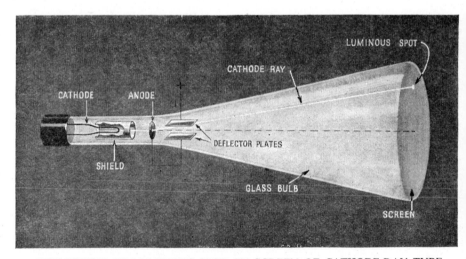

DEFLECTION OF LUMINOUS SPOT ON SCREEN OF CATHODE-RAY TUBE

FIG. 24. *The cathode ray is a continuous stream of electrons projected from the cathode through the centre of the anode. If a deflector plate is made positive, the ray is attracted causing the luminous spot to be deflected in a corresponding direction.*

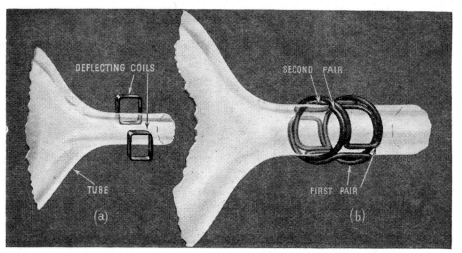

HOW ELECTROMAGNETIC DEFLECTION MAY BE OBTAINED

Fig. 25. *(a) One pair of coils is used to produce vertical deflection of the spot, while in (b) two pairs are employed so that the spot may be moved horizontally and vertically.*

pattern obtained on the screen of a cathode-ray tube can be regarded as a time axis; in other words, a distance measured along this axis can be used as measure of time if a suitable scale is chosen.

One of the early uses of the cathode-ray tube was in the measurement of the heights of the E and F layers which exist in the earth's upper atmosphere. We have already seen that such layers affect the propagation of radio signals and cause fading. The lower, or E layer, is sometimes called the Kennelly-Heaviside layer, because these two scientists, the former American and the latter English, first suggested their existence.

The upper or F layer is called the Appleton layer, because it was Sir Edward Appleton who discovered it and who made the first experiments enabling the height of this and the E layer to be measured.

Now, the effect of one of these layers on a radio wave travelling up from the ground is similar to the effect of a sheet of glass on a ray of light. Some of the light is transmitted through the glass, while some is reflected back. Similarly, a radio wave travelling up to a layer is partly transmitted and partly reflected. By measuring the time taken for the wave to return to the starting point, the height of the layer may be calculated.

Let us consider a transmitter as shown in Fig. 26 with the receiver at a known distance from it. If the transmitter radiates a signal, the receiver will detect a ray which has travelled along the direct or ground path and a little later it will receive a wave which has travelled upwards to the F layer and down again. Although the waves travel with a very high velocity, there is a definite difference between the lengths of the paths and, consequently, a definite time interval between the arrival of the two waves.

To determine this time interval, the transmitter is arranged to send out a special kind of signal consisting of a series or train of short-time pulses. If the receiver incorporates a cathode-ray tube provided with a suitable time base, these pulses received along the direct path appear on the screen of the cathode-ray tube as shown. The wave shown below the pulses is that due to a timing oscillation; if the frequency of the timing oscillator is known to be, say, 1000 cycles per second, then the time interval between successive waves is one-thousandth of a second.

The reflected wave is also picked up by

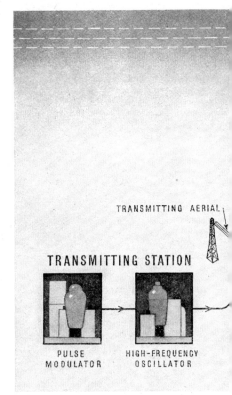

FIG. 26. *Transmitter radiates high-frequency pulses in all directions: some reach the receiver aerial by a direct path and others by reflection from the upper layer. Owing to the longer path travelled, the reflected wave reaches the receiver after the direct pulse ; the delay time is measured by the timing wave and thus the height of the layer is determined.*

the receiver as an echo and appears on the screen of the cathode-ray tube. It is, of course, smaller and its time delay may easily be determined by reference to the scale provided by the timing wave. From a knowledge of this time and the distance between transmitter and receiver, the height of the layer may be calculated. This use of the echo is an elaboration of the rough technique of a ship's pilot, who uses the echo from a sharp blast on the vessel's whistle to estimate his approximate distance from the face of a cliff.

The general layout of the apparatus used in these measurements is shown in Fig. 26. The high-frequency oscillator is pulse modulated so that short pulses of high-frequency oscillations are sent out by the

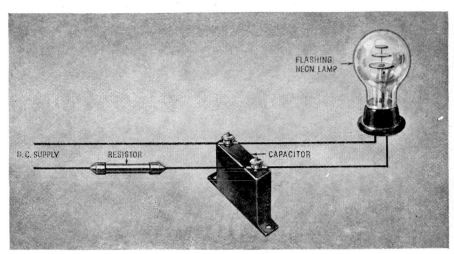

CONNECTIONS OF A SIMPLE TIME BASE

FIG. 27. *When the D.C. supply is switched on, the capacitor charges relatively slowly until a voltage is reached which is sufficient to "strike" the neon lamp; the latter flashes and rapidly discharges the capacitor, and the process is repeated indefinitely.*

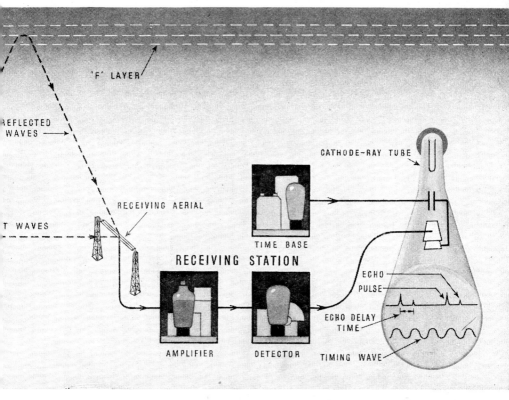

'F' LAYER

REFLECTED WAVES ———►

T WAVES

RECEIVING AERIAL

CATHODE-RAY TUBE

TIME BASE

RECEIVING STATION

ECHO PULSE

ECHO DELAY TIME

AMPLIFIER   DETECTOR   TIMING WAVE

transmitter aerial. The direct and reflected waves are picked up by the receiver, where they are amplified, and after detection are supplied to the "vertical" plate of the cathode-ray tube, i.e. the plate giving the vertical deflection. The "horizontal" plate is connected to the time base.

Constructing a Time Base

A simple time base may be made as shown in Fig. 27. When the direct-current supply is switched on, the capacitor charges up through the resistor until the voltage across it reaches the striking value for the neon lamp. This is usually of the order of 170 volts, so that the D.C. supply voltage must be greater than this value. When the neon lamp glows, it short-circuits the capacitor, which thus discharges through the lamp; the latter is then extinguished and the process is repeated indefinitely, the neon lamp flashing regularly at a rate depending upon the product of the values

of resistance and capacitance. If they are both large, the flashing rate is low and it may be as low as once per second if the resistor is of the order of 1 megohm and the capacitor is of the order of 1 microfarad.

When used as a time base, it is the voltage across the capacitor which is employed to supply the "horizontal" plates of the cathode-ray tube.

Radar Stations

The word "radar" means radio detection and range finding. The first radar stations were known as Chain Home or CH stations and the wavelength used was 10 to 13 metres. The transmitting array consisted of fixed horizontal aerials and reflectors suspended from 350-ft. towers and was not unlike the conventional telegraph transmitting array. The receiving aerial system, which was mounted on a wooden tower 240 ft. high, comprised one pair of aerials for direction finding and one pair for elevation measurements.

On the approach of an aircraft to these shores, the reflected ray was detected as indicated in Fig. 28; the angle of elevation *A* was measured on one pair of receiving aerials, the bearing angle *B* was determined by the second pair, while the range *R* was given by the echo delay time on the cathode-ray tube. In this way the position of the aircraft was completely specified.

Operating on Ultra-short Waves

The CH stations proved to be very satisfactory for the location of the large formations of aircraft, but they were not so successful in dealing with small formations, particularly at low altitudes of a few hundred feet. For this purpose the CHL (Chain, Home, Low) stations were devised. The transmitters, which were capable of ranges exceeding 100 miles, operated on a wavelength of 1·5 metres.

The employment of such a short wave-length enabled a relatively small aerial array to be used; the dimensions of this array were of the order of 7 yd., so that it was possible to mount the aerial on a turntable which rotated at six revolutions per minute. The whole arrangement was mounted on towers 185 ft. high when used at sea level or on 20-ft. gantries when installed on cliffs; the width of the beam transmitted was about 20 deg.

For maximum sensitivity, it was clearly necessary to use a beam-receiving aerial and it was also essential that the receiving aerial should always be in line with the transmitting aerial. Now, the latter was transmitting for only short periods at a time, while the receiving aerial could be usefully employed only during the intervals between the transmitted pulses. Hence, the same aerial could be used for both transmission and reception and this principle was adopted.

Another fundamental difference between the CH and CHL stations was that whereas

LOCATING THE POSITION OF AN AEROPLANE

FIG. 28. *Aeroplane's position is determined by receiving waves sent out by a neighbouring transmitter and reflected by the aircraft. The receiving aerial system comprises one pair of aerials for measuring elevation angle* A, *and another for determining the bearing angle* B, *while range* R *is measured by the echo delay time on a cathode-ray tube.*

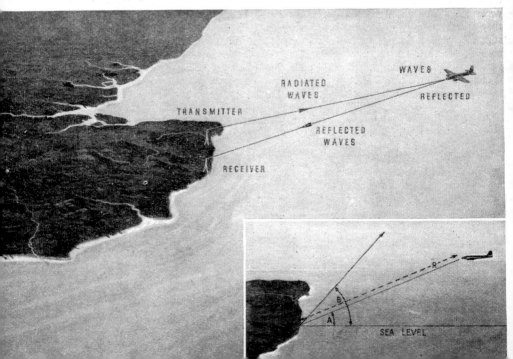

Labels on photograph: SANDS BAY · ENEMY SHIPPING · CRUISER "KÖLN" · JELÖ · HORTEN

Map labels: DRAMMEN · OSLO FJORD · Horten · Tönsberg

RADAR "MAGIC EYE" IN OPERATION

With the aid of radar apparatus, airmen are able to pin-point their targets and bomb with maximum effect and accuracy, even when the target is totally obscured. From the installation in the aircraft is transmitted a beam of radar waves; the returned "echo" passes through various stages and finally appears on the face of a cathode-ray tube in the form of a map. How accurate these "echo maps" are is clearly seen in the above photographs in which the appropriate map section appears alongside the radar "magic eye" map

the former used a horizontal time base, the latter used a radial time base; this was arranged to rotate at the same speed as the beam and to point in a corresponding direction.

Since, also, the received pulses were used to brighten the spot on the cathode-ray tube, the target, when detected, produced a bright spot on the screen at a distance and in a direction from the centre of the tube which corresponded with the distance and direction of the target from the station. This is indicated in Fig. 29. The method just described of indicating the position of the target directly on the screen of a cathode-ray tube was called the plan position indicator, or P.P.I.

Ground Control Interception

This led to a new system called the G.C.I., or ground control interception, by means of which night fighters were guided to their targets directly from the cathode-ray tube on the screen of which the plan position indicated the actual position of the enemy. Prior to this it had been necessary

to employ plotters, whose job it was to move coloured plaques on a map to indicate the enemy positions.

The aerial system rotated on a turntable, while underground was the radar station which combined the functions of locating enemy raiders and directing our fighter aircraft to intercept them. The switching mechanism connected the aerial to the transmitter when the latter was sending out its pulses, while during the "silent" interval between pulses the aerial was connected to the receiver to pick up the echo. The position of the raider was indicated directly on the plan position indicator and the fighters were directed accordingly.

Later, a magnetron valve, generating high power at a wavelength of a few centimetres, was produced, to be followed by a valve called the reflection klystron, which was used in combination with the former.

The use of very short waves enabled a very small aerial to be employed and this was mounted at the focus of a parabolic reflector, which projected a narrow beam

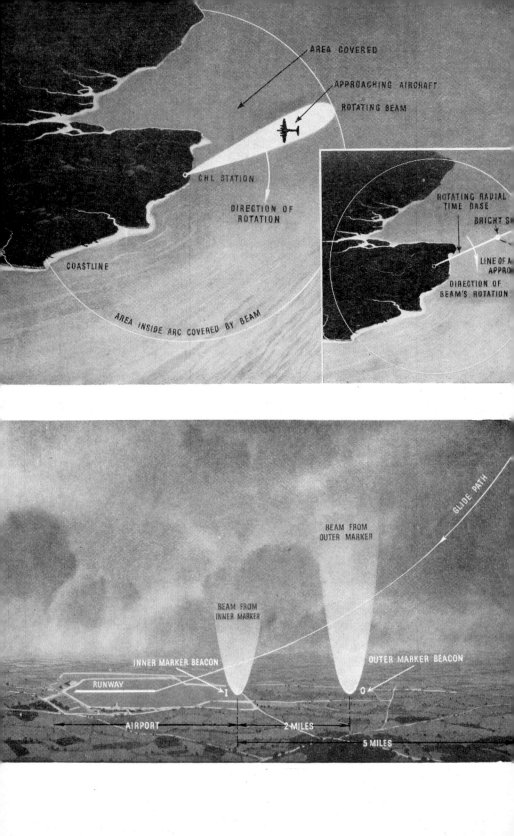

AREA COVERED

APPROACHING AIRCRAFT

ROTATING BEAM

C.H.L. STATION

DIRECTION OF
ROTATION

COASTLINE

AREA INSIDE ARC COVERED BY BEAM

ROTATING RADIAL
TIME BASE

BRIGHT S

LINE OF A
APPRO

DIRECTION OF
BEAM'S ROTATION

GLIDE PATH

BEAM FROM
OUTER MARKER

BEAM FROM
INNER MARKER

INNER MARKER BEACON

OUTER MARKER BEACON

RUNWAY

AIRPORT

2 MILES

5 MILES

FIG. 29 *(Left)*. *At a CHL station operating on a wavelength of 1·5 metre, the rotating aerial was used alternately for transmitting the pulse signal and for receiving the echo. The radial time base of the receiver rotated in synchronism with the aerial, while the received signal brightened the spot of the cathode-ray tube. In this way, position of the target was indicated on the screen, which thus became a plan position indicator, or P.P.I.*

FIG. 30 *(Below)*. *When making a "blind" landing, a pilot approaches the airfield at a height of 1500 ft. and is guided towards the runway by signals from a radio transmitter. At a distance of five miles from the airport, a radio beam is entered, the signals from which remain at a constant intensity if the aircraft descends along the appropriate glide path. When two miles from the aerodrome, the pilot flies the aeroplane through the vertical beam of an outer marker beacon and receives corresponding signals, while at the airport boundary further distinctive signals are received on crossing the radio beam of the inner marker beacon.*

forward. The reflector was rotated in circles of first increasing and then decreasing radius, so that the beam traced and then retraced a spiral in the sky. This system, in conjunction with a radial time base, enabled the target to be located as in the case of the CHL stations.

The foregoing account of radar development has been concerned with the echoes of radio signals when reflected from aircraft. Such echoes, however, could be caused by objects other than airplanes, for example, ships at sea and buildings on the ground.

Although radar was developed during wartime and as a war weapon, it has many possible uses in peacetime. It provides a means of navigation and the avoidance of collisions at sea, in the air and on land. It is particularly useful as an altimeter, which enables an aircraft pilot to determine his height above ground when obliged to land in fog.

In making a "blind" approach to an airfield, i.e. when visibility is zero, the pilot is entirely dependent upon instruments. On approaching the airfield, he is guided by signals from a radio transmitter, called the localizer, so that he flies along the line of the runway. The height of the plane should be kept at about 1500 ft., and when the machine arrives at a distance of about five miles from the airfield, signals are received from a second radio transmitter; the beam from the latter is shaped so that if the pilot loses height at such a rate that the signals remain constant, he will be flying along a "glide path" which will guide him accurately down to the runway, as shown in Fig. 30.

Marker Beacons

To provide the pilot with additional information, two "marker" beacons are also installed; these radiate vertical beams and each provides its own distinctive signal. For example, the outer marker beacon, which is usually situated about two miles from the airfield, may give a low-pitched note in the headphones and cause a lamp to flash slowly. The inner marker beacon, which is usually situated near the boundary of the airfield, would

PATH OF PLANE

1500 FEET

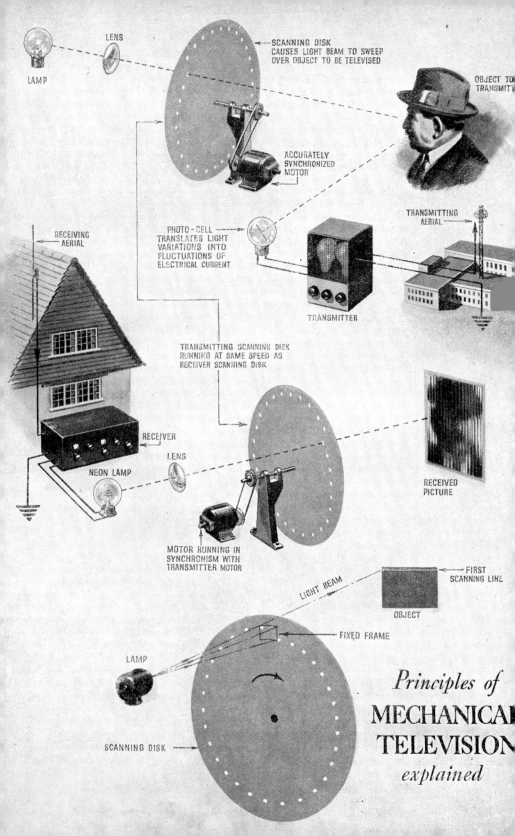

LAMP

LENS

SCANNING DISK
CAUSES LIGHT BEAM TO SWEEP
OVER OBJECT TO BE TELEVISED

OBJECT TO
TRANSMIT

ACCURATELY
SYNCHRONIZED
MOTOR

TRANSMITTING
AERIAL

RECEIVING
AERIAL

PHOTO-CELL
TRANSLATES LIGHT
VARIATIONS INTO
FLUCTUATIONS OF
ELECTRICAL CURRENT

TRANSMITTER

TRANSMITTING SCANNING DISK
RUNNING AT SAME SPEED AS
RECEIVER SCANNING DISK

RECEIVER

LENS

NEON LAMP

RECEIVED
PICTURE

MOTOR RUNNING IN
SYNCHRONISM WITH
TRANSMITTER MOTOR

LIGHT BEAM

FIRST
SCANNING LINE

OBJECT

FIXED FRAME

LAMP

Principles of
MECHANICAL
TELEVISION
explained

SCANNING DISK

produce a distinctive signal such as a high-pitched note in the headphones and a rapid flashing of the lamp.

By maintaining the correct course and keeping the glide-path indicator at a constant reading, the aircraft should touch down correctly on the runway.

Television

One of the most outstanding achievements in the field of radio engineering is the accomplishment of television.

In order to transmit a picture or scene from one place to another by television it is necessary to analyse the picture into a large number of elements, convert the elements into corresponding electrical impulses, transmit these to the receiving end, where they may be reconverted into picture elements and reassembled to form an image of the televised object.

The analysis of the picture is effected by some kind of scanning, the early form of which was performed by means of a rotating disk, as shown in Fig. 31, opposite. In this system, light from a lamp passes through a lens on to a disk which rotates at high speed.

The disk, shown in Fig. 31, has a number of holes arranged in the form of a single-turn spiral; a frame is provided so that light passes through one hole at a time, forming a narrow beam which is swept across the object as the disk rotates. As soon as one horizontal strip of the object has been scanned by one beam, another beam is formed by the next hole, which scans an adjacent strip and so on until the last hole causes the last strip of the object to be scanned, whereupon the whole process is repeated.

As each element of the object is illuminated by the beam, light is reflected on to a photo-electric cell; the latter is a device which is capable of generating an electrical impulse corresponding in magnitude to the light received from the object.

Thus, as the transmitter scanning disk rotates, electrical impulses are generated in the photo-electric cell corresponding in magnitude and sequence to the light and shade of the elements of the object and to the order in which these elements are scanned. These impulses are fed to the transmitter, which in turn is connected to the transmitting aerial. The electromagnetic waves so radiated are picked up by the receiving aerial, in which the small voltages generated are fed to the receiver.

The amplified electrical impulses produced by the latter are supplied to a lamp containing neon or other suitable gas; the light produced by the latter varies with the strength of the signal, i.e. with the light and shade of the object. The light so obtained passes through a lens on to a scanning disk, which is similar to and rotates at exactly the same speed as the transmitter scanning disk.

The light beams from this disk are allowed to fall on a screen, which is thus scanned in exactly the same way as the object. Although only one spot on the screen is illuminated at any time, an eye viewing this screen would see a complete picture, since the impression made by each illuminated spot remains in the eye while the others are being scanned. Therefore, if perfect synchronism between the scanning disks is maintained, a picture is built up which is a fair reproduction of the object being televised. Many modifications, such as the mirror drum, have been introduced into mechanical scanning systems, to improve the definition.

Iconoscope

In the cathode-ray system, a scanning camera is used at the transmitting end. The heart of this is the Iconoscope, shown in Fig. 32 (a); this consists of a cathode-ray tube in which is mounted a signal plate. On one side of the latter is deposited a coating of light-sensitive material; this is in the form of a mosaic of millions of tiny globules of the metal cæsium, each of which constitutes, in effect, a minute photo-electric cell.

In practice, the scene to be televised is focused by means of a lens on to the mosaic side of the signal plate, so that each globule of light-sensitive material is caused to emit electrons, the number of which depends upon the intensity of light falling upon the particular globule. The cathode of the tube emits electrons in the usual way and these are projected by the electron gun to form a beam which falls on the mosaic.

Around the neck of the Iconoscope are two pairs of scanning or deflecting coils, supplied with sawtooth currents derived from a scanning panel external to the camera. A sawtooth current is one which grows uniformly with time, collapses suddenly and then grows again, repeating this cycle indefinitely in such a way that a graph of the current takes the form of a sawtooth. Such a current is generated by a linear time base, an elementary type of which has already been considered.

Two such time bases are employed; the current from one of them causes the scanning beam to move from left to right across the mosaic about 10,000 times every second, while the current from the other causes the beam to move from top to bottom across the mosaic at fifty times every second. The combined action produces the effect shown in Fig. 32 (b).

Main Principles of Scanning

The scanning spot commences at, say, *A* and moves uniformly along the line *AB* in a small fraction of a second; at *B* it moves almost instantaneously back to *C* and then traverses the lines *CD*, and so on. When about two hundred of these lines have been so traversed, the scanning spot approaches

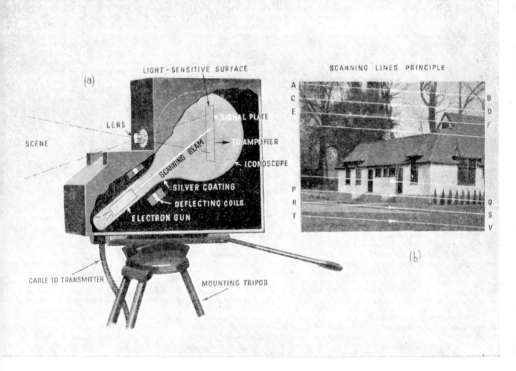

HOW A TELEVISION CAMERA WORKS

FIG. 32. *(a) Television camera is shown in detail. The scene to be televised is focused by a lens on to a light-sensitive mosaic formed on the signal plate; the deflecting coils around the neck of the Iconoscope cause the scanning beam of electrons to traverse the image, thus releasing electrical impulses which are fed to an amplifier and then to the transmitter. (b) The scanning process. The scene to be televised is scanned line by line in sequence until the last line* TV *is reached, when the whole operation is repeated.*

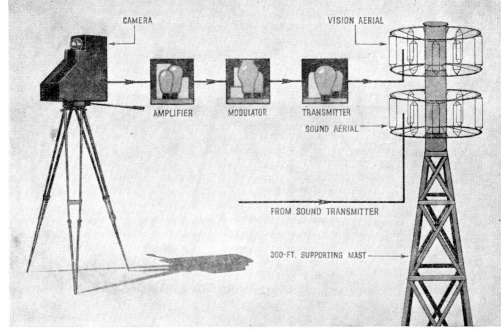

SIMPLIFIED REPRESENTATION OF A TELEVISION TRANSMITTER

FIG. 33. *Scene to be televised is focused by the camera lens on to the light-sensitive mosaic of the Iconoscope. As the scanning beam sweeps over the mosaic, electrical impulses corresponding to the light and shade of the picture are passed to an amplifier from which they are caused to modulate the carrier wave. From the transmitter the modulated signal is passed to the vision aerial; a separate aerial is used to radiate the sound waves.*

the bottom of the mosaic, following the lines *PQ*, *RS* and *TV*. The beam is then returned rapidly to *A*, whereupon the whole procedure is repeated fifty times every second. In practice, a modification of this system, known as interlaced scanning, is adopted. This does not, however, affect the main principles just described.

Amplifying the Electrical Impulses

As the scanning beam sweeps over the mosaic, electrical impulses are sent from the signal plate to an amplifier and ultimately to the transmitter, so that signals can be radiated which are electrical representations of the light and shade of the scene to be transmitted. At the same time, electrical impulses corresponding to the sounds which accompany the televised scene are transmitted along separate channels and eventually fed to the transmitting aerial.

At Alexandra Palace the sound and vision aerials are mounted at the top of a 300-ft. mast; the general layout, excluding that relating to the sound channels which is similar to that in a normal sound broadcast system, is shown in Fig. 33.

Reception Aerial

Turning now to the cathode-ray television receiver, both the "vision" signals and the "sound" signals are received on a single aerial, which usually consists of a vertical rod, about 10 ft. 6 in. long, connected at its centre to the feeder which joins it to the receiver. Such an aerial is called a dipole and is shown in Fig. 34. Both signals are passed through the sound and vision amplifier, where amplification takes place first at radio frequency and then at the intermediate frequency. Since the frequency of the local oscillator is about 42 Mc/s and the sound and vision signal frequencies are 41·5 and 45 Mc/s, the corresponding intermediate frequencies are

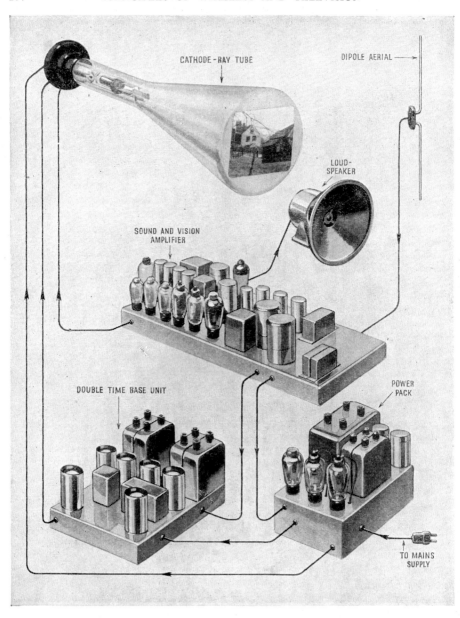

PICTORIAL REPRESENTATION OF A TELEVISION RECEIVER

FIG. 34. *In this illustration is shown the arrangement of the main units in a cathode-ray television receiver. Note the dipole aerial, upon which both vision and sound signals are received. Power pack provides the supplies for the cathode-ray tube, the double time base unit and the sound and vision amplifier. Output signals from the amplifier operate the loudspeaker and control the light and shade of the picture. The double time base unit provides impulses which deflect the beam, causing it to scan the screen of the tube.*

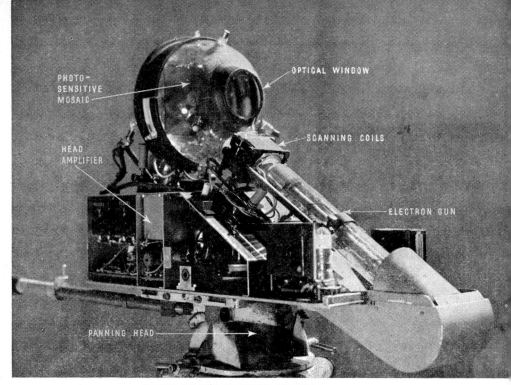

EMITRON TELEVISION CAMERA

This shows one type of camera used in British television. It operates on the same principles as the Iconoscope illustrated in Fig. 32 on page 262.

approximately 0·5 and 3 Mc/s respectively. The sound signal is then passed to the detector, audio-frequency amplifier and loudspeaker in the usual manner.

Separating the Signals

The vision signal and the synchronizing signals, which will be referred to later, are passed through the vision intermediate-frequency amplifier to the detector, after which the synchronizing signals are separated from the picture signals. The latter are transmitted to the controlling electrode of the cathode-ray tube, where they cause the brightness of the ray to be varied in accordance with the light and shade of the scene to be televised.

The cathode-ray tube in a television receiver is similar to that already described, but may vary in size from about 5 in. screen diameter to about 16 in., depending upon the size of the receiver. Deflection by coils around the neck of the tube is usually preferred to electrostatic deflection.

The tube may be mounted horizontally in

the receiver, in which case the picture is seen by viewing directly the end of the tube, or it may be mounted vertically with the screen uppermost; in the latter case, the picture is seen in a mirror arranged in the receiver lid to be above and inclined at an angle to the screen of the tube.

It will be appreciated that, to form a picture on the screen of the receiving tube, the cathode ray of the latter must scan the receiving screen in exactly the same way as the mosaic in the Iconoscope is scanned. This involves two time bases in the television receiver, one of which is a low-frequency time base for scanning the frame of the picture and the other a high-frequency time base for line scanning.

Scanning Must be in Step

The scanning of the receiver tube must be performed not only at the exact speed of scanning in the Iconoscope, but it must also be in step or in synchronism with the latter. In this way, the screen is scanned line by line and picture by picture in step with the scanning of the scene to be televised. This is achieved by the transmission of locking or synchronizing signals from the transmitter at the end of each line and at the end of each picture frame. This signal is received and filtered out by the receiver and is used to keep the time bases in perfect step.

The whole process is illustrated in Fig. 35, where it is seen that both vision and sound signals pass from the dipole to the radio-frequency amplifier and frequency changer, after which they are separated and flow along the vision and sound channels respectively. The vision signals, after detection, consist of picture frequency signals and synchronizing impulses; the former are fed to the control electrode of the cathode-ray tube, where they control the brightness of the spot in whatever position it happens to be; this position is determined by the two time bases, which are controlled by the synchronizing impulses.

Uniformity of Spot Movement

The high-frequency time base or line generator causes the spot to move uniformly from left to right across the screen, returning rapidly to the left to scan similarly the next line down and so on until the bottom of the picture is reached; it is then returned rapidly to the top left of the picture by the fly-back of the low-frequency time base or frame generator, whereupon the whole process is repeated. Fig. 36 (a) shows the arrangement of the components

PROGRESS OF THE SIGNALS

FIG. 35. *In a television receiver, the "vision" and "sound" signals are received on a dipole aerial and pass through a radio-frequency amplifier and frequency changer, at the output of which the signals divide. The sound signal passes along its channel to the loudspeaker as in a normal super-heterodyne receiver. The vision signal is amplified at its intermediate frequency, is detected and then consists of picture-frequency signals and synchronizing*

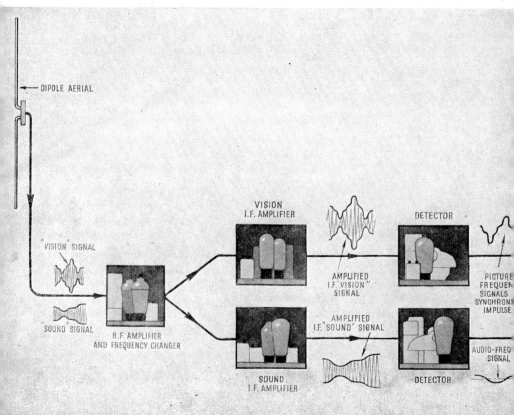

DIPOLE AERIAL

VISION SIGNAL

SOUND SIGNAL

R.F. AMPLIFIER
AND FREQUENCY CHANGER

VISION
I.F. AMPLIFIER

AMPLIFIED
I.F. "VISION"
SIGNAL

AMPLIFIED
I.F. "SOUND" SIGNAL

SOUND
I.F. AMPLIFIER

DETECTOR

DETECTOR

PICTURE
FREQUEN
SIGNALS
SYNCHRON
IMPULSE

AUDIO-FREQ
SIGNAL

in a typical television receiver employing a horizontally disposed tube, while Fig. 36 (b) illustrates the method of viewing the picture in a receiver which has a vertical tube.

One of the disadvantages of the cathode-ray system of television reception is the relatively low luminous output obtained. An optical system, invented and developed by Scophony Ltd., enables bright black and white pictures to be produced on a screen 24 in. wide by 20 in. high, for home reception, while pictures measuring 6 ft. by 5 ft. are possible for use in small cinemas.

In this system, light is derived from a high-pressure mercury lamp which is claimed to be the most efficient and brilliant source known. This is focused by means of

a lens on to a device known as the light control, which consists of a container, filled with a liquid, at one end of which is a quartz crystal. The container has on either side of it a lens so that light can be passed through the container in a direction transverse to that of the waves set up in the liquid. Light emerging from this unit passes through another lens on to a high-speed scanner; the latter is a stainless steel polygon rotated at a speed of 30,375 revolutions per minute by a motor which consists of two separate sections built in one case. One section is an asynchronous motor, used to run quickly up to the required speed, while the other is a synchronous motor to which are fed the amplified synchronizing signals; the function of the high-speed scanner is to

THROUGH A TELEVISION RECEIVER

impulses. The combined signal is fed to the control electrode of the cathode-ray tube, where it suppresses the beam during the fly-back period, and controls the brightness of the spot to provide the light and shade of the picture. Synchronizing impulses are filtered in the impulse separator and used to control two time bases, so that the spot scans the receiver screen in exact synchronism with the transmitter scanning, thus reproducing the picture.

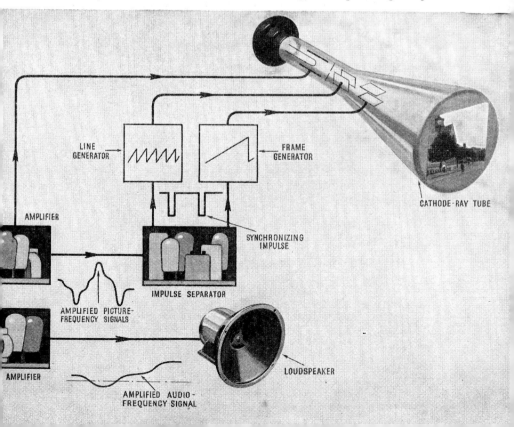

LINE GENERATOR

FRAME GENERATOR

CATHODE-RAY TUBE

AMPLIFIER

SYNCHRONIZING IMPULSE

IMPULSE SEPARATOR

AMPLIFIED PICTURE-FREQUENCY SIGNALS

LOUDSPEAKER

AMPLIFIER

AMPLIFIED AUDIO-FREQUENCY SIGNAL

produce the line scanning of the picture.

Light then passes through another lens on to the low-speed scanner and thence through a projection lens on to the 2-ft. screen. The low-speed scanner produces the frame scan and thus governs the picture repetition frequency; it is provided with twelve mirrors and is driven by means of a synchronous motor running at 1500 revolutions per minute, geared down to a final speed of 250 revolutions per minute. The alternating current required to drive the motor is produced by amplifying the frame synchronizing pulse obtained from the vision radio receiver.

Russia's National System

The output of the main vision receiver is fed through a low-impedance output valve and co-axial cable to the light control drive unit, which consists of a video amplifier and R.F. amplifier. The R.F. amplifier valve is connected to the quartz crystal on the light control and is grid modulated by

the video amplifier. This system has been adopted as the national television system in Russia.

The idea of transmitting pictures or scenes in colour is almost as old as the conception of television itself. Apart from the artistic appeal made by such a rendering, the presence of colour imparts a greater sense of reality to the picture, small objects seem more perceptible, outlines in general are more clearly defined and a certain impression of depth is obtained.

The three primary colours of light are red, green and blue: these are the component colours of white light and the colour of any part of an object or scene may be reproduced by a correct combination of these three colours. This fact is the basis of all colour reproduction, though the processes involved may be simplified by the use of two complementary colours such as red-orange and blue-green.

In an early method, the simple scanning disk used for monochrome television was

TWO METHODS OF MOUNTING THE CATHODE-RAY TUBE

FIG. 36. *(a) The cathode-ray tube of this television receiver is mounted horizontally so that the picture is seen by viewing directly the screen of the tube. (b) Tube mounted vertically, the picture being seen in an inclined mirror contained in the receiver lid.*

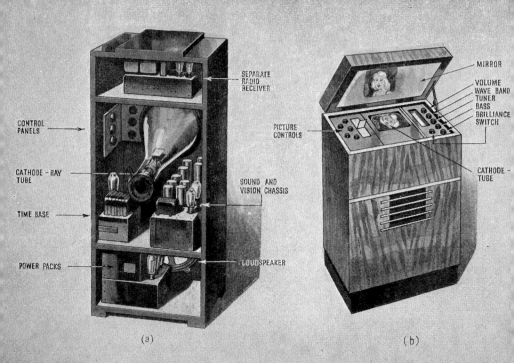

(a)   (b)

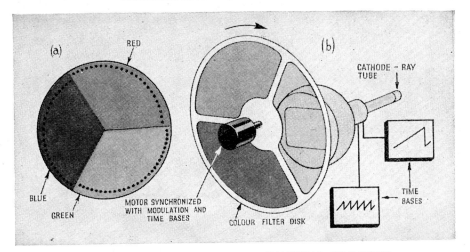

COLOUR FILTERS USED IN MECHANICAL SCANNING

FIG. 37. *(a) Triple spiral disk in which three sets of perforations are covered with red, green, and blue filters, for use in colour television by mechanical scanning. (b) Colour reception in an electronic scanning system in which receiving tube is viewed through a colour filter disk rotated in synchronism with a corresponding disk at the transmitter.*

replaced by a triple spiral disk in which the three sets of perforations were covered with red, green and blue filters respectively, as shown in Fig. 37. Thus, considering the action at the transmitter, the object is scanned first by a red beam of light, then by a green beam and subsequently by a blue beam, whereupon the process is repeated.

Colour Reproduction

Now, a red portion of the object appears to be so coloured because it reflects red light; therefore, when an object of this colour, say a red dress, is being scanned by the red beam, considerable reflection takes place and the photo-cells generate a relatively large voltage; when, however, the red dress is scanned by a green beam, no light is reflected and the photo-cell voltage is zero during this period, though reflection again occurs when the green beam passes over grass or any green-coloured object. Similarly for the blue scanning process.

When a portion of the object contains a combination of two or more of the primary colours, then some reflection takes place during the scanning by each colour and

corresponding voltages are generated. These voltages are passed to the amplifier and transmitter in the usual way.

At the receiver, a scanning disk precisely similar and rotating in exact synchronism with that at the transmitter is used and arrangements are made to provide red, green and blue illumination as the corresponding impulses are received.

The impression made on the eye of the observer results in the formation of a picture in colours which resemble those of the object.

The next step in the evolution of colour television was to replace the scanning disks by devices employing electronic scanning. The transmitter then employed consisted of a cathode-ray tube, the moving spot of which was projected by means of a lens on to the scene to be transmitted. Between the tube and the lens was interposed a disk with red, blue, and green filters, while photo-electric cells with a colour response approximating to that of the human eye were employed to receive the reflected light.

At the receiver, the picture was reproduced on the end of a cathode-ray tube; this could either be projected on to a screen

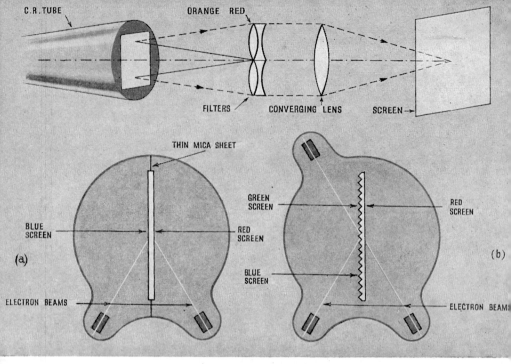

TELEVISION RECEPTION IN TWO AND THREE COLOURS

Fig. 38. *In the two-colour system, two images, one corresponding to the orange-red and the other to the blue-green, are formed in sequence, one above the other, on the receiving cathode-ray tube. Light rays from these images pass through a pair of light filters and a system of lenses, which cause the corresponding images to be superimposed on the receiving screen. (a) Double-screen cathode-ray tube for colour television on the two-colour system. (b) Tube designed for television reception in three colours.*

through a colour disk run in synchronism with the disk at the transmitter, or be viewed directly through a colour filter disk as shown in Fig. 37.

In the experimental colour television systems already described, the projection of successive colour frames were dependent upon the employment of rotating disks carrying colour filters and interposed between the reproduced picture and the observer. In a recent system, the filter disk is no longer used, so that moving parts are completely eliminated.

Forming Separate Images

The apparatus, which is shown diagrammatically in Fig. 38, employs the principle of forming separate images on a cathode-ray tube and combining them on a viewing screen. On the screen of the receiving cathode-ray tube, three images are formed, corresponding to the three primary

colours, red, green and blue; if the two-colour system is used, two images are formed corresponding to the blue-green and orange-red combinations.

In Sequence on the Screen

These images are formed one above the other in sequence on the fluorescent screen; a system of lenses, three if the three-colour system is employed and two for the two-colour, is arranged with the optical centres on perpendiculars, through the centres of each of the images and at a distance from them equal to the focal length of the lenses. In this way, parallel beams are projected on to a large converging lens spaced from the receiving screen by a distance equal to its focal length, so that the images are caused to overlap on the screen producing the final pictures in approximately true colours.

A still later method is entirely electronic

in action, but the colour image appears directly upon the fluorescent screen of the cathode-ray tube. The latter is of special construction and has two separate beams in the two-colour system and three in the three-colour. These beams are modulated by the incoming signals corresponding to the primary colour picture and impinge upon superimposed screens coated with fluorescent powders of the appropriate colours.

In the two-colour system, the two cathode-ray beams scan the opposite sides of a thin plate of transparent mica, one side of which has been coated with orange-red fluorescent powder and the other with blue-green fluorescent powder. In this way the screen has formed on its front face an image containing the orange-red colour components and on its back face an image containing the blue-green components; the combined images reproduce the picture in natural colours. Such a tube is shown in Fig. 38 (a).

Third Cathode-ray Beam

For use with the three-colour system, one side of the screen is ridged as shown in Fig. 38 (b) and a third cathode-ray beam is added. The front face of the screen then gives the red component, one side of the ridges on the reverse side gives the green component, while the other ridge gives the blue component. The tubes described give a very bright picture due to the absence of colour filters and to the fact that special powders are used to give only the desired colours which are seen in combination.

Test Yourself

1. What causes electrons to flow from the cathode to the anode of a diode? Explain the meaning of the term "saturation."
2. A broadcasting station transmits on a wavelength of 150 metres. To what frequency does this correspond?
3. Explain the purpose of a rectifying valve in a radio receiver and distinguish between half-wave and full-wave rectification.
4. What is meant by a tuned-anode amplifier? In what type of circuit is it used?
5. Give a definition of the term "demodulation" and enumerate three systems of "demodulation" used in practice.
6. What is understood by a multiple valve? Give examples of such valves used in modern radio receivers.
7. Describe the essential features and action of a microphone of the ribbon type.
8. Explain the action of a frequency changer in a super-heterodyne receiver and point out the advantages obtained by using such a device.
9. Write a brief description of the construction and action of a modern loudspeaker.
10. Why are the signals received in an aerial subject to fading and how are the corresponding fluctuations in receiver output minimized?
11. If the upper horizontal plate of a cathode-ray tube is made positive with respect to the anode and the left-hand vertical plate is made equally negative, in what direction is the fluorescent spot deflected?
12. By what process is the scanning of the picture in a television receiver maintained in step with the scanning of the scene to be televised?
13. Explain the basic principle of colour television.
14. What is the purpose of a beam station? In what way does such a station differ from a broadcasting station?

Answers will be found at the end of the book.

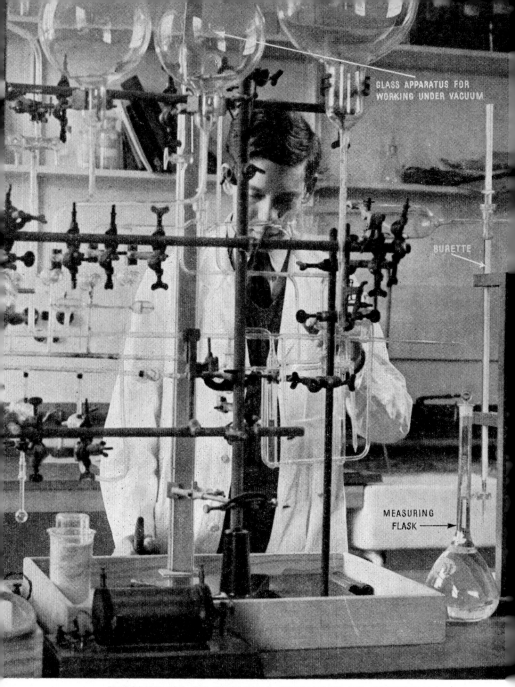

GLASS APPARATUS FOR
WORKING UNDER VACUUM

BURETTE

MEASURING
FLASK

IMPORTANCE OF CHEMICAL RESEARCH TO INDUSTRY
Throughout the world every large manufacturing concern has its own laboratories in which highly-trained professional chemists grapple daily with important production problems. Without chemistry, an industrial nation could never progress or prosper. The future is, indeed, for weal or for woe, based on the application of chemical science and on the results of its continual research. Here is a picture taken in one of these industrial "labs."

CHAPTER XIII

OUTLINES OF CHEMISTRY

MAN is an inquisitive being. From the remotest antiquity he has tried to discover the nature and composition of the stuff of which he himself, plants, animals, birds, fishes, the earth, the air, the sea and, indeed, the whole universe is made. The study of matter, the changes which may take place when two or more kinds of matter are brought into contact with one another, the mechanism of the living process, all fall within the ambit of Chemistry.

Therefore, the scope of chemistry is so extremely wide that it constitutes a considerable part of our rudimentary knowledge of Nature. Dealing, as it does, with the substance of which everything is made, whether it be brought into position with the aid of life or by the forces of nature or by the skill and labour of man, the accumulated knowledge is so vast that purely for the sake of convenience it has been found necessary to divide the subject into several sections.

Formerly, it was thought erroneously that one type of matter was involved in the living processes and another was the stuff of which the inanimate objects such as the earth and the sea are made. That branch of the subject which in any way was connected with life was designated *Organic Chemistry*, and that with dead matter *Inorganic Chemistry*.

Moreover, it used to be thought that matter containing the element *carbon*, i.e. charcoal in its purest form, when in chemical combination with other elements, particularly oxygen, hydrogen and nitrogen, could be formed only in the living organism such as the body of man or animals or the plant or the tree, and so organic chemistry became chiefly the chemistry of carbon compounds.

Numerous carbon compounds have since been prepared which have not and could not have the slightest connexion with any living process. Furthermore, many carbon compounds that are formed in the animal body, some of which are excreted in urine, can be prepared without the aid of any living agency whatsoever.

Thus Wöhler, in 1828, found that urea, a compound consisting of atoms of carbon, oxygen, hydrogen and nitrogen, which is formed in the animal body and can be isolated from urine in the form of white crystals, is gradually formed when another totally different compound, ammonium cyanate, prepared in the chemical laboratory, is dissolved in water and allowed to stand.

Urea is now manufactured synthetically from air, water and coke. It is used in the manufacture of certain types of plastics and as a valuable fertilizer to supply the growing plant with essential nitrogenous matter. Thus we see that a chemical compound, which is made in the body of living beings, can also be prepared by methods that are in no way connected with the mechanism of living.

On the other hand, there exist many carbon compounds that, hitherto, have been made only in laboratories and factories; many being detrimental to life.

Two Divisions of Chemistry

The term *organic chemistry* nowadays refers to "the chemistry *of the carbon compounds*," irrespective of the way they are formed. It would have been better if the term "organic" had been dropped; yet, though it is a misnomer, it misleads no chemist. *Inorganic chemistry* is that branch which deals with all other matter. Perhaps a more appropriate name would have been "mineral chemistry," as much of the matter classified under inorganic chemistry is of mineral origin.

Both inorganic and organic chemistry are concerned with the synthesis (chemical building) of compounds, and conversely with the disruption and analysis of large compounds and mixtures. Within the last

Modern Chemist

SOME IMPORTANT DATES IN THE DEVELOPMENT OF CHEMISTRY

Alchemist

A.D. 1900 —

Modern Chemistry established and developed.

1800 — Priestley discovered Oxygen; Cavendish, Scheele, Lavoisier.

Boyle—the Founder of Modern Chemistry.

1600 — Van Helmont—Medical or Iatro Chemistry. Search for "Elixir of Life."

Paracelsus ⎫ Period of Alchemy.

1400 — Basil Valentine ⎬ Transmutation of Base Metals

1200 — Roger Bacon discovered Gunpowder ⎭ into Gold—Philosophers' Stone.

· Albertus Magnus wrote Treatise in Latin on Alchemy.

1000 —

800 — Jabir Ibn Hayyan, or Geber (Bagdad), wrote Treatise on Alchemy.

Muslim Empire extended to Spain. Spread of Alchemy.

600 — Arabs conquered Egypt; became students of *Chemeia;* wrote books on subject of *Alchemy.*

400 —

— Emperor Diocletian ordered books on *Chemeia* to be burnt in Alexandria.

200 — First Books on *Chemeia* (The Divine Art), written by Greeks in Alexandria.

Gold Amalgam (Gold dissolved in Mercury). Art of Gilding baser metals (Romans).

— Brass (alloy of Copper and Zinc) used in Roman Coinage.

1000 B.C. —

— Large-scale Manufacture of Glass at Tel el Amarna.

2000 B.C. — Pottery, Glaze, Glass; Vegetable Dyes, Medicines, Poisons. (Egypt.)

Zinc used in Chinese Bronzes.

3000 B.C. — Alloys first made, e.g. Bronze (Copper and Tin). (Egypt.)

3500 B.C. — Metals: Gold, Copper, Silver, Lead, Iron, Tin were isolated from their minerals and used. (Egypt.)

Brass used in Roman Coinage

Ancient Pottery (Egypt)

Metal Replaces Flint

Working on Gold Vase (Egypt)

hundred years, and especially since the beginning of the present century, a further branch, physical chemistry, has been developed and, as the name implies, it consists of the application of the principles and methods of physics to the study of chemical compounds.

Physical Chemistry

Its introduction has added materially to our knowledge of the cause of chemical processes, and the impact of physics on chemistry has resulted in many spectacular advances in our chemical knowledge which, in turn, have been exploited and thus have led to the introduction of important new industries and products, for example, the synthetic production of ammonia and nitrogenous fertilizers from air and water, the manufacture of plastics, artificial rubber, etc. Strictly speaking, physical chemistry is not a distinct section of chemistry. It permeates inorganic and organic chemistry. As might be expected, physico-chemical principles and methods play an important role in analytical chemistry.

Within the last fifty years, chemists engaged in investigating the chemical substances formed in the living body or plant and, indeed, the very substances of which the body or plant is made, have classified their knowledge under the heading *Biochemistry*. As living material is composed of certain carbon compounds, which fall within the province of organic chemistry, and of mineral matter, which belongs to inorganic chemistry, it will be appreciated that biochemistry is applied chemistry and is a composite subject of physical, organic and inorganic chemistry.

Closely allied biological subjects are Physiology, which relates principally to the body in health, and Pathology, to the body in disease. Because of the progress of fundamental chemistry, biochemistry has also made important strides, and these have been transmitted to physiology and pathology and thus to medicine in general.

The structure of matter in the physical sense was discussed in Chapter IV and a brief introduction to radioactivity given.

Now, there are three series of radioactive elements: the actinium series, the thorium series and the uranium series. As shown in Fig. 1, one element is changed into another by the loss from the nucleus of the atom of an alpha- or a beta-particle.

The diagram gives a pictorial representation of the nuclear changes that occur in the main course of the successive disintegration of an atom of uranium I through the many nuclei until, finally, non-radioactive lead is formed. The numbers enclosed in rectangles refer to the relative weights of the nuclei. The atomic number, i.e. the number of unit positive charges, is given on the right (top). The lower equal numbers refer to the positive and negative charges, which have coalesced to produce the same number of neutrons. This is indicated by the right-hand bracket and the letter n.

As the proton and neutron have masses each roughly equal to unity, taking that of an oxygen atom as 16, we see in the case of uranium I that the weight contributed by 92 protons and 146 neutrons is $92+146 = 238$. As each atom of uranium I loses one α-particle from its nucleus during its transformation into uranium X_1, and as the α-particle is composed of 2 protons and 2 neutrons, the weight of which is $2+2=4$, it follows that the uranium X_1 nucleus must contain $92 - 2 = 90$ protons and $146 - 2 = 144$ neutrons, which together weigh $238 - 4 = 234$.

Loss of an Alpha-particle

In effect, *the loss of an α-particle leads to a diminution of two in the atomic number and a loss of 4 units of weight.* On the other hand, *the loss of a β-particle, i.e. an electron, from the nucleus, causes an increase of 1 in the atomic number, but an almost imperceptible change in atomic weight.* This will be understood by the conversion of uranium X_1 into uranium X_2. To eject an electron from the nucleus, a neutron must be disrupted, leaving behind a proton which gives an increase of one in the number of positive nuclear charges.

Thus, *one* of the 144 neutrons in uranium X_1 breaks down to give the negative charge that is ejected; hence, the total number of positive charges becomes $90+1=91$, and

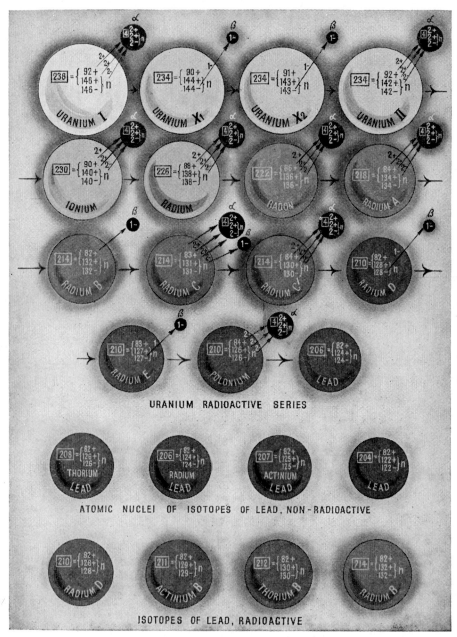

NUCLEAR DISINTEGRATIONS

FIG. 1. *Radioactive disintegration of the nucleus of an atom and how the weight of the atom depends on the weight of unit positive charges and neutrons. Lower part of the picture shows the nuclei of lead atoms which are no longer radioactive, comparing them with lead isotopes that are radioactive, these being stages in the disintegration of radioactive elements.*

the nuclear weight remains at 234=91+ 143. Occasionally gamma- or X-rays accompany the emission of charged particles, but, obviously, they can have no effect on either the atomic number or the atomic weight.

Lead in Two Forms

The last member of each of the radioactive series, actinium, uranium and

Lead derived from the disintegration of thorium has an atomic weight of 208, whilst that from actinium is 207. To account for this apparent anomaly, Soddy, in 1910, suggested that ordinary lead may be a mixture of atoms of all three types of lead in such a proportion as to give the experimentally determined atomic weight.

To these different atoms which have the

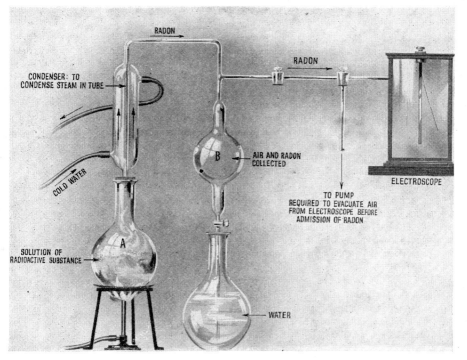

METHOD OF ESTIMATING THE RADIUM IN A RADIOACTIVE SUBSTANCE

FIG. 2. *This method is based on the fact that in a given time an exceedingly small but definite proportion of the radium will have become the gas radon (or niton), which is then driven out of solution in A by boiling and collected in B. This gas, when passed into the evacuated electroscope, previously charged, will cause it to be discharged at a definite rate. By calibrating the apparatus with a radioactive body of known percentage content of radium, it is possible to compute the percentage of radium in the sample.*

thorium, is a non-radioactive element of atomic number 82, which, as far as its chemical properties are concerned, is identical with ordinary lead. But the atomic weight of lead, as determined by chemical methods, is 207·22, whereas the atomic weight of the lead derived from uranium I, via radium, is precisely 206.

same atomic number, but *different atomic weights,* he gave the name of *isotopes.* The word isotope is derived from two Greek words meaning "equal" and "place"; since isotopic elements occupy the same place in what is known as the Periodic Classification. We now have conclusive evidence that nearly all of the so-called elements are mixtures of isotopes, the sole characterizing features of elements being their atomic numbers. Determinations of the atomic weight of lead extracted from different radioactive minerals have, indeed, revealed differences.

Radium in Uranium

Owing to the radioactive changes that are always proceeding at definite rates inside a mineral, it is not surprising that the proportion of the amount of radium to that of its parent, uranium, in the many uranium minerals of comparable geological age, is remarkably constant, viz., 1 part of radium to every 3,000,000 parts of uranium. This means that in order to obtain 1 lb. of radium from a good uranium mineral containing about, say, 40 per cent of uranium, no less than 3000 tons of ore must be worked.

Fortunately, the radioactivity of radium, and particularly that of the gas, radon (niton, or radium emanation, as it is variously called), into which it immediately begins to degenerate, serves as a ready method not only for the detection of the presence of radium, but also for the estimation of the quantity existing in a mixture.

To do this, the uranium-radium mixture is brought into solution, allowed to stand for some suitable time so as to allow some radon to be generated. Then the gaseous radon is driven out of solution by boiling, and the gas led into a previously evacuated vessel containing a charged gold-leaf electroscope. From the rate at which the gold leaf falls, the percentage of radium originally in the mixture can be calculated (Fig. 2).

As shown in Fig. 1, the transformation of an atom of uranium into one of lead involves the loss of eight α-particles. Eventually, they acquire from the surroundings the sixteen electrons that are required to convert them into eight atoms of gaseous helium (Fig. 3). Helium results from radioactive disintegration. The constancy of the amount of helium in the air (0·00014 per cent by volume) is due to the radioactive disintegrations that are occurring in the crust of the earth. The existence of helium, sometimes to the extent of 1 per cent, with hydrocarbons in the "natural gas" found in the earth's crust in the U.S.A., must also be attributed to radioactivity.

In the case of radioactive minerals of comparable age that have become her-

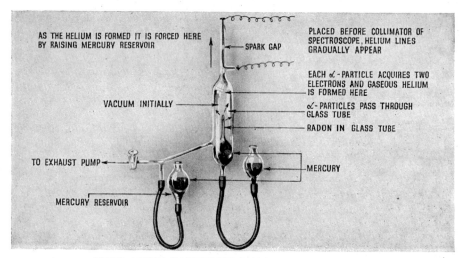

HOW ALPHA-PARTICLES BECOME HELIUM GAS

Fig. 3. *Rutherford and Royds' experiment showing the birth of helium gas by union of alpha-particles with electrons. The gradual production of the characteristic spectrum lines of helium as seen through a spectroscope proves that helium is actually formed.*

CHEMISTS OF THE FUTURE

This picture shows students under training in analytical chemistry in one of the Washington Singer Laboratories of the University College of the South-West, at Exeter.

metically sealed within the earth's crust, it is found that the amount of the radioactive progenitor, e.g. uranium, bears a definite ratio to the amount of helium liberated down through the ages and which is still enclosed by the mineral. By calculations based on this ratio it is possible to determine the age of the rock.

Calculating a Mineral's Age

Similarly, the precise ratio of the amounts of uranium to lead in radioactive minerals, in conjunction with a knowledge of the rate at which the complete disintegration occurs, makes it possible to calculate the age of the mineral. The table below gives some

AGES OF ROCKS AND MINERALS

Geological Period of Mineral	Weight of Lead / Weight of Uranium	Computed Age (years)
Pre-Cambrian (Sweden) ..	0·125	1,025,000,000
	0·155	1,270,000,000
Devonian ..	0·045	370,000,000
Carboniferous	0·041	340,000,000

computed ages of rocks from the analysis of the radioactive minerals contained therein.

Besides emitting α-, β- and γ-rays, radioactive bodies evolve much energy in the form of heat. Thus, radium develops enough heat to raise its own weight of water from freezing point to boiling point every hour.

Someone has calculated that, as a gram of radium will continue to be appreciably radioactive for 2500 years, it will during its life produce the same amount of heat as would be obtained by burning nine-tenths of a ton of coal.

Radium and Heat Energy

Expressed somewhat differently, radium furnishes 250,000 times as much heat energy as is evolved by the combustion of an equal weight of coal. Energy is also emitted in the form of light, whilst the invisible radiations emitted by radium will cause substances, particularly diamonds, to be luminous in the dark.

In one year, one gram of radium emits 1,170,000,000,000,000,000 α-particles (i.e. $1·17 \times 10^{18}$), and, after absorbing electrons,

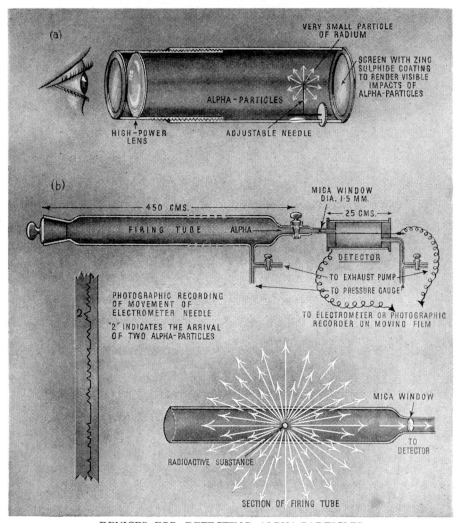

DEVICES FOR DETECTING ALPHA-PARTICLES

Fig. 4. *Two experiments which prove that, in disintegrating, radioactive substances do actually eject alpha-particles. (a) Illustrating Sir William Crookes's Spinthariscope. Every time an alpha-particle hits the zinc sulphide screen, the point of impact is momentarily rendered luminous. (b) Rutherford and Geiger's Counter. When an alpha-particle passes into the detecting chamber, the electrometer needle is momentarily deflected. From a knowledge of the area of the mica window, through which the alpha-particle must pass, the distance of the radioactive body from the window, and the number of "kicks" of the needle, it is possible to calculate the number of alpha-particles emitted in a given time.*

the resulting helium gas will occupy 0·043 cubic centimetres. We know that 4 grams (i.e. the molecular weight expressed in grams) of helium occupy 22,400 cubic centimetres when the temperature is 0 deg. C. and the pressure is equal to that of the atmosphere (= 76 centimetres of mercury). As each α-particle ultimately becomes a

one-atom molecule of helium, we have:
Number of helium molecules in
0.043 c.c. $= 1.17 \times 10^{18}$
$\therefore$ Number of helium molecules in
$22,400$ c.c. $= \frac{22,400 \times 1.17 \times 10^{18}}{0.043}$
$= 6 \times 10^{23}$ approx.

From the half-life period of radium (1590 years, i.e. the time taken for one half of a given quantity of radium to disintegrate) and the rate of decay given above, calculation shows that 1 gram of radium consists of 2.67×10^{21} radium atoms, whence it follows that 226 grams of solid radium (i.e. the gram-atom or the atomic weight expressed in grams) is made up of $2.67 \times 10^{21} \times 226 = 6 \times 10^{23}$ atoms.

The number, 6×10^{23}, or, according to recent work, 6.02×10^{23}, being the actual number of molecules, or atoms, which make up 1 gram-molecule, or gram-atom, respectively, of an element, in either the gaseous or solid form, is known as the *Avogadro Number*.

Fig. 4 illustrates two types of apparatus which have been used to investigate the discharge of α-particles. In (a), Crookes's Spinthariscope, an exceedingly small piece of a radium salt is attached to the end of a needle placed at a suitable distance from a screen covered with a zinc sulphide preparation. When viewed through a high-powered microscope, each impact of an α-particle with the screen will be indicated by a fluorescent scintillation.

Counting Alpha-particles

In the Rutherford and Geiger method of counting the number of α-particles emitted in a given time, the radioactive body is fixed in a long tube (firing tube) at a known distance from a mica window of known dimensions, which is placed immediately before a detecting chamber. Both firing tube and detecting chamber are almost evacuated, so as not to impede the motion of the charged particles by collision with molecules of air.

As shown in Fig. 4 (b), the α-particles are discharged equally in all directions, so that it can easily be calculated what fraction of the total emitted in a given time will pass through the mica window into the detecting chamber. The arrival of an α-particle causes a "throw" of the electrometer needle. The succession of "throws" can be recorded photographically. The "2" represents a pulse of twice the amplitude of the other pulses and signifies the simultaneous passage of two α-particles through the mica window into the detecting chamber.

So far as the radioactive elements are concerned, it can now be understood why lead is found with them in their minerals. On the other hand, the reason why similar *non*-radioactive metals frequently occur together is not so obvious. It is possible that they, too, are the products of radioactive transmutations.

Looking at the elements from the standpoint of their relative atomic weights, W. Prout, in 1815, was so struck by the fact that so many of the atomic weights were nearly exact multiples of that of hydrogen that he was led to believe that all elements must have been formed from atoms of hydrogen. Despite numerous atomic weight determinations, there still remained, as Strutt remarked at the beginning of this century, more elements having atomic weights that are almost whole numbers than could be considered fortuitous on the basis of the laws of chance.

Arising out of some work by Sir J. J. Thomson (1910-12), on the effect of magnetic and electrostatic fields on the passage of positive rays through certain gases, Aston elaborated the apparatus known as the Mass Spectrograph (Fig. 5), in which beams of particles with electric charges acquired from the positive rays are focused on a photographic plate. The apparatus can be calibrated so that the weights of the charged atoms can be calculated from the positions where they strike the photographic plate.

When gases had to be used, they were admitted at low pressure into the apparatus, but in order to investigate solids, the apparatus was so modified that it was only necessary to coat the anode with a suitable salt mixture of the element in question. The mass spectrograph, and other methods, have shown conclusively that the majority of non-radioactive elements are, indeed, mixtures of isotopes that have atomic weights which are whole numbers, and which in the case of any one element differ from one another by small numbers of units. The following table records a few examples:

ISOTOPES OF SOME NON-RADIOACTIVE ELEMENTS

	Atomic Weight	Atomic Number	Isotopes— Atomic Weights in Order of Abundance
Hydrogen	1·008	1	1, 2
Helium	4·003	2	4
Lithium	6·940	3	7, 6
Beryllium	9·02	4	9
Boron	10·82	5	11, 10
Carbon	12·01	6	12, 13
Nitrogen	14·008	7	14, 15
Oxygen	16·000	8	16, 17, 18
Fluorine	19·00	9	19
Neon	20·183	10	20, 22, 21
Chlorine	35·457	17	35, 37
Argon	39·944	18	40, 36, 38
Potassium	39·096	19	39, 41, 40
Iron	55·85	26	56, 54, 57, 58
Tellurium	127·61	52	130, 128, 126, 125, 124, 122, 123 (120)
Iodine	126·92	53	127
Mercury	200·61	80	202, 200, 199, 198, 201, 204, 196

The difference between the weights of the isotopes of any particular element is to be attributed to the number of neutrons in their nuclei. Many attempts have been made to separate the isotopes of various elements.

So far, complete success has been reached in separating heavy hydrogen, isotopic weight 2, from ordinary hydrogen, isotopic weight 1. To heavy hydrogen, the name *deuterium*, because its mass is 2, has been given. Its nucleus is called a *deuteron*. Its separation was accomplished by Washburn and Urey in 1932 in America. During the electrolysis of water containing alkali, the light hydrogen is first evolved at the negative pole, and after the electrolysis has been continued for a considerable time, and much of the water has been decomposed, deuterium begins to be evolved. This will be understood when it is remembered that ordinary hydrogen gas consists of 6500 times as much of the hydrogen isotope, mass 1, as the heavy deuterium isotope.

Heavy water, i.e. D_2O, freezes at $+3·82$ deg. C. instead of $0·0$ C. for ordinary water, H_2O; and boils at $101·42$ deg. C. instead of $100·00$ C. It has been put to many uses. One use is in the physiological study of the length of time water is retained in the human body.

An introduction to artificial transmutation has already been given in Chapter V.

In some thirty instances of artificial disintegration of atomic nuclei, radio-

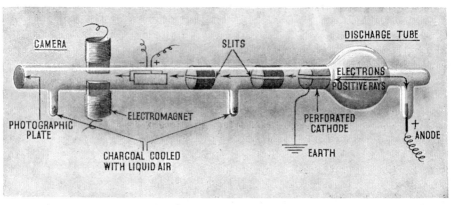

ASTON'S MASS SPECTROGRAPH

FIG. 5. *An instrument used to detect isotopes and to estimate their relative masses.*

MEDICAL STUDENTS STUDYING CHEMISTRY

All large hospitals have medical schools attached to them in which medical students are instructed in chemical principles as a preliminary to their professional training. Here is a corner of the St. Thomas's Hospital chemical laboratory in its former country retreat.

activity continues for some time after the bombardment has been stopped. This phenomenon is known as Induced Radioactivity, and the process may well serve to produce radioactive bodies that will take the place of the very expensive radium in the treatment of cancer. By bombarding bismuth with high-speed deuterons, radioactive Radium-E is formed. The conversion of the nucleus of the bismuth atom into that of Radium-E is shown in Fig. 6 (a).

"Oneness" of Things

Generally, the cause of induced radioactivity is to be found in the initial formation of unstable isotopes of elements which subsequently break down with the emission of electrically charged particles to yield stable nuclei. These radioactive changes require short periods of time; at most a few days only. As examples, the formation of the unstable isotopes of sodium and phosphorus, and their subsequent passage to stable isotopes, may be considered (Fig. 6 (b-e)). In the first case, the radioactivity is due to the ejection of β-particles

(*electrons*) and, in the second, of *positrons.*

Positrons are unit positively charged particles, which, unlike protons, have the same masses as electrons.

These examples show that the idea, which was tenaciously held by the alchemists (early chemists), of the possible changing of one metal into another, has in recent years become a reality, though our knowledge of transmutation is still very much in its infancy. What is perhaps more important is that we are forced to a belief in the "oneness" of matter, even though matter may manifest itself in the form of many elements, and we also see how great a part energy plays in holding together the protons, neutrons and electrons, which appear to be the basic units of matter.

Colossal amounts of energy operate to keep the nuclei of atoms intact and this is especially true of the three heaviest elements, viz., thorium, protoactinium and uranium.

Hahn (a former student of Rutherford) and Strassmann, in Berlin in 1939, observed that by bombarding uranium

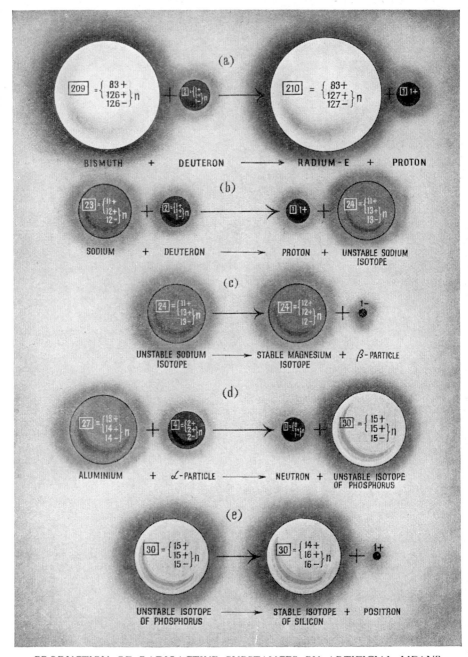

PRODUCTION OF RADIOACTIVE SUBSTANCES BY ARTIFICIAL MEANS

FIG. 6. *(a) How radium-E is formed. (b) Converting a stable sodium atom into an unstable isotope of sodium. (c) Spontaneous radioactivity of sodium isotope. (d) Production of radioactive phosphorus isotope. (e) Spontaneous radioactivity of phosphorus isotope.*

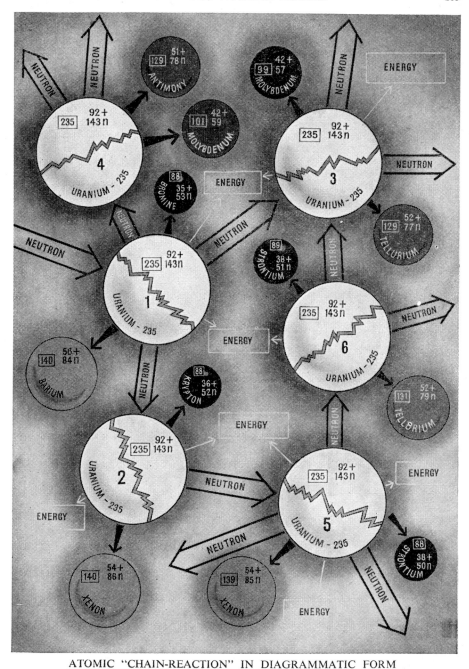

ATOMIC "CHAIN-REACTION" IN DIAGRAMMATIC FORM

FIG. 7. *Neutron colliding with the nucleus of a uranium atom No. 1 disrupts it, releasing 3 neutrons. These cause the breaking-up of other nuclei (2, 3 and 4), whilst a neutron from No. 2 nucleus is hurled at nucleus 5, which ejects a neutron to cause the splitting of nucleus 6.*

with neutrons its nuclei could be split asunder, giving nuclei of smaller atoms, e.g. barium. Professor Niels Bohr (who escaped from Denmark in a small boat during the Second World War) developed a theory to account for the fission of uranium in which he attributed the disruption to the impact of slow-moving neutrons on the rare isotope of uranium of weight 235, which is present in the uranium extracted from pitchblende to the extent of 7 parts in every 1000 parts.

Separating the Uraniums

During the last war, chemical and physical methods were devised to separate the 235-isotope from uranium. This alone was a remarkable achievement. Although a diffusion process proved to be fairly satisfactory, it appears to have been superseded by an electromagnetic method based on the principle of Aston's mass spectrograph.

Another valuable discovery was made by Joliot in Paris in 1939. It was that neutrons are amongst the products of the nuclear fission of uranium. He also observed that the velocity of neutrons could be suitably reduced by passing them through "heavy water." Just before the fall of France, Professor Joliot sent his two collaborators, Doctors Halban and Kowarski, to England with 165 litres of "heavy water," it being nearly the whole world's stock that had been purchased by the French Government from Norway just before that country was invaded by the Germans.

It seems that when a slow-moving neutron hits the nucleus of the uranium-235 isotope, the neutron is first absorbed, thereby deforming the nucleus, with the immediate result that it flies apart as the nuclei of lighter elements having atomic numbers that are *roughly* one-half of that of uranium. A few of these fission products are unstable isotopes that consequently possess short-lived radioactivity until they become stable nuclei (Fig. 7).

Uranium-235 itself is stable in amounts smaller than a certain "critical quantity." When there is a greater quantity than this amount, spontaneous fission and explosion occurs, owing to the impact of neutrons which pervade the atmosphere partly through the incidence of "cosmic rays."

The first atomic bomb, dropped on Hiroshima in 1945, appears to have been one of uranium-235 in which some device was employed to bring two or more small quantities of the isotope, each of which was less than the critical quantity, together suddenly so that the total quantity well exceeded the critical quantity. Fission of some nuclei immediately ensued with the liberation of neutrons, which in turn caused the fission of the nuclei of contiguous atoms and so on throughout the whole charge, provided, of course, that some undisrupted uranium-235 had not already been projected into space by the extremely rapid chain of previous fission explosions.

In 1940, American scientists confirmed Bohr's prediction that ordinary uranium-238 should undergo fission when bombarded with fast-moving neutrons. They also found that when bombarded with neutrons that were moving at moderate speeds, which were within narrow limits, fission did not occur, but, instead, that the neutrons were strongly retained by the uranium-238 nuclei. The resulting product first emits γ-rays or X-rays and becomes the unstable uranium-239 isotope, which, through the emission of an electron, becomes a new element, neptunium, atomic number 93, requiring twenty-three minutes for one half to be changed, and finally the neptunium is transmuted into a fairly stable, though radioactive, new element, plutonium, atomic number 94, with the emission of electrons and X-rays, half change, two to three days.

Artificial Element

Plutonium has not been found in the earth's crust. Like uranium-235, it will undergo spontaneous fission accompanied by the liberation of neutrons if the amount is greater than a critical quantity. To use it as a bomb, a mechanism is necessary that will bring "safe" quantities suddenly together such that the total exceeds the critical quantity.

Some idea of the catastrophic potentialities of a bomb using such a charge may be

PHYSICAL CHEMISTRY IN AN OXFORD LABORATORY

Here is a tank fitted with a delicate thermostatic device capable of maintaining the tank temperature constant to within $\frac{1}{100}$th of a degree C. Where exact measurements have to be made, it is often essential to be able to control the temperature to this degree of accuracy.

obtained from the fact that the energy released is about 100 million times as great as that released in chemical reactions, including those caused by the ordinary nitrogenous explosives.

Having gained some insight into the structure of the nucleus of the atom and seen that the factor which characterizes an element is its atomic number, we shall now consider the experimental evidence that led to the idea that matter consists of atoms and molecules. It is a story of much patient work and of careful deductive reasoning which ultimately led to the bold conclusion of John Dalton that the different elements must exist as infinitesimally minute particles that are incapable of further subdivision by chemical means.

The foregoing pages, however, show that the atoms of radioactive elements subdivide as a natural process, and that atoms of non-radioactive elements may be compelled to suffer subdivision if they are bombarded with certain missiles with sufficient violence.

Chemists are particularly concerned with the properties possessed by the atoms of different elements of combining with one another to form *compounds*, which, once formed, have properties that are peculiar to the compounds themselves and, at the same time, may have certain properties that are attributable to the elements. On the other hand, many of the properties of the individual elements are lost.

For instance, a molecule of common salt is the result of the union of the elements sodium and chlorine. Sodium is an extremely violent element in its properties— it readily decomposes water with the vigorous liberation therefrom of hydrogen, whereas chlorine is an exceedingly poisonous and reactive gas, yet salt is neither poisonous nor readily reactive; in fact, it is a comparatively stable compound and resists being reacted upon except by the more potent chemical reagents, such as concentrated sulphuric acid.

Mixtures, on the other hand, possess the properties of each of their constituents.

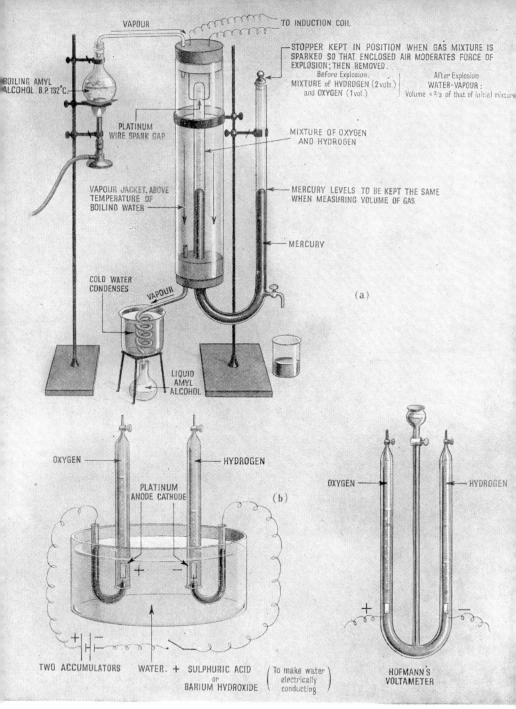

TO INDUCTION COIL

VAPOUR

STOPPER KEPT IN POSITION WHEN GAS MIXTURE IS
SPARKED SO THAT ENCLOSED AIR MODERATES FORCE OF
EXPLOSION; THEN REMOVED.

Before Explosion.   After Explosion
MIXTURE of HYDROGEN (2 vols.)   WATER-VAPOUR :
    and OXYGEN (1 vol.)   Volume = ²/₃ of that of initial mixture

BOILING AMYL
ALCOHOL. B.P. 132°C.

PLATINUM
WIRE SPARK GAP

MIXTURE OF OXYGEN
AND HYDROGEN

VAPOUR JACKET, ABOVE
TEMPERATURE OF
BOILING WATER

MERCURY LEVELS TO BE KEPT THE SAME
WHEN MEASURING VOLUME OF GAS

MERCURY

COLD WATER
CONDENSES

VAPOUR

(a)

LIQUID
AMYL
ALCOHOL

OXYGEN   HYDROGEN

PLATINUM
ANODE CATHODE   (b)

OXYGEN   HYDROGEN

+   −

+   −

+   −

TWO ACCUMULATORS   WATER. + SULPHURIC ACID   (To make water)
                              or   electrically
                      BARIUM HYDROXIDE   conducting

HOFMANN'S
VOLTAMETER

SYNTHESIS AND ANALYSIS OF WATER

FIG. 8. *(a) How steam may be made directly from hydrogen and oxygen. Showing
that 2 volumes of steam result from the chemical combination of 2 volumes of hydrogen
and 1 volume of oxygen. (b) Electricity may be used to split water into hydrogen and oxygen.*

The mixture called gunpowder was one of the first mixtures to engage the attention of man in the earliest times. Gunpowder is a mixture of approximately 75 per cent of potassium nitrate, 15 per cent of carbon (finely ground charcoal) and 10 per cent of sulphur. Its explosive power depends on the properties of its components. Thus, both carbon and sulphur burn in oxygen, and the potassium nitrate on heating supplies the necessary oxygen. Combustion takes place explosively through the spontaneous production of a large volume of gas consisting principally of carbon dioxide, carbon monoxide and nitrogen; 1 kilogram giving more than 300 litres of gas.

Compounds also differ fundamentally from mixtures in their *fixity* of composition. This fact has been designated the *Law of Constant Composition, or of Fixed or Definite Proportions*. This law merely states that the percentage weights of the elements which are chemically bound together in any given compound are fixed and, consequently, that the weights of the constituent elements are related to one another in definite proportions.

Arising from this law is the principle of *combining or equivalent weights*. From the analyses of compounds it can be found how much of an element will combine with a given weight of a particular element. This reference element is now taken as *oxygen*, and the given weight of it is *8 parts*. Such weights are *combining* or *equivalent weights*.

How Atoms Combine

Sometimes an element may combine with another element in more than one fixed proportion. Thus, copper forms two oxides; the red one, cuprous oxide (used in electrical rectifiers), and the black oxide, cupric oxide. From their analyses we find that in the first, 8 parts of oxygen have combined with 63·57 parts of copper, whereas in the second, 8 parts of oxygen had combined with half that amount, viz., 31·79 parts of copper. The Law of Fixity of Composition is not transgressed, but it will be seen that copper has two combining weights, 63·57 and 31·79; i.e. 8 grams of oxygen may combine with either 63·57

grams or 31·79 grams of copper. Looked at in this way, it is readily seen that 63·57 : 31·79 is as 2 : 1.

These observations, and many others like them, demonstrate that yet another principle may be involved in chemical combination. This was first enunciated by John Dalton in 1802-1804 in his *Law of Multiple Proportions*. It states that "if two elements combine to form more than one compound, the different proportions in which one of the two elements combines with the other bear a simple ratio to one another."

The question which now arises is "Why does Nature obey these laws so rigidly?" Dalton was forced to the conclusion that atoms are real entities in order to account for the laws of combination which had come to light through experimental work. Previously, the idea of atoms had been a mere conjecture. Unfortunately, Dalton's atomic theory was not altogether satisfactory, for he stubbornly refused to consider any relationships that may be involved in chemical combination other than that of combination by weight.

Somewhat before the time of Dalton, knowledge had been accumulating in regard to the relative volumes of gases of different elements which took part in chemical combination. The production of water from hydrogen and oxygen received the first attention, apparently through "a mere random experiment" which the Rev. Dr. Joseph Priestley made in 1781 in order "to entertain a few philosophical friends."

He exploded a mixture of air and hydrogen in a large vessel by means of an electric spark and observed that *water was formed*. This caused the Hon. Henry Cavendish in the same year to repeat the experiment, first with air and then with oxygen and, in the latter experiment, made the epoch-making observation that, to produce water, twice the volume of hydrogen to that of oxygen was consumed (Fig. 8).

These "combination by volume" experiments were extended by Gay-Lussac in the Sorbonne in Paris and, in 1808, on the results of these he enunciated his important *Law of Combining Volumes*, viz., "that when different gases react with one another, the volumes of the gases which have reacted bear a simple integral ratio one to the other, and also to the volume of the gas resulting from the reaction."

It was in 1811 that the Italian, Amadeo Avogadro, realized the significance of combination by *weight* and by *volume*, and published his celebrated theory, which has in recent years been shown to be a fact rather than an hypothesis. It is that "under the same temperature and pressure, equal volumes of different gases contain the same number of molecules." Avogadro confined the term *atom* to the smallest particle which can enter into chemical composition, whereas he introduced the word *molecule* (meaning *little mass*) to signify the smallest particle of an element or compound which can have a separate existence.

Atoms in Molecules

By studying the formation of compounds in terms of the weights of the elements which combine, together with the volumes of the reacting elements and the compound (when they are in the gaseous state), it is possible to find the atomic weights of the reacting elements and to find how many atoms of an element exist in the form of a molecule.

Thus we can find that the molecule of hydrogen contains two atoms and if we represent the atom of hydrogen by H, then the molecule will be H_2. Likewise, the molecule of oxygen is diatomic (i.e. it consists of two atoms) and its formula is O_2.

When two volumes of hydrogen and one volume of oxygen are subjected to an electric spark, an explosion occurs and two volumes of steam are immediately formed. If x molecules are contained in one volume of hydrogen or oxygen, then the reaction which occurs must actually take place between $2x$ molecules of hydrogen and x molecules of oxygen forming $2x$ molecules of water vapour (steam), i.e.

$$2x \ H_2 + x \ O_2 \longrightarrow 2x \ H_2O.$$

Dividing this equation by x, we have,

$$2H_2 + O_2 \longrightarrow 2H_2O.$$

The formula of a molecule of water is, therefore, H_2O.

Now, by taking into consideration the weights of the gases which combine, we are able to arrive at the relative weights of the atoms. To produce water, 1·008 part by weight of hydrogen combines with 8 parts by weight of oxygen. If, however, we represent the weight of an atom of hydrogen as 1·008, then the H_2 in H_2O will be 2·016, so that to keep the ratio of 1·008 : 8, O must be 16. The atomic weight of oxygen is, therefore, 16.

Formerly, the weight of an hydrogen atom was taken as unity, in which case the atomic weight of oxygen was 15·88. As oxygen forms compounds with all elements, except the rare gases (helium, neon, argon, etc.), oxygen is now taken as being of standard atomic weight 16·00, thus making that of hydrogen 1·0080.

Unfortunately, this method is not always directly applicable, for the simple reason that many elements, especially the metals, at ordinary temperature do not exist in the gaseous state, but usually as solids. It happens, however, that most elements form one or more compounds, very often the chlorides, that can be vaporized at high temperatures. The densities of the vapours can then be determined to which Avogadro's hypothesis can be applied, which, in conjunction with the analyses of the compounds by weight, make it possible to calculate the atomic weight of the element.

In chemistry, we understand by the vapour density the weight of a given volume of vapour compared with the weight of the same volume of hydrogen *under the same conditions of temperature and pressure* (Fig. 9). Hence:

Vapour density =
$$\frac{\text{Weight of a volume of vapour}}{\text{Weight of an equal volume of hydrogen}}.$$

Applying Avogadro's hypothesis,

Vapour density =
$$\frac{\text{Weight of } x \text{ molecules of vapour}}{\text{Weight of } x \text{ molecules of hydrogen}} =$$
$$\frac{\text{Molecular weight of vapour}}{\text{Molecular weight of hydrogen } (H_2)} =$$
$$\frac{\text{Molecular weight of vapour}}{2 \times 1\cdot008},$$

or Molecular Weight $= 2 \times 1\cdot008 \times$ Vapour Density.

If the percentage by weight of a metal in, say, the volatile chloride of that metal be known, e.g., x per cent, then we know

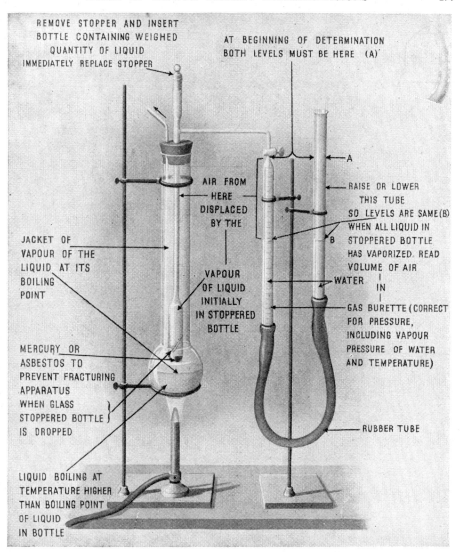

REMOVE STOPPER AND INSERT
BOTTLE CONTAINING WEIGHED
QUANTITY OF LIQUID
IMMEDIATELY REPLACE STOPPER

AT BEGINNING OF DETERMINATION
BOTH LEVELS MUST BE HERE (A)

A

AIR FROM
HERE
DISPLACED
BY THE

RAISE OR LOWER
THIS TUBE
SO LEVELS ARE SAME(B)
WHEN ALL LIQUID IN
STOPPERED BOTTLE
HAS VAPORIZED. READ
VOLUME OF AIR
IN

JACKET OF
VAPOUR OF THE
LIQUID AT ITS
BOILING
POINT

B

VAPOUR
OF LIQUID
INITIALLY
IN STOPPERED
BOTTLE

WATER

GAS BURETTE (CORRECT
FOR PRESSURE,
INCLUDING VAPOUR
PRESSURE OF WATER
AND TEMPERATURE)

MERCURY OR
ASBESTOS TO
PREVENT FRACTURING
APPARATUS
WHEN GLASS
STOPPERED BOTTLE
IS DROPPED

RUBBER TUBE

LIQUID BOILING AT
TEMPERATURE HIGHER
THAN BOILING POINT
OF LIQUID
IN BOTTLE

DETERMINATION OF VAPOUR DENSITIES

FIG. 9. *Victor Meyer's method (modified) of determining the densities of the vapours of volatile liquids. The absolute density (weight per unit volume) of the vapour is equal to* $\dfrac{Weight \ of \ liquid \ (grams)}{Volume \ of \ vapour \ (c.c.s)}$ *but the relative density ("vapour density") equals* $\dfrac{Absolute \ density \ of \ vapour}{Absolute \ density \ of \ hydrogen}$ *at same temperature and pressure (0 deg. C., 760mm. mercury).*

that $\frac{x}{100}$ × Molecular Weight is the weight of the metal in a molecule of its chloride. This weight will be that of one or a definite number of atoms. By carrying out similar determinations of the analyses and vapour densities of any other volatile compounds of that element, it will be possible to find which is the smallest weight of the metal that enters into chemical combination. This weight will be the atomic weight of the metal. This method is that first proposed by Cannizzaro.

The smallest weight of oxygen that is ever found in any compound is 16, but we saw that the combining weight of oxygen is 8. Thus, in water there are 8 parts by weight of oxygen for every 1·008 part of hydrogen, which is the same as 16 to $2 \times 1·008$ parts by weight respectively. Hence, one atom of oxygen, weight 16, combines with two atoms of hydrogen, each weighing 1·008, to form water, H_2O. The valency of the oxygen atom is 2, because it can combine with two atoms of hydrogen. The value

$$2 = \frac{\text{Atomic weight}}{\text{Combining weight}} = \frac{16}{8}.$$

What Valency Is

In general,

$$\frac{\text{Atomic weight of an element}}{\text{Combining weight of the element}} = \text{Valency},$$

so that *valency* may be defined as *the number of equivalent or combining weights of another element, or group of elements, with which a particular element can combine*. The atomic weight of any element is fixed but, whereas certain elements possess only one equivalent weight and, therefore, react in accordance with only one valency, many elements (e.g. copper, phosphorus) have more than one combining weight and these may combine in accordance with either of their valencies.

Atomic and molecular weights are purely *relative*, the atomic weight of oxygen being quite arbitrarily taken as 16. We sometimes talk about the *gram-atom* and the *gram-molecule*, by which we mean the weight equal to the atomic weight or molecular weight when expressed in grams. Regarding gases, it has been found experimentally that at 0 deg. C. and at normal atmospheric pressure (i.e. 760 mm. mercury), the volume occupied by a gram-molecule of any gas is 22·4 litres. Slight deviations from 22·4 litres occur with gases which at 0 deg. C. are not far from their respective critical points.

On the basis of Avogadro's hypothesis, we infer that 22·4 litres of different gases

should contain the same number of molecules. This is now an experimental fact and the actual number of molecules has been determined by a variety of methods with an accuracy of 1 per cent. The number (designated the Avogadro Number) is $6·02 \times 10^{23}$, or

602,000,000,000,000,000,000,000.

From this fact we are able to calculate the weight of actual molecules. For example, 1 gram-molecule of hydrogen, $H_2 = 2 \times 1·008$ grams = weight of $6·02 \times 10^{23}$ molecules; therefore, 1 molecule of hydrogen weighs $\frac{2 \times 1·008}{6·02 \times 10^{23}}$ gram $= 3·35 \times 10^{-24}$ $= 0·000,000,000,000,000,000,000,003,35$ gram.

Similarly, the oxygen molecule, O_2, is found to be sixteen times as heavy, and the carbon dioxide molecule, CO_2, is twenty-two times as heavy, as the hydrogen molecule.

The gram-atom of an element in the solid state contains the Avogadro Number of atoms. In 1818, Dulong and Petit made the important discovery that *the specific heat of an element* (i.e. the number of calories of heat which must be absorbed by 1 gram of the element to raise its temperature through 1 deg. C.) multiplied by its *atomic weight* gave the same value, 6·3 calories, for the majority of the elements. This quantity is the *gram-atomic heat*. Hence, the amount of heat absorbed by an individual atom, in the solid state, to raise its temperature through 1 deg. C. should be the same for all elements. At ordinary temperatures there are a few exceptions, notably the diamond, boron, aluminium, beryllium and silicon, but at high temperatures they also conform to the rule.

The advantage of Dulong and Petit's Law is that it enables one to calculate the approximate atomic weight of an element, thus:

Atomic weight × Specific heat
= 6·3 (approx.).
∴ *Approximate* atomic weight
= 6·3/ Specific heat.

The equivalent weight of an element can always be accurately determined. Knowing that the Equivalent weight × Valency = Accurate atomic weight, and by comparing this with the *approximate atomic weight*,

STUDYING THE PROCESS OF DISTILLATION

*Young pupils of a school at East Ham, London, who intend to follow chemistry as a career.
Here we see them enthusiastically conducting a simple experiment in distillation.*

the *true valency* can be found (viz., Approximate atomic weight/Equivalent weight = Approximate valency). The actual valency is the nearest whole number.

Another method of ascertaining the atomic weight of an element is based on the analyses of crystals in which the element is present, and of crystals of a similar compound that are almost identical in crystalline form in which the place of one of the elements is taken by another of which the atomic weight is known. Such crystals are *isomorphous*, and the foregoing principle is that discovered by Mitscherlich in 1821 and enunciated as the Law of Isomorphism, viz., that the ratio of the weights of the two different elements that are combined with the same weights of the other elements in isomorphous compounds is equal to the ratio of the atomic weights of the respective elements.

It was observed that there appeared to be several families of three similar elements (Triads) and, moreover, that the members of each family appeared to be related to one another by their atomic weights, the atomic weight of the middle member being approximately equal to the average of the atomic weights of the lightest and heaviest element, e.g. Lithium, 6·94; Sodium, 23·00; Potassium, 39·10. $\frac{6·94 + 39·10}{2} = 23·02$. Later, however, it was demonstrated that the Triads were only parts of larger families. Thus, the elements mentioned are but three members of a family of five, known as the "Alkali Metals" (because their oxides dissolve in water to form strongly alkaline solutions), the remaining members being Rubidium and Cæsium.

In 1853, Dr. Gladstone attempted a classification by arranging the names of the elements in the order of increasing atomic weights, and this idea was carried a stage further by Chaucourtois in 1862, who arranged the elements in a spiral ("the Telluric Screw") round a vertical cylinder, the surface of which was divided into sixteen vertical columns, and by J. A. R. Newlands in 1864, who arranged the elements in eight columns (the "Law of Octaves") in that the elements showed a periodicity as far as the resemblance of their properties is concerned.

The same year, Lothar Meyer, in Germany, demonstrated very forcibly the periodicity in the magnitude of the atomic volumes of the elements when plotted against their atomic weights. (The atomic volume of an element is the volume occupied by 1 gram-atom, and is equal to atomic weight divided by the density.)

Completing the international interest in classifying the elements, Dmitri Mendeléeff, a Russian, succeeded in 1869-1870 in evolving a satisfactory system based on increasing atomic weights, with few important exceptions, in which he was able to bring out the periodicity of *Eights* of Newlands and the periodicity of *Sixteens* of Chaucourtois.

Atomic Number and Weight

Thanks to the researches of Moseley, it is now known that the true basis for the classification of the elements is their atomic numbers and not their atomic weights. Save for a few exceptions, both, somewhat fortuitously, lead to the same sequence of the elements. One reason for these exceptions is to be found in the fact that elements are generally mixtures of isotopes, and that the apparent atomic weight of an element depends on the precise proportions of the isotopes of which the element-mixture is composed. Thus, for example, the weights of the two isotopes

of argon are 40 and 36 and those of the potassium are 39 and 41, but argon contains more of 40 isotope than potassium does of the 41 isotope. Hence the atomic weight of potassium is less than that of argon, whereas the reverse is the case in regard to their atomic numbers.

The advantages of the periodic system are manifold. Besides indicating the natural families of elements, it shows the interrelationship of the elements. It has, in this respect, materially assisted in the discovery of new elements, and it has assisted in ascertaining the probable valency of certain elements, particularly beryllium. It has supplied evidence which has greatly assisted in the development of the electronic theory of valency.

It may be considered that the orbital electrons belong to one or other of a series of "shells" surrounding the nucleus of an atom and that energy at different levels is possessed by the electrons existing in the various shells. The 86 electrons surrounding the radon nucleus are supposed to be held in "shells," starting from the nucleus outwards, thus:

Shell . . . K L M N O P
Number of Electrons 2 8 18 32 18 8

in which the K, L, M, and N shells are supposed to be holding their full quota of electrons. The orientation of the electrons in the atoms of the rare gases are given in the table at the foot of the page.

An element which comes before or after a rare gas in the periodic system, in reacting with another element, is supposed to acquire the arrangement of the electrons possessed by that particular rare gas. As

CONFIGURATION OF ELECTRONS IN ATOMS
OF THE RARE GASES

Element	Atomic Number	Shell					
		K	L	M	N	O	P
Helium (He)	$2 = 2 \times 1^2$	2	—	—	—	—	—
Neon (Ne)	$10 = 2 \ (1^2 + 2^2)$	2	8	—	—	—	—
Argon (A)	$18 = 2 \ (1^2 + 2^2 + 2^2)$	2	8	8	—	—	—
Krypton (Kr)	$36 = 2 \ (1^2 + 2^2 + 2^2 + 3^2)$	2	8	18	8	—	—
Xenon (Xe)	$54 = 2 \ (1^2 + 2^2 + 2^2 + 3^2 + 3^2)$	2	8	18	18	8	—
Radon (Rn)	$86 = 2 \ (1^2 + 2^2 + 2^2 + 3^2 + 3^2 + 4^2)$	2	8	18	32	18	8

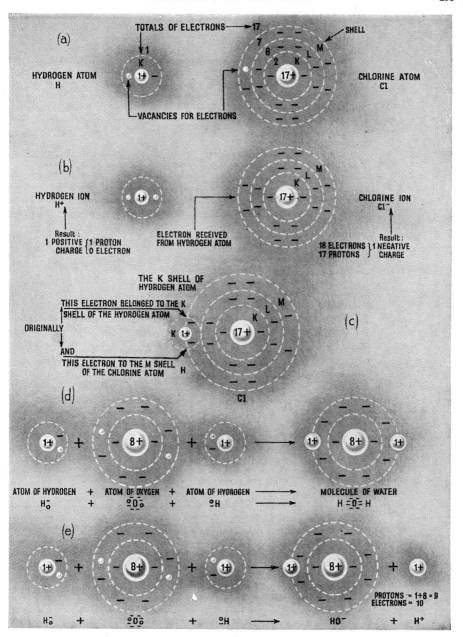

ELECTRON LINKAGES IN ATOMS

FIG. 10. *(a) How electrons are arranged in hydrogen and chlorine atoms. (b) Electrovalent linkage. (c) Covalent linkage. A pair of electrons, mutually shared by the constituent atoms. (d) Formation of a water molecule from one atom of oxygen and two of hydrogen by means of two covalent linkages. (e) One covalent linkage and one electrovalent linkage.*

the rare gases are chemically unreactive, their electron arrangements are considered to be stable. This is done either by giving or taking the requisite number of electrons to or from the atoms of the reacting elements.

Chemical combination leads to a change in the distribution of the valency electrons of the reacting elements in order that the atoms in the resulting compound may have more stable electron-configurations than they possessed in the free state. These stable configurations correspond with either (a) eight electrons in the outermost shell, or (b) that of the nearest rare gas in the periodic classification. So far, three types of valency have been recognized, but it must be understood that the theory in its present form is far from complete and it is quite possible that other types of valency may come to light ere long. The recognized types are:

(1) *Electrovalency*, or *Polar Valency*. This occurs when one atom in the act of union gives valency electrons to the other atom.

(2) *Covalency*. This involves the sharing of two or more electrons by the combined atoms, one electron belonging originally to one atom and the second electron to the other.

(3) *Co-ordinate Valency*, or *Semi-polar Linkage*. This occurs when combination results from both atoms sharing a pair of electrons that originally belonged to one of the atoms.

Exchange of Electrons

In the first place, let us consider the union of an atom of hydrogen with one of chlorine to form hydrogen chloride (Fig. 10 (a)). The hydrogen atom has only one K electron, whereas the chlorine atom has a full complement of two in its K shell and eight in its L shell, but only seven in the M shell. To complete the number of electrons possessed by the next rare gas, viz., argon K2, L8, M8, the chlorine atom must obtain another electron for its M shell, and this it does by taking one K electron from the hydrogen atom. The hydrogen atom becomes an ion, a proton, thus carrying a single positive charge, and the chlorine atom becomes a negatively charged chloride ion, for it possesses seventeen positive and eighteen negative charges, as shown in Fig. 10 (b). Such a compound is *electrovalent*, because owing to transference of a single electron from one atom to the other, the hydrogen atom becomes positively charged and the chlorine atom negatively charged, so that when hydrogen chloride is dissolved in water, these positively and negatively charged parts (ions) exist as individual ions.

Serious doubts, however, have been expressed as to the possibility of a proton having a permanent existence in solution, and for that reason the type of union depicted in (c) has been thought more probable. Here, the chlorine gives an electron to the hydrogen atom, to make up the stable helium number of 2, and at the same time the hydrogen gives an electron to the chlorine to complete its M shell as in the stable argon M shell. To do this, the hydrogen atom must move into very close proximity with the chlorine atom in order that the electron requirements of the two atoms may be simultaneously satisfied.

This process of giving an electron by one atom to another and taking an electron from it at the same time, in chemical language, "donating" and "accepting," constitutes a *covalent linkage*. Hydrogen chloride, when dissolved in water, is considerably ionized. The hydrogen ion (proton), H^+, no doubt attaches itself to one or more molecules of water; the precise number is by no means certain, although a single molecule of water is often assumed, i.e. H_3O^+.

Fig. 11 shows the combination of an atom of sodium with one of chlorine to form common salt. Here a covalent linkage is theoretically possible, but the compound formation is certainly one of electrovalence. In the solid state, the salt is undoubtedly polar, the sodium bearing a positive charge and the chloride a negative charge (b), whereas in solution the salt splits asunder to form individual ions.

Water offers considerable resistance to the passage of electricity. This is because water is almost un-ionized, for it is the ions that are positively (kations) and negatively (anions) charged that are respon-

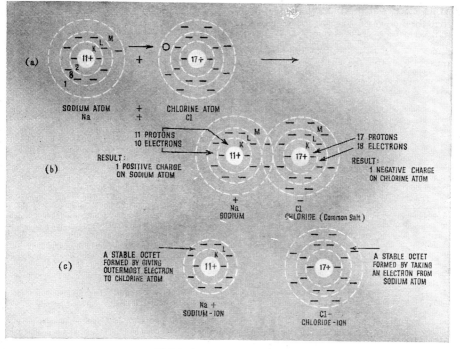

ELECTROVALENT LINKAGE

FIG. 11. *(a) and (b) show what takes place when an atom of sodium combines with an atom of chlorine to form sodium chloride (common salt), and (b) and (c) clearly explain why a molecule of sodium chloride splits asunder as a sodium-ion and a chloride-ion.*

sible for the conduction of electricity. In actual fact, it can be calculated from the electrical conductivity of the purest water that out of 556 millions of molecules of water only one is ionized. Expressed in the simplest manner, the ionization or the electrolytic dissociation of water is:

$$H_2O \rightleftharpoons H^+ + OH^-$$
water molecule   hydrogen ion   hydroxyl ion

Two ways by which a molecule of water may be formed by the union of two atoms of hydrogen and one atom of oxygen are shown in Fig. 10. As the atomic number of oxygen is 8, it has two electrons in the K shell and six in the L shell. To acquire stability, the oxygen atom must increase its L electrons to eight, and this it does almost exclusively by means of covalent linkages with the hydrogen atoms as shown. The process in the bottom sketch shows how this may be done by using a covalent

linkage with one hydrogen atom and a electrovalent linkage with the other. The fact that this takes place to so very small an extent suggests that the excess negative charge on the L shell must exert a considerable attractive force on the hydrogen ion and, in effect, converts the electrovalent bond into one of covalency.

The formation of ammonia by the direct union of hydrogen with nitrogen is an example of three atoms of hydrogen being bound by three covalent linkages, thereby making it possible for the nitrogen atom to secure eight electrons in its L shell. Of these, two electrons remain as they were in the original nitrogen atom (Fig. 12 (a)).

The union of ammonia with hydrogen chloride is interesting in that it illustrates how these two electrons are utilized in establishing a co-ordinate linkage (Fig. 12 (b)). Representing hydrogen chloride

as an electrovalent compound, it appears
that the hydrogen ion is attracted by the
pair of electrons on the nitrogen of the
ammonia when the positive ionic charge is
transferred to the ammonium group,
thereby becoming an ammonium ion,
NH_4^+.

The nitrogen still retains the eight

$$\left[\begin{array}{c} H \\ H \rightarrow N \longrightarrow H \\ H \end{array} \right]^+$$

Air is a mixture of approximately 1 part
by volume of oxygen and 4 parts of nitrogen, with relatively small amounts of

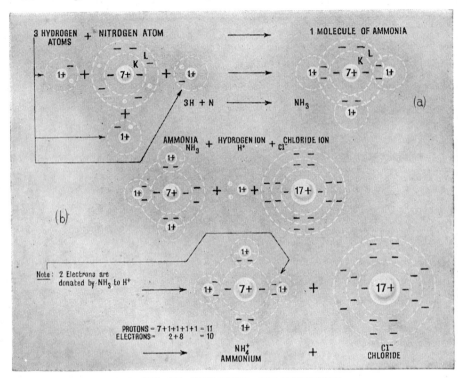

CASES OF CHEMICAL COMBINATION

FIG. 12. *(a) Formation of ammonia from three atoms of hydrogen and one atom of nitrogen.*
(b) Formation of ammonium chloride (sal ammoniac) by the union of hydrogen chloride
(in its electrically conducting state) and ammonia. Note novel way in which hydrogen ion
attaches itself to the ammonia molecule to produce a positively charged ammonium ion.
Two electrons saturate the shell of the hydrogen ion and the number of electrons in the L shell
of the nitrogen atom is maintained at 8. This forms an example of a co-ordinate linkage.

electrons, but the pair of electrons also
satisfies the hydrogen in bringing its electron requirements up to those of the stable
helium atom. This is an instance of a
co-ordinate valency. It is represented by
a small arrow pointing in the direction
of the donation of the electron pair
(see top of next column).

carbon dioxide and the rare gases, viz.,
helium, neon, argon, xenon, krypton, and
variable quantities of water vapour. The
ratio in the air of oxygen to nitrogen is
surprisingly constant all over the world,
yet despite its constancy of composition
air is *not* a compound.

It can be shown that air is a mixture,

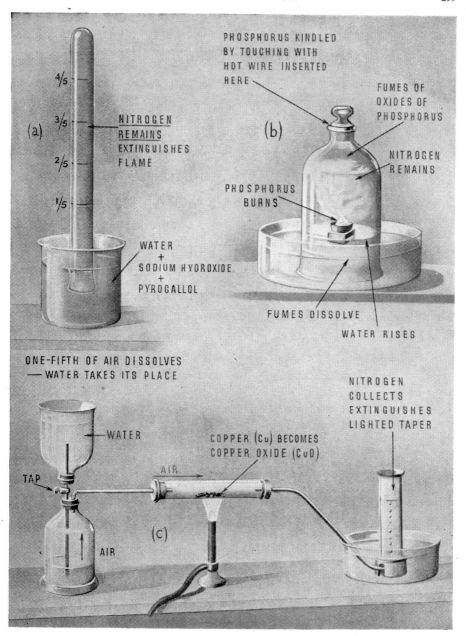

PROVING THAT AIR IS A MIXTURE OF GASES

Fig. 13. *Three interesting experiments. (a) The oxygen combines with the dissolved pyrogallol, leaving nitrogen in the tube. (b) The oxygen combines with the phosphorus and the resulting oxide of phosphorus dissolves in the water, leaving nitrogen in the bell jar. (c) The oxygen combines with the heated copper and the remaining nitrogen collects in the gas jar.*

TESTING FOR METALS

Fitting up a laboratory model of Heyrovsky's Polarograph, which is used to detect and to estimate electrically the amounts of different metals that may be present in a solution.

by shaking air with water. If air were a compound it would either dissolve or not dissolve; if it dissolved in the water it would dissolve as such and on boiling would be driven out of solution as such. But owing to the different, though slight, solubilities of the two gases, the mixture driven out of solution by boiling is relatively richer in oxygen than is the air itself.

Air is a Mixture

Another way of proving air to be a mixture is to take advantage of the solubility of oxygen in a solution of pyrogallol and sodium hydroxide. One-fifth of the air (viz., the oxygen) will be removed.

Other methods are: (i) To pass air over heated copper. The oxygen will combine with the copper and leave the nitrogen behind. (ii) To burn phosphorus in an enclosed volume of air. The phosphorus burns vividly until all the air is consumed, giving intense white fumes of oxides of phosphorus. If the vessel had been placed over water, the white fumes would dissolve and the water would rise in the vessel to take the place of the oxygen consumed, viz., one-fifth (Fig. 13).

Oxygen is the constituent of the air that makes burning possible. In pure oxygen, many elements will burn with great vigour and rapidity; the products are oxides. Thus, glowing charcoal becomes a bright flame and carbon dioxide, CO_2, results. Sulphur burns with a blue flame to form sulphur dioxide, SO_2.

The oxides produced by the combustion of non-metallic elements, e.g. carbon, sulphur and phosphorus, although not being acids themselves, dissolve in water to give solutions that are acidic in nature.

The solutions contain the respective acids: carbonic acid, H_2CO_3 ($CO_2+H_2O \longrightarrow H_2CO_3$); sulphur*ous* acid, H_2SO_3 ($SO_2+H_2O \longrightarrow H_2SO_3$); sulphur*ic* acid, H_2SO_4 ($SO_3+H_2O \longrightarrow H_2SO_4$); phosphor*ic* acid, H_3PO_4 ($P_4O_{10}+6H_2O \longrightarrow 4H_3PO_4$); phosphor*ous* acid, H_3PO_3 ($P_4O_6 +6H_2O \longrightarrow 4H_3PO_3$). Two oxides of phosphorus are formed: P_4O_{10}, phosphor*ic* oxide; P_4O_6, phosphor*ous* oxide; the former with a plentiful supply of oxygen and the latter with a restricted supply.

The property of forming soluble oxides that in water yield acids is characteristic of the non-metals.

It must not be thought that acids are formed only by the dissolution of certain oxides in water. Thus the gas, hydrogen chloride, HCl, which is evolved when concentrated sulphuric acid is poured on common salt, NaCl,

$$NaCl + H_2SO_4 \longrightarrow NaHSO_4 + HCl \uparrow$$

sodium sulphuric   sodium hydrogen
chloride acid   bisulphate chloride

is very soluble in water and then produces a powerful acid, hydrochloric acid — a concentrated solution being sold as "spirits of salt," whilst a very dilute solution is present in human gastric juice (Fig. 14).

The name *oxygen* means *acid producer*, and this idea is more evident in the German name for the gas, *Sauerstoff*, i.e. sour stuff, sourness being associated with the taste of acids.

The naming of acids, due in the first place to Lavoisier, was based on the relative amounts of oxygen they contain— the suffix *ic* indicating more oxygen than in the acid designated by the suffix *ous*. For example: (i) H_3PO_4 is phosphor*ic* acid, and H_3PO_3, phosphor*ous* acid, a molecule of the former containing four atoms of oxygen, whilst the latter contains three; (ii) sulphur*ic* acid, H_2SO_4, and sulphur*ous* acid, H_2SO_3.

It was formerly believed that the cause of acidity was oxygen. This is not so. Hydrochloric acid, HCl, is a more potent acid than either phosphoric or sulphuric acids, yet, as its formula shows, it contains no oxygen. Here the suffix *ic* is used to signify that it is a strong acid, but the prefix *hydro* (short for hydrogen) suggests that the acidity is to be attributed to the hydrogen.

The essential element in the molecule of any acid is now known to be hydrogen and not oxygen. When an acid dissolves in water it dissociates into ions that are electrically charged, positively or negatively, to precisely the same extent as are protons and electrons, e.g.,

$$HCl \rightleftharpoons H^+ + Cl^-$$

hydrochloric   hydrogen   chloride
acid   ion   ion

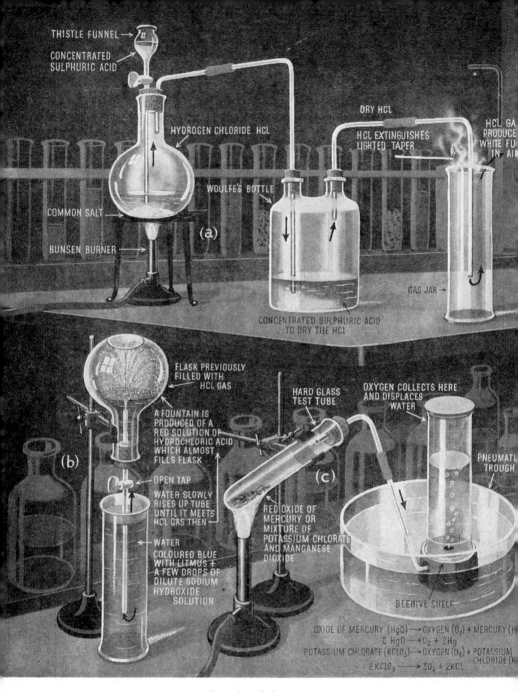

THISTLE FUNNEL

CONCENTRATED
SULPHURIC ACID

HYDROGEN CHLORIDE HCL

DRY HCL

HCL EXTINGUISHES
LIGHTED TAPER

HCL GA
PRODUCE
WHITE FU
IN AI

WOULFE'S BOTTLE

COMMON SALT

BUNSEN BURNER

(a)

CONCENTRATED SULPHURIC ACID
TO DRY THE HCL

GAS JAR

FLASK PREVIOUSLY
FILLED WITH
HCL GAS

HARD GLASS
TEST TUBE

OXYGEN COLLECTS HERE
AND DISPLACES
WATER

A FOUNTAIN IS
PRODUCED OF A
RED SOLUTION OF
HYDROCHLORIC ACID
WHICH ALMOST
FILLS FLASK

(b)

OPEN TAP

WATER SLOWLY
RISES UP TUBE
UNTIL IT MEETS
HCL GAS THEN

WATER
COLOURED BLUE
WITH LITMUS +
A FEW DROPS OF
DILUTE SODIUM
HYDROXIDE
SOLUTION

(c)

RED OXIDE OF
MERCURY OR
MIXTURE OF
POTASSIUM CHLORATE
AND MANGANESE
DIOXIDE

PNEUMATI
TROUGH

BEEHIVE SHELF

OXIDE OF MERCURY (HgO) → OXYGEN (O$_2$) + MERCURY (H
2 HgO → O$_2$ + 2Hg
POTASSIUM CHLORATE (KClO$_3$) → OXYGEN (O$_2$) + POTASSIUM
CHLORIDE (K
2 KClO$_3$ → 3O$_2$ + 2KCL

PREPARATION OF HYDROGEN,

FIG. 14. *Some experiments to demonstrate their properties. (a) How hydrochloric acid gas (hydrogen chloride) may be prepared from common salt. (b) Illustrating the extreme solubility of hydrogen chloride gas. (c) How oxygen gas may be obtained from oxide of mercury or potassium chlorate. The manganese dioxide mainly assists the potassium chlorate to give up its oxygen. (d) Shows how burning phosphorus inflames in oxygen with dazzling brilli-*

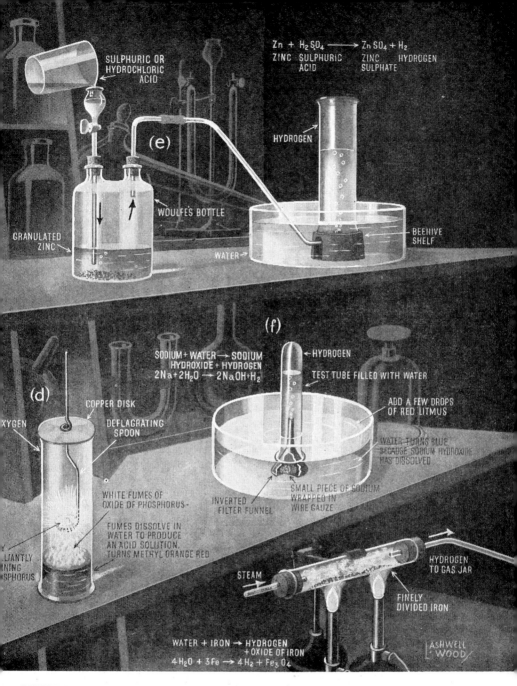

Zn + H₂ SO₄ ⟶ Zn SO₄ + H₂

$$Zn + H_2SO_4 \longrightarrow ZnSO_4 + H_2$$

ZINC   SULPHURIC   ZINC   HYDROGEN
ACID   SULPHATE

SULPHURIC OR
HYDROCHLORIC
ACID

(e)

HYDROGEN

WOULFES BOTTLE

GRANULATED
ZINC

BEEHIVE
SHELF

WATER

(f)

SODIUM + WATER ⟶ SODIUM
HYDROXIDE + HYDROGEN
$$2Na + 2H_2O \longrightarrow 2NaOH + H_2$$

HYDROGEN

TEST TUBE FILLED WITH WATER

ADD A FEW DROPS
OF RED LITMUS

(d)

COPPER DISK

DEFLAGRATING
SPOON

XYGEN

WATER TURNS BLUE
BECAUSE SODIUM HYDROXIDE
HAS DISSOLVED

WHITE FUMES OF
OXIDE OF PHOSPHORUS

INVERTED
FILTER FUNNEL

SMALL PIECE OF SODIUM
WRAPPED IN
WIRE GAUZE

FUMES DISSOLVE IN
WATER TO PRODUCE
AN ACID SOLUTION.
TURNS METHYL ORANGE RED

Y
LIANTLY
NING
SPHORUS

STEAM

HYDROGEN
TO GAS JAR

FINELY
DIVIDED IRON

WATER + IRON ⟶ HYDROGEN
+ OXIDE OF IRON
$$4H_2O + 3Fe \longrightarrow 4H_2 + Fe_3O_4$$

ASHWELL
WOOD

OXYGEN AND HYDROGEN CHLORIDE

ance, and how the resulting oxide of phosphorus dissolves in water, with which it forms
phosphoric acid. (e) How hydrogen may be prepared by making use of the ability of zinc
to displace the combined hydrogen from sulphuric acid. (f) Experiments showing how
(i) sodium reacts with and dissolves in water, releasing hydrogen and forming the alkali
sodium hydroxide in the water; (ii) iron splits up steam, releasing hydrogen gas.

The degree of ionization determines the reactivity of the acid.

Vinegar contains acetic acid, but, unlike either hydrochloric, nitric or sulphuric acids, it is but slightly ionized and, in consequence, it is considerably less active as an acid than are these so-called mineral acids. Acidity is produced by hydrogen ions, and of two acids the one which in the same volume of water yields the greater number of hydrogen ions (molecule for molecule) is the more reactive or stronger acid.

Some metals, especially if finely divided and previously heated until they glow, burn vigorously in pure oxygen. Sodium, potassium and calcium burn brilliantly, so also does red-hot, finely divided iron. Again, oxides are formed, but, being oxides of metals, the oxides have radically different properties from those of non-metals.

Metals to Alkalis

Sodium forms sodium oxide, Na_2O, and calcium forms calcium oxide, CaO (which, as it may also be obtained by "burning" lime, calcium carbonate, $CaCO_3$, when carbon dioxide, CO_2, is driven off, is also called *burnt lime*). Sodium oxide combines with, and then dissolves in, water thus:

$$Na_2O + H_2O \longrightarrow 2\,NaOH.$$

A solution of sodium hydroxide NaOH ("caustic soda"), imparts a soapy feeling. It is most reactive and combines with acids to form salts, e.g.

$$NaOH + HCl \longrightarrow NaCl + H_2O$$

sodium + hydro-   sodium + water,
hydroxide chloric   chloride
      acid

a process known as *neutralization*, for in salts both acid and alkali properties disappear. Sodium hydroxide, NaOH, is an alkali and its chemical potency depends on the fact that in solution it, too, splits up into ions, thus:

$$NaOH \rightleftharpoons Na^+ + OH^-$$

sodium   sodium   hydroxyl
hydroxide   ion   ion

Neutralization of an acid with an alkali really takes place between the hydrogen ions of the acid and the hydroxyl ions originating from the alkali, to form mole-

cules of water that are almost entirely un-ionized, e.g.

$$Na^+ + OH^- + H^+ + Cl^- \longrightarrow H_2O + Na^+ + Cl^-.$$

Subtracting the ions, Na^+ and Cl^-, from each side of the equation, we get,

$$H^+ + OH^- \longrightarrow H_2O.$$

This union of the two ions is accompanied by the evolution of much heat.

There are available indicators which have various colours (and in some cases are colourless) in acid solution and have quite different colours in alkaline solution. One or two drops of a solution of an indicator added to a solution undergoing neutralization will, by the production of an intermediate colour in proceeding from acidity to alkalinity, or vice versa, indicate when neutralization is complete. Many indicators are available for this purpose, e.g. methyl orange, methyl red, litmus, phenolphthalein, thymolphthalein. They are used in the volumetric analysis of acids and alkalis (Fig. 15).

Calcium oxide does not immediately dissolve in water. Dropping water on it causes much heat to be evolved, and the powder to swell appreciably and eventually to disintegrate into a very fine state. The process is called "slaking," in which calcium hydroxide (slaked lime) is formed:

$$CaO + H_2O \longrightarrow Ca(OH)_2.$$

The calcium hydroxide dissolves in water to a small extent. It, too, is caustic and is alkaline in reaction, and it is largely due to this that the lime-washing of walls has a cleansing action.

Other metallic oxides, though they may be insoluble in water, will dissolve in acids to form salts.

Oxygen is also the element on which all life depends, for the process of living consists of a series of chemical reactions with oxygen that ultimately lead to the two chief products of combustion, carbon dioxide and water.

Most foods contain carbohydrates. If a definite weight of a carbohydrate were burnt in an excess of oxygen, the amount of energy, liberated in the form of heat, would be the same as the total of the energy set free in the body by the series of chemical reactions that take place before

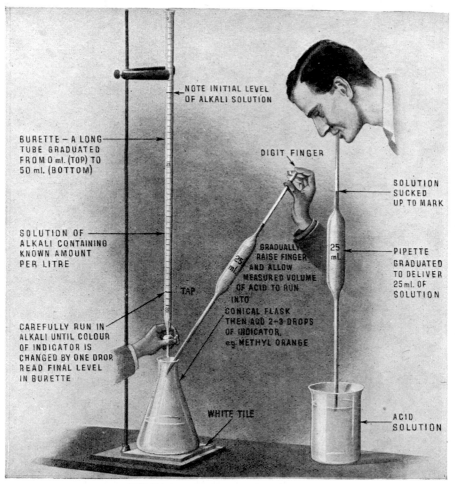

NOTE INITIAL LEVEL
OF ALKALI SOLUTION

BURETTE — A LONG
TUBE GRADUATED
FROM 0 ml. (TOP) TO
50 ml. (BOTTOM)

DIGIT FINGER

SOLUTION
SUCKED
UP TO MARK

SOLUTION OF
ALKALI CONTAINING
KNOWN AMOUNT
PER LITRE

GRADUALLY
RAISE FINGER
AND ALLOW
MEASURED VOLUME
OF ACID TO RUN
INTO
CONICAL FLASK
THEN ADD 2–3 DROPS
OF INDICATOR,
e.g. METHYL ORANGE

25
ml.

PIPETTE
GRADUATED
TO DELIVER
25 ml. OF
SOLUTION

TAP

CAREFULLY RUN IN
ALKALI UNTIL COLOUR
OF INDICATOR IS
CHANGED BY ONE DROP
READ FINAL LEVEL
IN BURETTE

WHITE TILE

ACID
SOLUTION

VOLUMETRIC ANALYSIS OF ACIDS

Fig. 15. *Alkaline solution of known concentration is run from burette into the acid solution in the conical flask until the acid is just neutralized, this point being shown by the sudden colour-change of an "indicator" dye in the solution. Knowing the amount of alkali used to neutralize the acid, the precise amount of acid present can be calculated. (Right) An exact amount of the solution is measured with a pipette by suction. When the exact volume is reached, the finger tip is clamped on the end of the pipette in the mouth.*

the carbon dioxide is produced and then carried back by the venous blood to the lungs and discharged therefrom.

In the body, however, some of this energy is converted into mechanical energy by the muscles, though much is utilized directly in the form of heat to keep the body heated to its normal temperature, 98·4 deg. F. Any variation from this tem-perature is an indication that the combus-tions are proceeding abnormally.

The body-combustion reactions are intimately connected with the proportion of oxygen in the air and proportion of the diluent, nitrogen. Nitrogen serves no purpose than to keep oxygen-content down to 20·95 per cent of dry air by volume.

As a gas, nitrogen is quite harmless to

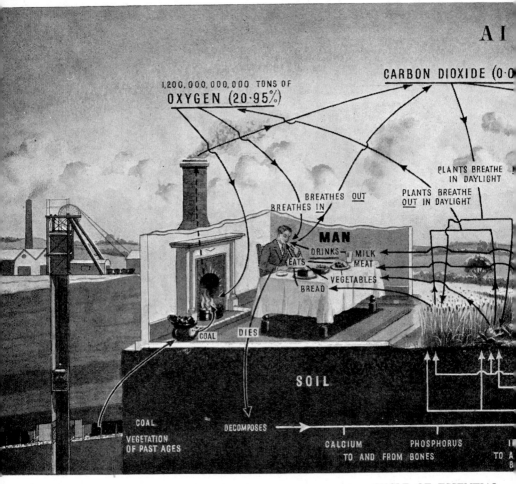

CYCLE OF ESSENTIAL

FIG. 16. *Showing diagrammatically how man is dependent on air, earth and water for his whole existence. He takes in oxygen when breathing in, and returns carbon dioxide to the*

life; in fact, it is just negative. It is most unreactive, except under extreme conditions. It will not support life and, if the atmosphere consisted only of nitrogen, combustion and, therefore, life would both be impossible. It would suffocate and this fact is perpetuated in the old French name for nitrogen, *l'azote*—suffocator. Clearly, the 78·08 per cent of nitrogen in the atmosphere is intended to retard the rate of combustion and of living. One can only imagine what the effects might be if the nitrogen content of the air were to alter. Life would undergo a radical change.

In most industries, considerable amounts of coal are burnt and carbon dioxide in vast quantities is returned to the atmosphere; animals and human beings are everywhere polluting the air with carbon dioxide; fermentation and putrefactive processes are frequently taking place to yield carbon dioxide; whilst in some districts lime-burning adds still more carbon dioxide to the air, and *yet the average*

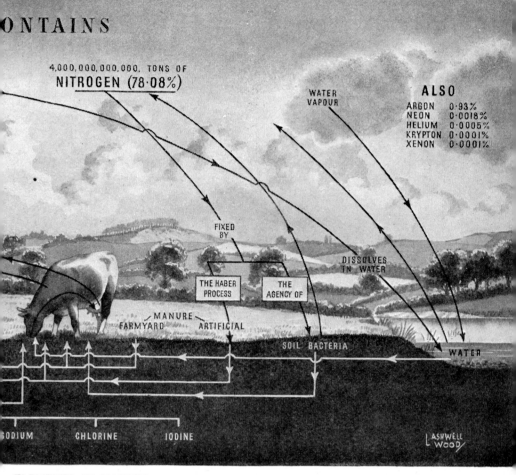

ONTAINS

4,000,000,000,000, TONS OF
NITROGEN (78·08%)

WATER
VAPOUR

ALSO
ARGON 0·93%
NEON 0·0018%
HELIUM 0·0005%
KRYPTON 0·0001%
XENON 0·0001%

FIXED
BY

DISSOLVES
IN WATER

THE HABER
PROCESS

THE
AGENCY OF

MANURE
FARMYARD ARTIFICIAL

SOIL BACTERIA

WATER

SODIUM CHLORINE IODINE

L ASHWELL WOOD

ELEMENTS IN NATURE
air when breathing out. Carbon comes from the sugars, starches, fats, oils and proteins in food. Nitrogen comes from protein, such as egg-white, lean meat, or cheese.

carbon dioxide content of open air remains at about 0·03 per cent (Fig. 16).

In crowded rooms, and particularly in industrial cities, the content rises. In a crowded hall in which the content in the air has risen to 0·5 per cent, no appreciable effect may be experienced by the people, but discomfort in breathing and an increase in pulse will be experienced when the carbon dioxide rises to 3 per cent. Moreover, carbon dioxide is a heavy gas and accumulates near to the ground.

Fig. 17 shows stages in the preparation of carbon dioxide.

Carbon dioxide is appreciably soluble in water, especially if it be in contact with limestone, which is sometimes present in river beds. The carbon dioxide, in dissolving in water, causes the calcium carbonate to dissolve by the chemical reaction:

$$CaCO_3 + H_2O + CO_2 \rightleftharpoons Ca(HCO_3)_2,$$

limestone   carbon   calcium bicar-
(insoluble)   dioxide   bonate (soluble in
                                   cold water)

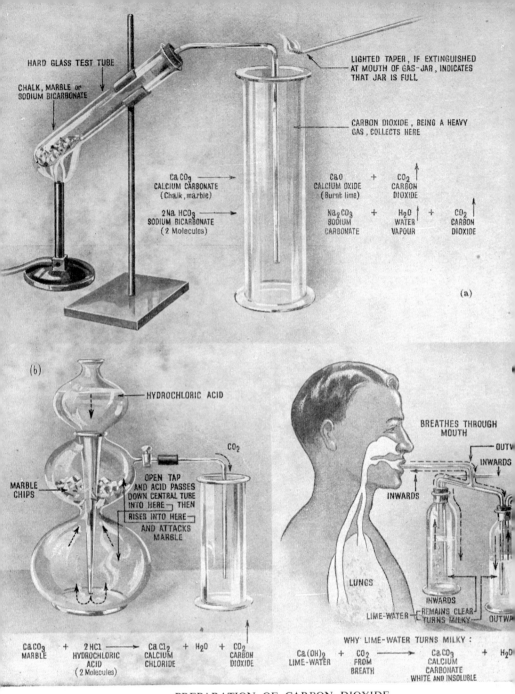

HARD GLASS TEST TUBE

CHALK, MARBLE or SODIUM BICARBONATE

LIGHTED TAPER, IF EXTINGUISHED AT MOUTH OF GAS-JAR, INDICATES THAT JAR IS FULL

CARBON DIOXIDE, BEING A HEAVY GAS, COLLECTS HERE

$CaCO_3$
CALCIUM CARBONATE
(Chalk, marble)

$\rightarrow$

CaO
CALCIUM OXIDE
(Burnt lime)

$+$

CO_2
CARBON
DIOXIDE

$2NaHCO_3$
SODIUM BICARBONATE
(2 Molecules)

$\rightarrow$

Na_2CO_3
SODIUM
CARBONATE

$+$

H_2O
WATER
VAPOUR

$+$

CO_2
CARBON
DIOXIDE

(a)

(b)

HYDROCHLORIC ACID

CO_2

OPEN TAP AND ACID PASSES DOWN CENTRAL TUBE INTO HERE — THEN RISES INTO HERE AND ATTACKS MARBLE

MARBLE CHIPS

BREATHES THROUGH MOUTH

OUTW

INWARDS

INWARDS

LUNGS

LIME-WATER

INWARDS
REMAINS CLEAR
TURNS MILKY

OUTWA

$CaCO_3$
MARBLE

$+$

$2HCl$
HYDROCHLORIC
ACID
(2 Molecules)

$\rightarrow$

$CaCl_2$
CALCIUM
CHLORIDE

$+$

H_2O

$+$

CO_2
CARBON
DIOXIDE

WHY LIME-WATER TURNS MILKY:

$Ca(OH)_2$
LIME-WATER

$+$

CO_2
FROM
BREATH

$\rightarrow$

$CaCO_3$
CALCIUM
CARBONATE
WHITE AND INSOLUBLE

$+$

H_2O

PREPARATION OF CARBON DIOXIDE

FIG. 17. (a) *Carbon dioxide is liberated when certain carbonates and bicarbonates are heated. (b) Kipp's apparatus, suitable for the intermittent preparation of gases. When* tap *is closed, the gas sets up a pressure in central chamber, forcing the acid down into the bottom bulb, some being ultimately forced up into the uppermost bulb. (c) The Living Process is one of slow combustion, resulting in the production of* carbon dioxide.

which shows that soluble calcium bicarbonate is formed. Calcium bicarbonate imparts to water "temporary hardness"; "temporary" because on boiling the bicarbonate decomposes and carbon dioxide is evolved, while the calcium carbonate separates as a white insoluble deposit such as is to be found in "furred" kettles. Water, then, is a veritable carbon dioxide scavenger.

The living plant, unlike the animal, is able to assimilate carbon dioxide directly from the atmosphere and, with the aid of sunlight, it is able to convert carbon dioxide and water into starch, sugars and other carbohydrates, including cellulose. During the daytime, the plant absorbs carbon dioxide from the air and simultaneously returns oxygen to it.

The reverse process occurs to a relatively small extent during daylight, but as night falls the absorption of carbon dioxide almost ceases and then the absorption of oxygen becomes the chief operation. It is possible that the vegetables we eat may have utilized some of the carbon dioxide emitted by the coal fire which we burnt, or possibly some of the vegetation of today may become the coal or peat for the people of the distant future.

This return of oxygen to the air by vegetation compensates for the removal of oxygen from the atmosphere by living beings.

Nitrogen, though almost unreactive, is one of the most essential elements in the living process, whether it be in the plant or animal kingdoms. The proteins, or body builders, are complex compounds of nitrogen, carbon, hydrogen, and oxygen.

Soil Lacks Nitrogen

Man gets his proteins principally from milk, meat and fish and a little from peas, bread and nuts. The plant absorbs nitrogen compounds, when dissolved in water, through its roots. The soil is, however, remarkably deficient in soluble nitrogen compounds and few deposits of nitrogen compounds are found in the earth—the chief deposits being in Chile in the form of nitrate of soda (Chile saltpetre).

Since very ancient times, the rotation of crops has been practised. Virgil, in the first century A.D., stated in a poem that the land on which wheat is grown should lie fallow for one year before wheat is sown again. A better scheme is to sow wheat one year and either pulse or vetch the next, in order to ensure a good crop of wheat in the following season. The reason is that many plants belonging to the *Leguminosæ* order, viz., peas, beans, lentils, clover, lucerne, sainfoin, vetch, not only flourish in soils that are devoid of nitrogen compounds, but they actually enrich the soils with nitrogenous matter.

Bountiful Bacteria

The fact is that these plants become infected with colonies of bacteria which thrive on their roots and produce wrinkled swellings thereon. These bacteria have the power of assimilating nitrogen directly from the air and of converting it into soluble nitrogen compounds in the soil, so that they can be absorbed by the roots of the plant.

The soil is also inhabited by denitrifying bacteria which cause soluble nitrogenous compounds, e.g. nitrates and nitrites, to decompose and to return the nitrogen again to the atmosphere.

Whilst the bacterial putrefaction and decomposition of animal matter that occur in the soil keep the nitrogen in the air at a constant percentage, the fact must not be lost sight of that we depend for our very existence on the productivity of the soil. Were adequate supplies of farmyard manure available, there would be no difficulty in keeping the soil fertile, but this is by no means the case. Artificial nitrogenous fertilizers are essential.

Until the beginning of this century there were two sources: (a) Chile saltpetre, and (b) sulphate of ammonia, the ammonia being extracted from coal during the production of coal gas. Neither was available in amounts equal to the demands of agriculture. In consequence, atmospheric nitrogen received consideration.

If air be heated to 2500–3000 deg. C., between $2\frac{1}{2}$ and 5 per cent of the oxygen will combine with the nitrogen to form nitric oxide, $NO : N_2 + O_2 \rightleftharpoons 2NO$, and the time required is about one-ten-thousandth part of a second. If, however, the air containing the nitric oxide be slowly cooled, then the small amount of nitric oxide formed will break down to form nitrogen and oxygen once again. Sudden cooling to 800 deg. C. prevents this decomposition.

By warming the colourless nitric oxide to 50 deg. C. in air, it will combine with still more oxygen to form a brown gas, nitrogen peroxide, NO_2, thus $2NO + O_2 \longrightarrow 2NO_2$. This will dissolve in water to give a mixture of nitric acid, HNO_3, and nitrous acid, HNO_2; but if the water be hot, only the nitric acid will remain in solution, for the nitrous acid decomposes in the form of gaseous oxides of nitrogen:

$$2NO_2 + H_2O \longrightarrow HNO_3 + HNO_2$$

nitric   nitrous
acid   acid

By neutralizing the nitric acid with slaked lime,

$$2HNO_3 + Ca(OH)_2 \longrightarrow Ca(NO_3)_2 + 2H_2O,$$

an excellent fertilizer, *nitrate of lime*, or *calcium nitrate*, $Ca(NO_3)_2$, is formed, which can be produced in crystalline form.

This is the principle of the process which was devised by Birkeland and Eyde in 1903, who started a factory in Norway at Notodden in 1907. It made use of 40,000 h.p. of electric power derived from waterfalls. The Germans also started a factory on similar lines in Norway in 1911. The drawback to the process was its considerable extravagance in electrical energy, and, whilst this could be offset by cheap waterpower in Norway, the process was uneconomic elsewhere.

Shortly before the First World War, the late Professor F. Haber, a German, and an Englishman, Mr. Le Rossignol, devised a much more economical method of entrapping atmospheric nitrogen. They found that nitrogen and hydrogen would combine at 500–700 deg. C. if the gases were subjected to a high pressure, about 200 atmospheres. Between 3 and 12 per cent of ammonia, NH_3, could thus be formed:

$$3H_2 + N_2 \rightleftharpoons 2NH_3.$$

But the reaction was slow. By passing the mixed gases through a layer of finely-divided platinum or osmium, maintained at the appropriate temperature, the rate of combination could be enormously accelerated. These finely divided particles thus serve as a *catalyst*, which is an agent that alters the speed of the reaction, although it takes no part chemically in the reaction itself (Fig. 18).

Nation's Nitrogen Needs

Various methods are available of extracting the nitrogen from the air and of obtaining the hydrogen from water. One way is to remove the oxygen from both the air and water by making it combine with carbon to form carbon monoxide, CO, and carbon dioxide, CO_2. This is done by squirting water into burning coke, the gases issuing therefrom being a mixture of nitrogen, hydrogen and the two oxides of carbon. The carbon monoxide combines with oxygen in the presence of a catalyst, very often iron oxide, to form carbon dioxide:

$$2CO + O_2 \longrightarrow 2CO_2.$$

The carbon dioxide may be dissolved in water, leaving a mixture of nitrogen and hydrogen.

It was by placing this method on the industrial scale that Germany was able to prolong the First World War, and it was by her vast extension of the nitrogen industry, out of all proportion to her agricultural needs, that she prepared for the Second World War.

Nitrogen Explosives

Not only is nitrogen fixed as ammonia, a vital plant food, but from it nitric acid can be easily made. And nitric acid is necessary for the manufacture of the principal kinds of explosives except, of course, the uranium isotope 235, used in the atomic bomb. Unlike uranium, nitrogen is most abundant, with the result that nitrogenous explosives may be made directly from air and water in vast quantities.

Sulphate of ammonia $(NH_4)_2SO_4$, may be made directly by neutralizing sulphuric acid with ammonia:

$$H_2SO_4 + 2NH_3 \longrightarrow (NH_4)_2SO_4.$$

As free sulphuric acid is expensive,

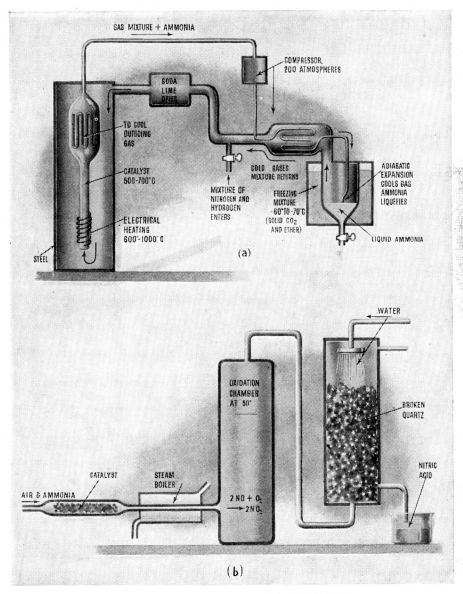

GAS MIXTURE + AMMONIA

COMPRESSOR,
200 ATMOSPHERES

SODA
LIME
DRIER

TO COOL
OUTGOING
GAS

CATALYST
500-700°C

ELECTRICAL
HEATING
800°-1000°C

STEEL

MIXTURE OF
NITROGEN AND
HYDROGEN
ENTERS

COLD GASES
MIXTURE RETURNS

FREEZING
MIXTURE
-60°TO-70°C
(SOLID CO₂
AND ETHER)

ADIABATIC
EXPANSION
COOLS GAS
AMMONIA
LIQUEFIES

LIQUID AMMONIA

(a)

WATER

OXIDATION
CHAMBER
AT 50°

BROKEN
QUARTZ

CATALYST   STEAM
             BOILER

AIR & AMMONIA

NITRIC
ACID

$2 NO + O_2 \rightarrow 2 NO_2$

(b)

TWO IMPORTANT CHEMICAL PROCESSES

Fig. 18. *(a) Haber's process for the synthesis of ammonia from nitrogen and hydrogen. (b) Ostwald's process of converting ammonia into nitric acid by means of air and water.*

ammonium sulphate is more often made by dissolving the natural calcium sulphate, known as *anhydrite*, in water, into which ammonia and carbon dioxide are passed.

This leads to the formation of ammonium sulphate, which remains in solution, whilst the insoluble calcium carbonate separates, is filtered off and the filtrate evaporated

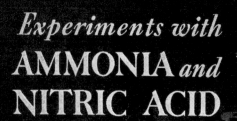

Experiments with
AMMONIA and
NITRIC ACID

BROWN FUMES OF NITROGEN PEROXIDE OWING TO COMBINATION OF NITRIC OXIDE WITH OXYGEN OF AIR

$$2NO + O_2 \longrightarrow 2NO_2$$

AMMONIA, BEING LIGHTER THAN AIR, MUST BE COLLECTED IN THIS WAY

OPEN A JAR OF NITRIC OXIDE TO THE AIR

COLOURLESS NITRIC OXIDE

WHEN JAR IS FULL, AMMONIA WILL EXTINGUISH LIGHTED TAPER

WHAT HAPPENS WHEN NITRIC OXIDE AND AIR MEET

PREPARATION OF AMMONIA

$$2NH_4Cl + CaO \longrightarrow CaCl_2 + H_2O \uparrow + 2NH_3 \uparrow$$

2 AMMONIUM CHLORIDE *(Sal ammoniac)*   CALCIUM OXIDE *(Burnt Lime)*   CALCIUM CHLORIDE   2 AMMONIA

AIR

BROWN FUME (OXIDE OF NITROGEN

PLATINUM W COIL GLOWS

SAL AMMONIAC AND BURNT LIME

AMMONIA GAS

CONCENTRATED SOLUTION OF AMMONIA

BUNSEN BURNER

AMMONIA BURNING

OIL LAMP CHIMNEY

OXYGEN

BURNING OF JET OF AMMONIA GAS IN ATMOSPHERE OF OXYGEN

N.B. AMMONIA WILL NOT BURN IN AIR, OWING TO INSUFFICIENT OXYGEN

AMMONIA

CATALYTIC REACTION OF AMMONIA WITH OXYGEN (IN AIR)

$$4NH_3 + 7O_2 \longrightarrow 4NO_2 + 6H_2O$$

4 AMMONIA + 7 OXYGEN → 4 NITROGEN PERO + 6 WATER

OXYGEN

LASHWELL WOOD

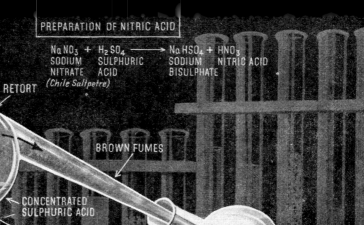

PREPARATION OF NITRIC ACID

$$NaNO_3 + H_2SO_4 \longrightarrow NaHSO_4 + HNO_3$$

SODIUM SULPHURIC SODIUM NITRIC ACID
NITRATE ACID BISULPHATE
(Chile Saltpetre)

RETORT

BROWN FUMES

CONCENTRATED
SULPHURIC ACID

NITRATE OF SODA
OR POTASH OR LIME

COLD WATER TO LIQUEFY
NITRIC ACID VAPOUR

CONCENTRATED NITRIC ACID

THISTLE FUNNEL

ACTION OF CONCENTRATED NITRIC ACID ON COPPER. PREPARATION OF NITRIC OXIDE

BROWN FUMES
(MIXTURE OF
BROWN GAS AND
COLOURLESS GAS)

COLOURLESS GAS
(NITRIC OXIDE)

CONCENTRATED
NITRIC ACID

BROWN GAS
(NITROGEN PEROXIDE)
DISSOLVES IN WATER
MAKING IT ACIDIC —
MIXTURE OF NITROUS
AND NITRIC ACIDS

COPPER FILINGS

ADD A FEW DROPS OF LITMUS OR
METHYL ORANGE – BOTH TURN RED

PNEUMATIC TROUGH

BEEHIVE SHELF

until the crystalline sulphate of ammonia separates:

$$CaSO_4 + H_2O + 2NH_3 + CO_2 \longrightarrow CaCO_3 + (NH_4)_2SO_4.$$

Nitric acid may be obtained from ammonia by passing ammonia and air over platinum, suitably prepared, at a definite rate. Under the right conditions, nitric oxide, NO, is formed thus:

$$4NH_3 + 5O_2 \longrightarrow 4NO + 6H_2O,$$

but there is distinct risk that the oxygen might combine with all the hydrogen atoms in the ammonia and regenerate nitrogen,

$$4NH_3 + 3O_2 \longrightarrow 2N_2 + 6H_2O.$$

Once nitric oxide is obtained, it is converted into nitric acid by the method outlined in Fig. 18.

Between the First and the Second World Wars, this fixation-of-nitrogen industry assumed enormous proportions in all the countries of the world; particularly in Germany. If used aright, this industry, by nourishing the soil so that it may bring forth abundant food, will save mankind from starvation.

Another useful nitrogenous fertilizer is calcium cyanamide, $CaCN_2$. It is made by the heating at 800 deg. C. of calcium carbide, CaC_2, with nitrogen under slight pressure,

$$CaC_2 + N_2 \longrightarrow CaCN_2 + C.$$

Calcium carbide is prepared by heating lime and anthracite in an electric arc furnace at 3000 deg. C. This process necessitates much electric power and is, therefore, operated only where plentiful and cheap power is available.

Carbon Chemistry

Modern organic chemistry consists of the study of carbon compounds. Formerly, the main object was to prepare new compounds, and thousands have been prepared, the majority of which have not been put to any practical advantage. But all the patient research that led to their discovery has not been in vain, for it has brought to light a great deal of fundamental knowledge of which use is constantly being made.

Today, interest is being focused more on products of industrial or physiological importance. Many of the substances in the human body are of extremely complex structure, but some, for instance, the vitamins and hormones, have already been studied and methods have been devised for their manufacture.

The usual method of investigating a natural product is, firstly, to analyse it to ascertain the number of atoms of the different elements that are present in the molecule; secondly, to study the chemical reactions of the substance so as to detect the different groupings of elements it contains; thirdly, to decompose the compound by the available chemical methods and to identify its decomposition products; finally, means are sought whereby the natural product may be synthesized from relatively simple chemicals.

Search for Synthetic Drugs

As the result of such labours, many organic chemicals, particularly new drugs, are being manufactured and widely used which formerly had to be extracted from animal or vegetable matter. Sometimes it has been possible to establish the active physiological principle of a drug, namely, the characteristic grouping which is responsible for its curative action and, in consequence, simpler compounds are prepared which contain the active principle, but which have either none or little of the undesirable properties of the original drug.

Much work remains to be done, and some of the commonest substances, e.g. the proteins, or "body-builders," hold many mysteries yet to be unravelled. The chemist has succeeded in decomposing the proteins and identifying many of the resulting products, viz., the aminoacids, but despite all this he has not yet succeeded in putting them together again to form any known protein.

The starting materials available for synthetic work are obtained from the vegetable or animal kingdoms or from coal tar. From the former are obtained such substances as ethyl and methyl alcohol; formic, acetic, malic, citric and tartaric acids, and glycerine, whilst coal tar provides benzene, toluene, phenol, pyridine, etc. Other starting materials, however, are now being made available by their direct synthesis (building

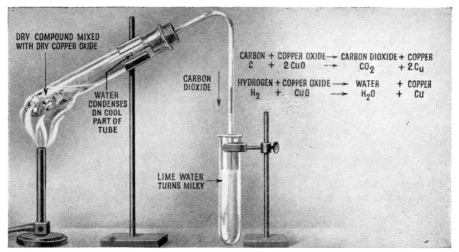

DRY COMPOUND MIXED
WITH DRY COPPER OXIDE

WATER
CONDENSES
ON COOL
PART OF
TUBE

CARBON
DIOXIDE

CARBON + COPPER OXIDE—→ CARBON DIOXIDE + COPPER
C + 2CuO —→ CO$_2$ + 2Cu

HYDROGEN + COPPER OXIDE —→ WATER + COPPER
H$_2$ +. CuO —→ H$_2$O + Cu

LIME WATER
TURNS MILKY

DETECTING THE ELEMENTS IN AN ORGANIC COMPOUND

FIG. 19. *Proving that an organic compound contains carbon and hydrogen. Oxygen from copper oxide combines with hydrogen, forming water; carbon, forming carbon dioxide.*

up) from simple substances such as air, water and coal, and the by-products of the distillation and "cracking" of petroleum.

Now let us try to remove the mystery that enshrouds the formulæ which chemists use to indicate not only the constituents but the quantities which exist in an organic substance. To establish a formula, we must ascertain which elements are present, then estimate precisely their percentage amounts and finally find the molecular weight. From the percentage analysis and the atomic weights of the elements we can calculate the ratio of the numbers of atoms of the elements in the molecule of the compound, but until we have found the actual weight of the molecule we cannot say precisely how many atoms of the different elements are present.

Testing for Carbon

Carbon and hydrogen are easily detected by heating a mixture of dry copper oxide and the dry compound in a hard glass tube, fixed in the mouth of which is a delivery tube with the other end dipping into lime water (Fig. 19). Any carbon present will be converted into carbon dioxide and this will turn lime water milky by forming insoluble calcium carbonate:

$$Ca(OH)_2 + CO_2 \longrightarrow CaCO_3 \downarrow + H_2O.$$

Likewise, hydrogen in the compound will remove oxygen from the copper oxide and form water as a film or drops on the upper part of the test tube. To prove that water is produced, you would place on suspected moisture a crystal of copper sulphate, from which the water of crystallization has been driven off by previous heating, thereby turning its colour from blue to white. On touching the moisture with the white crystal, the water immediately combines and blue colour will be restored.

Detecting Nitrogen

Nitrogen is more difficult to detect. The principle of the test is to convert the nitrogen and carbon in the compound into sodium cyanide, the sodium salt of prussic acid. This is done by heating the compound in a tube with molten sodium for a few minutes and then plunging the hot tube into a basin of cold distilled water, whereupon the tube is fractured and any sodium cyanide that may have been formed dissolves in the water. Caution: this is a dangerous process!

To a little of the solution add a few drops of ferrous sulphate solution and two or three drops of ferric chloride solution. Heat slightly and, after cooling, add dilute hydrochloric acid. A blue coloration or precipitate (Prussian Blue) shows that nitrogen is in the compound (Fig. 20).

If sulphur was present, the sodium in the previous test would have combined with it to form sodium sulphide. If this has occurred, a drop of the solution placed on a silver coin will make a black stain of sulphide of silver.

Detecting a Halogen

If another portion of the solution resulting from the fusion with sodium is taken and boiled for a few minutes with dilute nitric acid to destroy the cyanide, and then a little silver nitrate solution is added, the presence of one or all of the three halogens will be indicated by a white or yellow precipitate. If the element is chlorine, the precipitate will readily dissolve in dilute ammonia solution; if iodine, the precipitate will not dissolve, but if bromine, the precipitate will not dissolve unless a fairly concentrated solution of ammonia is employed.

The two elements, carbon and hydrogen, are estimated simultaneously. Perfectly dry air or oxygen is very slowly passed through a tube in which is placed, in a porcelain boat, an accurately weighed amount of the organic compound, the tube being uniformly heated, usually by numerous Bunsen burners. The compound burns and the products of combustion are made to pass through a length of tubing filled with coarse copper oxide (in wire form), which converts any carbon or carbon monoxide into carbon dioxide,

$$C \qquad + 2CuO \longrightarrow 2\,Cu \qquad + CO_2$$
Carbon   + 2 Copper⟶2 Copper + Carbon
            oxide   dioxide

or,

$$CO \qquad + CuO \longrightarrow Cu \qquad + CO_2$$
Carbon   + Copper ⟶Copper   + Carbon
monoxide   oxide   dioxide

and any hydrogen into water vapour,

$$H_2 \qquad + CuO \longrightarrow Cu \qquad + H_2O$$
Hydrogen + Copper ⟶Copper + Water
            oxide

The water vapour is quantitatively absorbed *in a previously weighed* U-tube containing fused calcium chloride, and the carbon dioxide is subsequently absorbed *in a previously weighed* system of bulbs containing a solution of potassium hydroxide. The experiment is continued for two or three hours until all traces of the compound have disappeared from the boat.

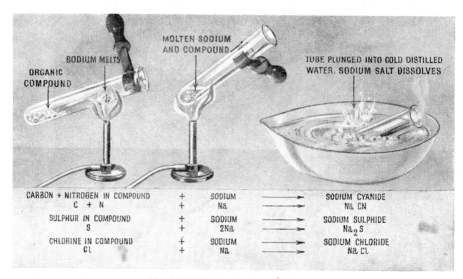

CARBON + NITROGEN IN COMPOUND   +   SODIUM   ⟶   SODIUM CYANIDE
        C + N   +   Na   Na CN

SULPHUR IN COMPOUND   +   SODIUM   ⟶   SODIUM SULPHIDE
        S   +   2Na Na_2S

CHLORINE IN COMPOUND   +   SODIUM   ⟶   SODIUM CHLORIDE
        Cl   +   Na   Na Cl

ANALYTICAL USE OF SODIUM

FIG. 20. *How the elements, nitrogen, sulphur, chlorine, bromine, iodine, are first made to combine with sodium in order to detect them by means of chemical tests.*

Afterwards, the U-tube and the potash bulbs are weighed again, the increase in the former being equal to the weight of water produced and that in the latter to the carbon dioxide formed.

Knowing that of water, H_2O, $\frac{2}{18}$ths is hydrogen, it follows that $\frac{1}{9}$th of the weight of water must have been that of the hydrogen originally in the compound. Similarly, carbon constituted $\frac{3}{11}$ths of the weight of carbon dioxide, so that $\frac{3}{11}$ths of the carbon dioxide collected in the bulbs is equal to the carbon that was originally in the compound. Hence, the percentage of hydrogen and of carbon in the compound can be easily calculated.

If the compound contains nitrogen, sulphur or chlorine, slight modifications in packing the combustion tube are necessary.

The method of estimating nitrogen is somewhat similar in principle. Carbon dioxide, generated by heating magnesite,

$$Mg\,CO_3 \longrightarrow MgO + CO_2,$$

| magnesium | magnesia | carbon |
| carbonate | | dioxide |

is passed through a long heated tube in which a weighed amount of the compound is intimately mixed with fine copper oxide, and a spiral of copper gauze is placed at the end of the tube in order to remove any oxygen from the oxides of nitrogen and thus liberate nitrogen itself (Fig. 21).

Collecting the Nitrogen

The nitrogen is collected in a gas burette, as shown, over a solution of potassium hydroxide which dissolves carbon dioxide but does not dissolve the nitrogen. Therefore, it collects in the burette, or nitrometer, as it is frequently called.

When the experiment is ended, the volume of nitrogen liberated is measured by raising the reservoir (right) until the level of the solution in it is the same as that in the nitrometer. The temperature and height of the barometer are observed, which make it possible to calculate the volume of nitrogen at 0 deg. C. and 760 mm. mercury pressure by making use of Boyle's and Charles's Laws. Then, knowing that a gram-molecule of any gas occupies 22·4 litres at 0 deg. and 760 mm., i.e. 28 grams of nitrogen occupy

this volume, it is possible to calculate the actual weight of nitrogen obtained and, consequently, the percentage of nitrogen in the compound.

Calculating Percentage Composition

Methods of estimating the other elements that may exist in organic compounds are also available, except in the case of oxygen. When oxygen is proved to be present and all the other elements have been estimated, the remaining percentage amount (viz., that required to make up 100 per cent) is taken to be that of oxygen.

The following example illustrates the calculation of the percentage composition of an organic substance from combustion data and shows how the simplest formula may be derived therefrom.

0·5 gram of an organic liquid on complete combustion yielded 1·137 grams of carbon dioxide and 0·468 gram of water. Calculate the percentage composition and find the empirical formula.

Weight of carbon in 1·137 gram CO_2
$$=\tfrac{3}{11}\times 1\cdot137 \text{ gram}$$
$$=0\cdot310 \text{ gram.}$$

Weight of hydrogen in 0·468 gram H_2O
$$=\tfrac{1}{9}\times 0\cdot468 \text{ gram}$$
$$=0\cdot052 \text{ gram.}$$

Percentage of carbon
$$=\tfrac{0\cdot310}{0\cdot500}\times 100$$
$$=62\cdot0.$$

Percentage of hydrogen
$$=\tfrac{0\cdot052}{0\cdot500}\times 100$$
$$=10\cdot4.$$

Total percentage of weight of carbon and hydrogen
$$=72\cdot4.$$

If no other elements could be detected in the compound, and if its properties indicated the presence of oxygen therein, then:

Percentage of oxygen
$$=100-72\cdot4$$
$$=27\cdot6.$$

∴ Compound contains 62·0 per cent of carbon, 10·4 per cent of hydrogen, and 27·6 per cent of oxygen.

The compound contains these three elements in the form of atoms. To calculate the simplest ratio of the numbers of the different atoms we must know the relative weights of the atoms; that of *carbon* is 12, *hydrogen* is 1, and *oxygen* 16.

It follows that $\frac{62 \cdot 0}{12 \cdot 0} : \frac{10 \cdot 4}{1} : \frac{27 \cdot 6}{16} =$ number of atoms of *carbon* : number of atoms of *hydrogen* : number of atoms of *oxygen*= $5 \cdot 167 : 10 \cdot 4 : 1 \cdot 725$.

Dividing by the smallest number, $1 \cdot 725$, we obtain the simplest atomic ratio, $\frac{5 \cdot 167}{1 \cdot 725} : \frac{10 \cdot 4}{1 \cdot 725} : \frac{1 \cdot 725}{1 \cdot 725} = 3 : 6 : 1$.

Therefore, the simplest formula, or, as it is usually called, the *empirical formula*, is C_3H_6O. All that it indicates, however, is the simplest ratio of the various atoms contained in a compound. It does *not* necessarily give the precise number of atoms of the different elements that actually exist in a molecule of the compound. For clearly, if x is a whole number, the ratio $3x$ atoms of C : $6x$ atoms of H : $1x$ atoms of O, would satisfy the percentage requirements equally well. The formula that gives the exact number of atoms in a molecule, viz., $C_{3x}H_{6x}O_x$, is the *Molecular Formula;* x, of course, being known.

Determining Molecular Weights

Before we can find the value of x it is necessary to determine the molecular weight. This may be done by several methods:

(i) by determining the vapour density;

(ii) from the extent by which the freezing point of some solvent is lowered, when a definite weight of the compound is dissolved in a known weight of that solvent;

(iii) from the elevation of the boiling point of a solvent when a definite weight of the compound is dissolved in a known weight of the solvent;

(iv) from the diminution in the vapour pressure of its solution compared with that of the solvent alone at any given temperature.

In the example under consideration, the vapour density of the compound is found to be 29, whence it follows that the molecular weight is $2 \times 29 = 58$.

The weight indicated by the simplest formula, C_3H_6O, is $(3 \times 12)+(6 \times 1)+(16) = 58$, which happens to be the same as the molecular weight. Hence, $x=1$ and

the Molecular Formula is C_3H_6O. Had the molecular weight been 2×58, then x would have been 2 and the Molecular Formula, $C_6H_{12}O_2$.

The molecular formula shows the actual number of atoms of the different elements in a molecule, but it gives no information about their arrangement. For instance, a compound having the formula C_3H_6O might be either C_2H_5CHO (propion-alde-hyde), or CH_3COCH_3 (acetone), these being quite different compounds. Not only have they very different odours, but they are unlike in their chemical properties. The latter formulæ are *Constitutional or Structural Formulæ*, for they give the characteristic groups, e.g. $-C_2H_5$, $-CH_3$, $-CHO_3$, $-CO$, and show how these groups are linked together within the molecule.

A compound has a definite Molecular Formula and one *Constitutional or Structural Formula*. In the example we have been studying, the Molecular Formula may represent either of two compounds, each having its own Constitutional Formula. Such compounds are said to be *isomeric* with one another; each being an *isomer* of the other. *Isomers* are compounds which contain the same number of atoms of identical elements, but which are arranged differently in their separate molecules. *Isomerism* is a common occurrence in organic chemistry.

If we consider the many compounds which carbon forms with hydrogen and calculate from their percentage compositions the apparent combining weights which carbon utilizes in the different compounds, we should find that carbon appears to violate the Law of Multiple Proportions. For example, in methane, 1 gram of hydrogen is combined with 3 grams of carbon; in ethane, 4 grams; in propane, $4 \cdot 5$ grams; in butane, $4 \cdot 8$ grams; in pentane, 5 grams, etc. But if we also take into consideration the molecular weights of these hydrocarbons (i.e. compounds of *hydrogen* and *carbon*) and remember that it is the atoms that actually combine, we shall arrive at the following molecular formulæ: methane, CH_4; ethane, C_2H_6; propane, C_3H_8; butane, C_4H_{10}; pentane, C_5H_{12}.

Now, organic chemistry is based on one

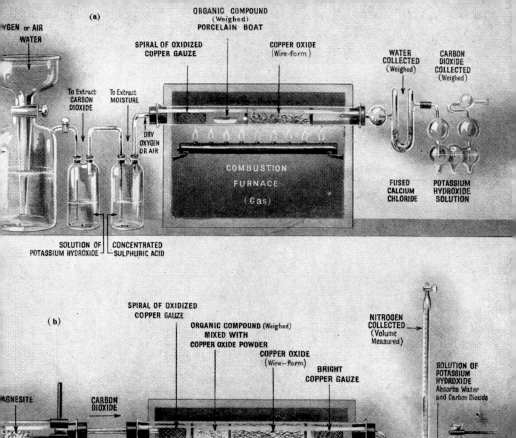

HOW AN ORGANIC COMPOUND IS ANALYSED

FIG. 21. *(a) Here is illustrated the apparatus which is required for the estimation of the percentage by weight of carbon and hydrogen in an organic compound. (b) Showing Dumas's apparatus as used to estimate the percentage of nitrogen by weight in organic compounds.*

fundamental principle, first enunciated in 1858 by Kekulé and Couper, that *the valency of carbon is always four*. With this in mind we shall attempt to assign structural formulæ to the above hydrocarbons. Thus, methane is

the four strokes representing the four valency bonds. It should be mentioned that this method of representing a structural formula is not altogether satisfactory, for molecules occupy space and, therefore, the structural formula should be represented in three dimensions (Fig. 22). Hence, as the four valency forces are the same, the carbon atom will be at the centre of a sphere and the four hydrogen atoms will

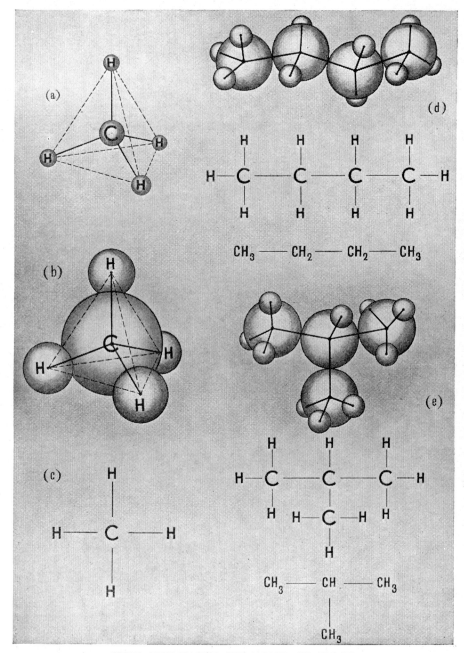

HOW ATOMS ARE ARRANGED IN SPACE

FIG. 22. *(a) Geometrical arrangement of the four hydrogen atoms at corners of a regular tetrahedron; the carbon atom is located in the centre of the molecule of methane. (b) Atoms in a molecule of methane. (c) Plane formula. (d) Normal butane. (e) Iso-butane.*

be oriented uniformly around its surface.

The valency of the carbon atom in ethane, C_2H_6, appears to be three, as its two carbon atoms hold six hydrogen atoms. The structural formula, however, reveals that the valency is *four*, for two carbon atoms are held together by a single valency, thus:

$$\begin{array}{cc} H & H \\ | & | \\ H-C\!\!-\!\!-\!\!-\!\!-C-H, & \text{or, in short. } CH_3CH_3. \\ | & | \\ H & H \end{array}$$

The structural formula of propane, C_3H_8, is:

$$\begin{array}{ccc} H & H & H \\ | & | & | \\ H-C\!\!-\!\!-\!\!-C\!\!-\!\!-\!\!-C-H, & & \text{i.e. } CH_3CH_2CH_3. \\ | & | & | \\ H & H & H \end{array}$$

Paraffin Hydrocarbons

Each of the hydrocarbons having four or more carbon atoms and exerting four valencies, viz., butane, pentane, hexane, heptane, octane, etc., may exist in several isomeric forms. Fig. 22 shows the structures of the two isomers of butane. *Normal butane* consists of a *single chain* of carbon atoms, whilst, as the formula shows, the *iso-butane* is a *branched* hydrocarbon.

Although the two butanes are gaseous at ordinary temperature and pressure, the chain-hydrocarbon liquefies at 10 deg. C. and the iso-compound at -17 deg. C. Under increased pressures, both gases become liquid at ordinary temperatures. As liquids under pressure, the butanes are sold, under various trade names, in tanks; on reducing the pressure by opening the valve, they again become gaseous and are used in country districts for heating and lighting purposes.

The number of isomers of pentane, C_5H_{12}, is 3; hexane, C_6H_{14}, 5; heptane, C_7H_{16}, 9; and octane, C_8H_{18}, 18; whilst the number of possible isomers of $C_{13}H_{28}$ is 802.

It will have been noticed that the general formula of the hydrocarbons in which the quadrivalency of carbon is maintained is C_nH_{2n+2}. These hydrocarbons are referred to as the *Saturated Hydrocarbons*, or *The Paraffins*.

Petroleum is a complex mixture of hydrocarbons which may have resulted from the decay of vegetation. The nature of the hydrocarbons varies with the source of origin. All petroleums contain many of the paraffins, but that obtained from Pennsylvania contains the greatest proportions of saturated hydrocarbons. Refining is carried out by fractional distillation; the

PENNSYLVANIAN PETROLEUM FRACTIONS

Boiling Range	Number of Carbon Atoms in Paraffins	Technical Name	Uses
Up to 30° C.	C_4–C_5	{ Cymogene ⟨ Rhigolene	Refrigerants
30°– 70°	C_5–C_6	Petroleum ether	Solvent
70°–120°	C_6–C_8	⎰ Petrol ⟨ Gasoline ⎱ Ligroin	Motor spirit / Dry cleaning / Solvent
120°–150°	C_8–C_9	Benzoline	Dry cleaning solvent
70°–150°	C_6–C_9	Petrol	Motor spirit
70°–250°	C_6–C_{13}	Tractor vaporizing oil	Tractor spirit
150°–300°	C_{10}–C_{18}	Paraffin ⎱ Kerosene ⎰	Illuminant
Above 300°	C_{23}–C_{28}	Paraffin-wax (melting point, 48°–62° C.)	Candles
,,	—	Oil	Lubricant
,,	—	Vaseline	Ointments

different fractions being used for particular purposes and are sold under various designations.

Two series of unsaturated hydrocarbons exist:

(i) *The Olefines*, general formula, C_nH_{2n};
(ii) *The Acetylenes*, general formula, C_nH_{2n-2}.

Ethylene Compounds

The simplest member of the *olefine* series is ethylene, C_2H_4 (Fig. 23). It is a reactive gas, burns with a smoky flame and forms an explosive mixture with air. It combines with chlorine and bromine simply by adding on two atoms of these elements to each molecule of ethylene, thus:

$$C_2H_4 \quad + Br_2 \quad \longrightarrow C_2H_4Br_2$$
ethylene   bromine   ethylene
dibromide

The explanation of these *addition-reactions* is to be found in the apparent valency of each of the carbon atoms. On the grounds that the valency of carbon is *four*, the structural formula of ethylene may be represented thus:

$$\begin{array}{cc} H & H \\ | & | \\ H-C-\!-\!-C-H \\ | & | \end{array}$$

in which both carbon atoms have an unused valency. That this is actually the case is shown by the way in which chlorine or bromine unites to form, respectively:

$$\begin{array}{cc} H & H \\ | & | \\ H-C-\!-\!-C-H \\ | & | \\ Cl & Cl \end{array} \quad \text{and} \quad \begin{array}{cc} H & H \\ | & | \\ H-C-\!-\!-C-H \\ | & | \\ Br & Br \end{array}$$
ethylene dichloride   ethylene dibro-
mide

Ethylene also combines with sulphuric acid, H_2SO_4, to form ethyl sulphuric acid, $C_2H_5HSO_4$, or, structurally:

$$\begin{array}{c} H \\ | \\ H-C- \\ | \\ H-C- \\ | \\ H \end{array} + \left\{ \begin{array}{c} H \\ HSO_4 \end{array} \right. \longrightarrow \begin{array}{c} H \\ | \\ H-C-H \\ | \\ H-C-HSO_4 \\ | \\ H \end{array}$$
ethylene   sulphuric   ethyl
acid   sulphuric acid

Instead of representing ethylene with *two loose valencies*, as shown above, it is considered that the unused valencies swing towards one another and ultimately satisfy one another in the form of a *double bond* between the carbon atoms:

$$\begin{array}{cc} H & H \\ | & | \\ H-C-\!-\!-C-H \\ | & | \end{array} \qquad \begin{array}{cc} H & H \\ | & | \\ H-C-\!-\!-C-H \\ \backslash & / \end{array}$$

$$\begin{array}{cc} & H \quad H \\ & | \quad | \\ & H-C = C-H \end{array}$$

The "double bond" in the last formula shows that the valencies of ethylene are unsaturated and that ethylene will combine in such a way as to make the carbon atoms four-valent, in other words, to convert an unsaturated hydrocarbon into a saturated compound.

Groups of atoms of carbon and hydrogen are given distinctive names. Thus, the term *methyl* is applied to CH_3-; *ethyl* to C_2H_5-; *propyl* to C_3H_7-, and so on. In these groups the carbon atoms are attached successively to one another in the form of a chain, e.g.

propyl, C_3H_7-, is $CH_3CH_2CH_2-$.

But the same formula, C_3H_7, refers equally well to the arrangement: CH_3

$$\begin{array}{c} CH_3 \\ | \\ H-C- \\ | \\ CH_3, \end{array}$$

which shows that the other element or group of elements is attached to the middle carbon atom instead of to a carbon atom at the end of a chain. Such a group is *isomeric* with the *normal* or chain group, and the fact is denoted by the prefix, *iso*, e.g. *isopropyl* $(CH_3)_2CH-$.

The presence of an $-OH$ (hydroxyl) group alone in an aliphatic compound indicates that it is an *alcohol*. Examples are: methyl alcohol, CH_3OH; ethyl alcohol, C_2H_5OH; *n.* propyl alcohol, C_3H_7OH; *iso*-propyl alcohol $(CH_3)_2CH.OH$. Compounds exist which have more than one alcohol group; for instance, the simplest dihydric alcohol is *ethylene glycol*, $\begin{array}{c} CH_2OH \\ | \\ CH_2OH \end{array}$, well known to motorists as an anti-freeze; and

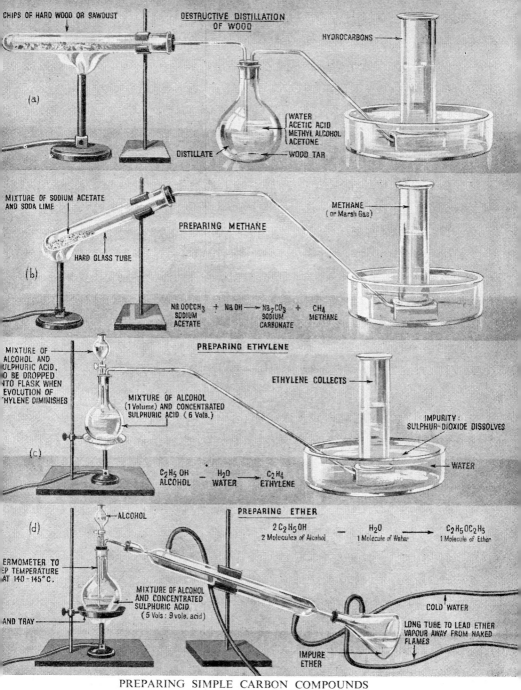

CHIPS OF HARD WOOD OR SAWDUST

DESTRUCTIVE DISTILLATION OF WOOD

HYDROCARBONS

(a)

WATER
ACETIC ACID
METHYL ALCOHOL
ACETONE

DISTILLATE

WOOD TAR

MIXTURE OF SODIUM ACETATE AND SODA LIME

PREPARING METHANE

METHANE (or Marsh Gas)

HARD GLASS TUBE

(b)

$Na OOCCH_3$ + $Na OH$ → $Na_2 CO_3$ + CH_4
SODIUM ACETATE   SODIUM CARBONATE   METHANE

PREPARING ETHYLENE

MIXTURE OF ALCOHOL AND SULPHURIC ACID. TO BE DROPPED INTO FLASK WHEN EVOLUTION OF ETHYLENE DIMINISHES

MIXTURE OF ALCOHOL (1 Volume) AND CONCENTRATED SULPHURIC ACID (6 Vols.)

ETHYLENE COLLECTS

IMPURITY: SULPHUR-DIOXIDE DISSOLVES

(c)

$C_2 H_5 OH$ — H_2O → $C_2 H_4$
ALCOHOL   WATER   ETHYLENE

WATER

PREPARING ETHER

(d)

ALCOHOL

$2 C_2 H_5 OH$ — H_2O → $C_2 H_5 OC_2 H_5$
2 Molecules of Alcohol   1 Molecule of Water   1 Molecule of Ether

THERMOMETER TO KEEP TEMPERATURE AT 140-145° C.

MIXTURE OF ALCOHOL AND CONCENTRATED SULPHURIC ACID (5 Vols : 9 vols. acid)

COLD WATER

SAND TRAY

IMPURE ETHER

LONG TUBE TO LEAD ETHER VAPOUR AWAY FROM NAKED FLAMES

PREPARING SIMPLE CARBON COMPOUNDS

FIG. 23. *(a) Obtaining chemical compounds by the heating of wood. (b) Making methane or "marsh gas." (c) By removing water from ethyl alcohol, ethylene gas is created. (d) How ether is made by the removal of a smaller proportion of water from alcohol. Methane, ethylene and ether are all highly inflammable. Hence they should be kept away from any naked flame, lest an explosion should result.*

the simplest, *trihydric alcohol*, is glycerol, or *glycerine*, as it is commonly called.

$$CH_2OH$$
$$|$$
$$CH\ OH$$
$$|$$
$$CH_2OH$$

Naming the Alcohols

One of the recommendations made at a conference of chemists held at Geneva was to simplify the names of alcohols, by adding the suffix *ol* to that of the parent hydrocarbon. Thus, instead of methyl alcohol, methan*ol* was suggested. Curiously enough, this name is applied to the industrial product which is used as a motor fuel. Formerly, methyl alcohol was prepared chiefly by the destructive distillation of wood but, nowadays, it is made synthetically by passing a compressed mixture of hydrogen and carbon monoxide over a heated catalyst. This mixture, or "water-gas," as it is known in industry, is obtained by spraying white-hot coke with water.

$$C + H_2O \rightarrow CO + H_2\ ;\ CO + 2H_2 \rightarrow CH_3OH$$

carbon hydro-   methanol
mon-   gen
oxide

"water-gas"

Enzyme Action

Alcohols, particularly ethyl alcohol, are obtained by the fermentation of sugar (molasses), starchy materials such as barley, potatoes, rice and maize, cellulose such as sawdust and wood, with the aid of suitable agents called enzymes. Enzymes and ferments, secreted by plants and animals, are organic catalysts, but unlike a catalyst used in inorganic chemistry, a particular enzyme has the power to catalyse, i.e. accelerate, a particular reaction. Enzyme is derived from two Greek words meaning "in yeast." One of the reactions that takes place during the fermentation of glucose (grape-sugar) is:

$$C_6H_{12}O_6 \longrightarrow 2C_2H_5OH + 2CO_2$$

glucose   ethyl   carbon
              alcohol   dioxide

Aldehydes are generally liquids with distinctive odours and tastes. They are largely responsible for the "bouquet" of fermented liquors, notably wines and spirits (Fig. 24).

Bacterial and enzyme actions are usually oxidations in which alcohols, aldehydes and acids are formed. The formation of acids explains the souring of beer and wine when left exposed to the air. Vinegar is produced by the enzyme action set up by the bacterium *Mycoderma aceti* (mother of vinegar), in which a dilute alcoholic liquor is oxidized to acetic acid. Although solutions containing 14 per cent of acetic acid may thus be prepared, ordinary vinegar contains 3 to 6 per cent.

In a really satisfactory nomenclature of the compounds derived from a hydrocarbon, the name of the parent hydrocarbon should appear in the name of each derivative. This is the case with the propane and butane derivatives, e.g. C_3H_8 (propane), C_3H_7OH (propyl alcohol), C_2H_5CHO (propionaldehyde), C_2H_5COOH (propionic acid). In other cases, however, whereas the hydrocarbon obtains its name from the number of carbon atoms (except butane), the corresponding acid (and aldehyde) receives a name based on its natural source. This will be seen from the table on page 327 of some fatty acids.

These acids, being saturated, have the general formula $C_nH_{2n+1}COOH$. Because they are usually found in natural fats, this series of acids is known as the Fatty Acids. Some of the acids from capric to cerotic are solid at ordinary temperatures and are fatty or wax-like in nature.

Acids in which double bonds appear in the carbon chains are designated unsaturated acids. Oleic acid is such an acid. It is an oily liquid and its formula is $C_{17}H_{33}COOH$, which may be compared with the formula of the corresponding saturated acid, stearic, $C_{17}H_{35}COOH$, a solid. Oleic acid has a double bond situated in the middle of the chain of carbon atoms. Oleic acid may be converted into stearic acid by making it combine with two atoms of hydrogen, which it does in the presence of "reduced" nickel. (Catalytic hydrogenation.)

Linseed oil contains, in a state of

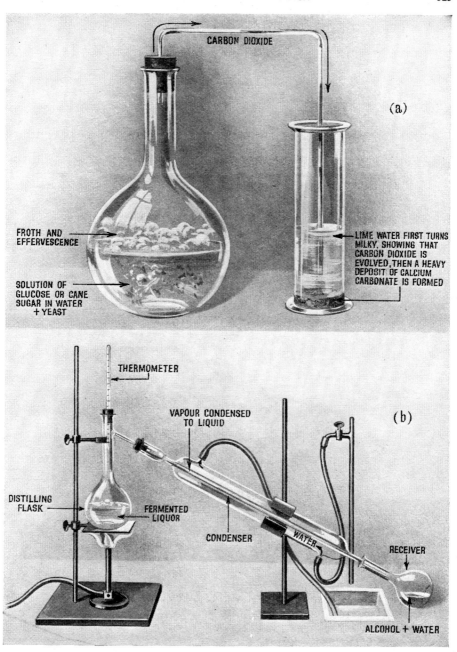

(a)

CARBON DIOXIDE

FROTH AND EFFERVESCENCE

LIME WATER FIRST TURNS MILKY, SHOWING THAT CARBON DIOXIDE IS EVOLVED, THEN A HEAVY DEPOSIT OF CALCIUM CARBONATE IS FORMED

SOLUTION OF GLUCOSE OR CANE SUGAR IN WATER + YEAST

THERMOMETER

VAPOUR CONDENSED TO LIQUID

(b)

DISTILLING FLASK

FERMENTED LIQUOR

CONDENSER

WATER

RECEIVER

ALCOHOL + WATER

DISTILLATION OF FERMENTED LIQUIDS

FIG. 24. (a) By fermenting a solution of sugar at about 25 deg. C., the principal compounds produced are ethyl alcohol and carbon dioxide. (b) How the alcohol is extracted from the fermented solution by simple distillation. The first fraction contains most of the alcohol.

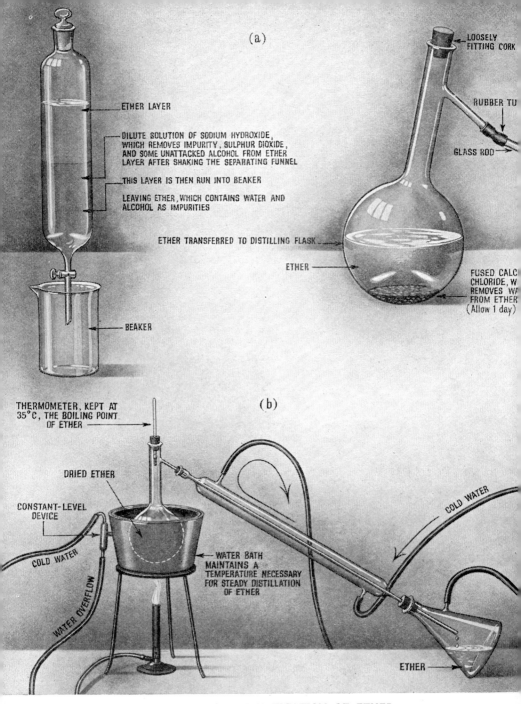

(a)

ETHER LAYER

DILUTE SOLUTION OF SODIUM HYDROXIDE,
WHICH REMOVES IMPURITY, SULPHUR DIOXIDE,
AND SOME UNATTACKED ALCOHOL FROM ETHER
LAYER AFTER SHAKING THE SEPARATING FUNNEL

THIS LAYER IS THEN RUN INTO BEAKER

LEAVING ETHER, WHICH CONTAINS WATER AND
ALCOHOL AS IMPURITIES

ETHER TRANSFERRED TO DISTILLING FLASK

ETHER

BEAKER

LOOSELY
FITTING CORK

RUBBER TU

GLASS ROD

FUSED CALC
CHLORIDE, W
REMOVES WA
FROM ETHER
(Allow 1 day)

(b)

THERMOMETER, KEPT AT
35°C, THE BOILING POINT
OF ETHER

DRIED ETHER

CONSTANT-LEVEL
DEVICE

COLD WATER

WATER OVERFLOW

WATER BATH
MAINTAINS A
TEMPERATURE NECESSARY
FOR STEADY DISTILLATION
OF ETHER

COLD WATER

ETHER

LABORATORY PURIFICATION OF ETHER

FIG. 25. (a) Extraction of impurities, viz., sulphur dioxide and water. (b) Distillation
of ether. Note how any ether vapour in the receiver is led away from the vicinity of a flame.
Traces of water and alcohol remaining in the ether may be removed by inserting bright
pieces of sodium metal, allowing it to stand, then re-distilling.

combination with glycerine, acids with two and three double bonds. The drying of the oil (in paints and varnishes) depends on oxygen from the air combining at the double bonds—the rate of which can be appreciably accelerated by "driers," e.g. manganese dioxide, included in the paint or varnish.

Marine animal (e.g. whale) oils are composed of glycerine compounds of highly unsaturated acids. They contain as many as four or five double bonds. The most important acids have about eighteen carbon atoms. They, too, can be hydrogenated to the corresponding saturated compounds.

The alcohols we have so far considered are the so-called *primary alcohols*. They have the general formula, RCH_2OH; R being H, CH_3, C_2H_5, etc.

Secondary Alcohols

Secondary alcohols have the general formula:

R
|
CHOH, in which R and R′ may be CH_3,
| C_2H_5, etc.
R′

An example is isopropyl alcohol,

$$CH_3$$
$$|$$
$$H—C—OH$$
$$|$$
$$CH_3$$

Secondary alcohols are distinguished from primary alcohols by the fact that oxidation, which may be effected either chemically or by fermentation (using an appropriate enzyme), yields a ketone, the characteristic group of the latter being

$$>C=O,$$

(i)

CH_3
iso-propyl alcohol

CH_3
dimethyl ketone or acetone

(ii)

C_2H_5
iso-butyl alcohol

C_2H_5
methyl ethyl ketone

Acetone is a product of faulty digestive metabolism and its sweetish smell can often be detected in the breath of sufferers. Acetone can be obtained by the dry distillation of wood. Industrially, it is prepared by the fermentation of the starch in rice, maize and horse chestnuts by Fernbach's culture, which yields a mixture of acetone (15 to 24 per cent) and n-butyl alcohol (30 to 48 per cent).

Odorous Esters

Organic acids and alcohols interact to form esters with the elimination of water. Esters have distinctive odours, often pleasant, and flavours that resemble those

SOME FATTY ACIDS

Fatty Acid		Formula	Present in
Formic acid	..	HCOOH	*formica* = ant: prepared by the distillation of ants
Acetic acid	..	CH_3COOH	*acetum* = vinegar
Butyric acid	..	C_3H_7COOH	*butyrum* = butter
Valeric acid	..	C_4H_9COOH	valerian plant roots, iso-acid
Caproic acid	..	$C_5H_{11}COOH$	*caper* = goat
Caprylic acid	..	$C_7H_{15}COOH$	in goat's butter m.p. 16·5° C.
Capric acid	..	$C_9H_{19}COOH$	,, 31° C.
Lauric acid	..	$C_{11}H_{23}COOH$	in laurel oil ,, 44° C.
Palmitic acid	..	$C_{15}H_{31}COOH$	in palm oil ,, 63° C.
Stearic acid	..	$C_{17}H_{35}COOH$	*stear* = tallow. Beef and Mutton fat ,, 69° C.
Cerotic acid	..	$C_{25}H_{51}COOH$	*cere* = wax
			in beeswax ,, 78·5° C.

of fruits. They are used in artificial fruit essences and in perfumery.

$$\text{C}_2\text{H}_5[\text{OH} + \text{H}]\text{OOC.C}_3\text{H}_7 \longrightarrow$$
ethyl alcohol + butyric acid $\longrightarrow$
$$\text{C}_2\text{H}_5\text{OOC.C}_3\text{H}_7 + \text{H}_2\text{O}$$
ethyl butyrate + water

Esters Form Fine Flavourings

Esters are generally volatile liquids. They dissolve in alcohol and it is in alcoholic solution that they are used as flavourings and perfumes. Ethyl butyrate in an alcoholic solution becomes "*Essence of Pineapple.*" Very often a number of different esters are mixed in suitable proportions to simulate the taste and aroma of some particular fruit.

Ethers are compounds formed when a molecule of water is removed from one molecule of any alcohol and another molecule of the same or a different alcohol. The particular ether used as an anæsthetic is the diethyl ether (Fig. 25). It may be prepared by extracting the water, with the aid of concentrated sulphuric acid, from two molecules of ordinary ethyl alcohol, thus :

$$\text{C}_2\text{H}_5\text{O}[\text{H} + \text{HO}]\text{C}_2\text{H}_5 \longrightarrow$$
ethyl alcohol (2 molecules)
$$\text{H}_2\text{O} + \text{C}_2\text{H}_5\text{OC}_2\text{H}_5$$
ethyl ether (1 molecule).

Test Yourself

1. It used to be thought that an element consisted of only one substance. Is this statement correct?

2. What is the characteristic property of an element?

3. What do you understand by (*a*) an atom; (*b*) a molecule?

4. How is the relative atomic weight of an element found?

5. What information must be gained before the precise number of atoms of the different elements present in the molecule of a compound can be found?

6. What is the importance of the Law of Multiple Proportions? The analysis of different compounds formed from two elements shows that one of the elements may have more than one combining weight. What relationship exists between these different combining weights?

7. What relationship exists between the various equivalent weights that an element may exhibit and the atomic weight of that element? What term has been assigned to the quotient: atomic weight divided by equivalent weight?

8. What are the essential features of the internal structure of an atom?

9. What is an electron, a proton and a neutron? What are their relative weights? Explain why helium has an atomic weight of 4 and an atomic number of 2?

10. Sodium has an atomic number of 11 and chlorine an atomic number of 17. What electronic re-arrangement is supposed to occur when these two elements combine to form common salt? What type of valency is involved and what justification is there for your statement?

11. Why is the formula, H_2O, ascribed to a molecule of water and not $\text{H}_{200}\text{O}_{100}$?

12. Sketch the electronic structure of a molecule of water and explain the type of valency that is brought into play by the oxygen atom in combining with two atoms of hydrogen? How may the fact that water conducts electricity very slightly be explained by an alteration in the electronic structure of the water molecule?

13. What is an isotope? Illustrate your answer by referring to deuterium and uranium-235.

14. How may the isotopes of an element be separated from one another? Refer to the separation of ordinary hydrogen from heavy hydrogen and the separation of the isotopes of uranium.

15. What is meant by radioactivity and radioactive disintegration? Suggest a reason why the heavy elements should be naturally radioactive.

16. What are artificial or induced radioactive elements? How may they be produced?

17. Explain *nuclear fission* and how it may be effected? Describe the atomic bomb in which uranium-235 is used.

18. What advances in chemical theory do you associate with the names of Dalton and Avogadro?

19. Describe the periodic classification of the elements.

20. Why is it unlikely that the elements, neptunium and plutonium, exist in the earth's crust?

21. Explain the term "fixation of nitrogen." How has the nitrogen of the air been "fixed" and for what purpose?

22. Why is combined nitrogen essential to life and how has it been misused? Describe the nitrogen cycle in nature.

23. The ratio of the amounts of oxygen and nitrogen in the air is almost constant. Is air, therefore, a compound? Give reasons.

24. What is an acid? What is its essential constituent?

25. What do you understand by the terms (i) neutralization; (ii) salt?

26. How would you demonstrate that carbon dioxide is present in the gas you "breathe out"? Why does the open air contain so little carbon dioxide, despite the fact that it is being constantly polluted with the gas?

27. Show how Kekulé's idea that the valency of carbon is always *four* may be justified in (a) ethane, C_2H_6; (b) ethylene, C_2H_4; (c) acetylene, C_2H_2. Explain the "bonds" that exist in ethylene and acetylene.

28. What is (a) hydrocarbon; (b) carbohydrate?

29. What is a "saturated" hydrocarbon? Give the simple formula for the hydrocarbon having 25 atoms of carbon and existing in paraffin wax.

30. What is an isomer? Write down the structural formulæ of the isomers of butane, C_4H_{10}.

31. What is the name of the agents that speed up fermentative reactions? Show, by means of an equation, how glucose is converted into ordinary alcohol.

32. What are aldehydes and ketones? From what types of alcohols may they be derived and how?

33. Write down the formulæ for methanol, glycol and glycerol, and explain why each compound is an alcohol.

34. What is acetone? From what sources may it be obtained?

35. Explain why "esters" may be regarded as "salts" of alcohols and acids.

36. How may the elements, hydrogen and carbon, be proved to be present in an organic compound?

Answers will be found at the end of the book.

SULPHUR
BURNER

HEAT EXCHANGER FOR
RECOVERY OF HEAT IN
SULPHUR TRIOXIDE GAS

SULPHURIC ACID PRODUCTION

Perhaps the most used of all acids, this highly corrosive, oily liquid is manufactured in enormous quantities. It finds a use in nearly every basic chemical industry, from the making of washing soda to the production of fertilizers, dyes, drugs and explosives. Here is a portion of the sulphuric acid plant operated by Messrs. Peter Spence & Co., Ltd.

CHAPTER XIV

CHEMISTRY AND INDUSTRY

THE chemical industry, that almost ideal union between applied chemistry and structural engineering, constitutes a sort of "universal provider" for the whole of civilized mankind.

Think for a moment of just a few of the multitudinous, ever-varied and continually increasing products of this industrial marriage between chemical and engineering science and you will readily be convinced of the above assertion.

Indispensable Products

Dyestuffs, medicines and drugs, anæsthetics, photographic materials, food preparations, soaps and other detergents, fertilizers, rubber, explosives, artificial fabrics, acids and alkalis, plastics, radium, not forgetting, also, the chemical wonder, penicillin — these and many other substances, old and new, are readily to be enumerated as their names pass through the inquiring mind as up-to-date, essential and, indeed, indispensable products of the modern chemical industry.

There must, in point of fact, be literally thousands of civilization's chemical commodities which are separately manufactured and marketed by one or other of the many branches of the chemical industry in our country alone, to say nothing of the myriads of trade products, which are usually simple mixtures or preparations of the more fundamental chemical materials and which are put up under the convenient guise (and sometimes convenient *dis*guise) of attractive trade names.

Indeed, we have no escape from the maze of the chemical industry's products if we lead a normal, civilized life, for we meet them and use them at every turn. From our early morning wash and shave, right through our daily avocations in home, office, workshop or factory, in our hours of relaxation and amusement, during our periods of ill-health and of actual illness, and even, sometimes, during our sleep, we are kept directly in touch with one product or another of the all-pervading, intensely practical and ever-utilitarian chemical industry.

For the purpose of realizing the truth of this statement, let the reader, for a moment or two, quietly count up the number of products of applied chemical science which he has encountered during any one day of his normal existence, products which will naturally vary according to his circumstances and interests. He may experience some measure of surprise at perceiving how chemistry's products, ranging from ink to aspirin and from petrol or paraffin to a favourite perfume or flavour, manage in one way or another to minister to his convenience and general ease of living and of earning a livelihood.

The position as regards our day-by-day utilization of chemical goods and materials is just this: Chemistry is, fundamentally, the science of material changes and transformations. Hence, because we are all necessarily users of material commodities and, also, since a very large proportion of our life's activities is associated with the routine employment of various prepared substances, it follows that the group of industries which supplies us with these necessary materials and substances in the exact forms in which we require them for our pleasures and our profits, for our well-being and for our means of livelihood, is, when considered collectively, very much the "industry of industries."

Allied Sciences

So that, in all truth, we have the great chemical industries of our time forming a sort of nucleus around which all other industries, so to speak, revolve and upon which they are all more or less dependent in one way or another.

Curiously enough, the major part of today's chemical industry is hardly more than a century and a half old. It is true

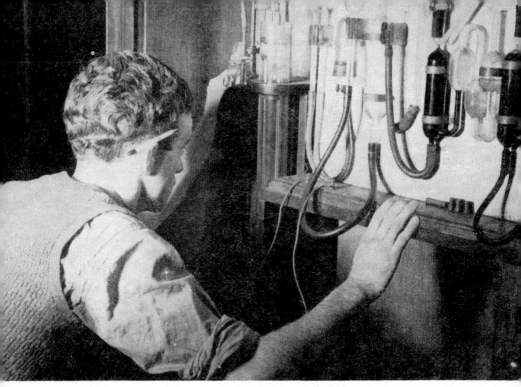

CHEMISTRY OF COAL

Chemists and other scientists have devoted years of patient research to the investigation of conditions making for greater safety in mines. Yet much work still has to be done. Here we see tests being conducted in a mining laboratory at Ashington on gases given off by coal.

enough, of course, that even in the early days of history a rudimentary species of chemical industry existed, a scattered and diminutive form of activity which produced materials such as vinegar, white lead, arsenic, sulphur, one which undertook the compounding of vegetable drugs and the making of perfumes, spices and so on.

But it was not until the Industrial Revolution, that industrial, social and economic upheaval which began in Britain during the eighteenth century, that a pressing need for an abundance of chemical products arose. During this period, scientific chemistry had been thoroughly grounded and established, so that, as a result, chemical knowledge was able to cope with the clamorous demands of the new civilization which was then in the making. Such, very briefly, were the circumstances in which the twin sciences of chemistry and engineering first came together in permanent association.

Present-day chemical making is a business which is conducted upon a vast scale, its products amounting in the aggregate to hundreds of thousands of tons annually. It is an industry which, being the creation of exact knowledge and scientific acumen, necessarily demands continued scientific control in all its processes.

Scientific Supervision

No other manufacturing industry functions under such stringent scientific supervision and control as do most of the present-day chemical trades, the reason for this being that the fundamental operations of chemical making are so delicately balanced that the slightest divergence from a given set of conditions is likely to upset the whole of the chemical reactions involved in the making of a chemical substance, and either to alter the nature of the final product or to prevent its formation at all.

It follows, therefore, that as trade competition grows, as nations vie with nations for supremacy and output in the chemical manufacturing world, and as chemical researchers pass on to industry the newly created chemical substances, the cry among the chemical trades is ever for more and more scientific control, for a continually increasing army of trained scientific workers and highly skilled chemists to watch over and to guide the intricate manufacturing processes along their appointed paths.

Work such as this in the modern chemical industry requires years of patient study and training. It necessitates not only technical knowledge and experience of a very high order, but it also makes considerable demands on the higher powers of judgment and mental alacrity.

No Noxious Fumes

There was a time when the average chemical factory was regarded by all and sundry as an offensively odoriferous place in the vicinity of which it was hardly possible to breathe with ease. Unhappily, such opinions were true enough at one period of the chemical industry's growth.

James Muspratt, for example, one of the "fathers" of the chemical industry in England, when he set up his alkali works near Widnes, in Lancashire, evolved so much hydrochloric acid gas from his factory that the acrid, pungent vapours devastated the green countryside for miles around.

"Sure," ejaculated this renowned chemical pioneer, when approached on the matter, "all the waters of Ballyshannon itself could not suffice to condense the acid which I make!"

But, not long afterwards, new factory legislation was enacted in Parliament and Muspratt was compelled to condense his corrosive fumes, with the result that the acid-scorched neighbourhood gradually returned to its normal condition and green meadows sprang up again in places which had formerly constituted a long, depressing and almost hopeless vista of blackened tracts of land.

Muspratt's case was, of course, an exceptionally bad one. Today, no such occurrence would be possible, because chemical manufacturers realize that an inordinately "smelly" factory is one from which some type of gaseous chemical product is escaping into the air. This escape obviously represents a certain amount of chemical wastage.

It so happens, however, that wastage is one of the factors which are completely anathema in any up-to-date chemical works. Hence the modern tendency is to make the average chemical factory more and more inodorous by means of effective fume condensation and, by so doing, to turn the condensed material into a by-product of value.

In general, the chemical industry of our present time may be split up into two great divisions, viz., the chemical *producing* industries and the chemical *converting* industries.

The chemical producing industries are obviously the more fundamental of the two. They are the industries which actually make chemical material in an almost untold variety, materials which range from bakelite moulding powders for plastic working to drugs and anæsthetics such as ether, chloroform, phenacetin and salicylic acid; from sulphuric, hydrochloric and nitric acids to ammonia and artificial fertilizers.

Chemical converting industries, on the other hand, comprise those very numerous trades which utilize the more fundamental chemicals and convert them into what our American friends term "consumer goods," that is to say, anything from a daintily bottled perfume or other article of cosmetic use to a blended tobacco, or a proprietary cough cure.

Producing and Converting

From a numerical standpoint, the world's chemical producing industry is relatively small, and it tends to be composed of a few large units rather than a larger number of smaller manufacturing entities.

The chemical converting industry, on the contrary, comprises a vast array of small manufacturing plants which derive their main supplies from the larger chemical producing units. To this latter division of chemical industry belong the innumerable trades which are direct users of fundamental chemicals, trades such as cosmetic manufacture, disinfectant and soap producers, makers of liquid and gaseous fuels and of industrial and household chemical specialities.

Manufacturers of insecticides, water-softening preparations, patent medicines, paints, varnishes, polishes, inks, bleaches, adhesives, etc., are also chemical converters, and their name is legion.

Fine and Heavy Chemicals

In our present survey of the subject, however, we are more concerned with the chemical producing industries than we are with the enormously more numerous chemical converting industries; and rightly so, because these main chemical producing trades form the backbone of all their subservient and dependent industries. An ink manufacturer, for example, would be in a pretty pickle without his dyes and his other ink-making ingredients, as also would a soap maker without his caustic soda for saponifying or chemically splitting up the soap-producing fats.

Now, there are two great divisions in the chemical producing industry, and these comprise (a) the heavy chemical trades and (b) the "fine" chemical industry.

The division of manufactured chemicals into "heavy" and "fine" is more one of convenience than of scientific accuracy. Caustic soda, sulphuric acid, vitamin-B, and radium bromide are all in the one sense "chemicals." But while caustic alkalis and strong acids are made in their millions of tons, the vitamin-B output is estimated in grams and that of radium bromide only in milligrams. "Heavy" chemicals, therefore, are those which are manufactured on the large scale and whose output from the world's chemical concerns is to be expressed in tons daily.

Acids and Alkalis

They include strong acids (nitric, sulphuric, hydrochloric); the alkalis (ammonia, caustic and common soda); fertilizers, such as superphosphate and ammonium sulphate; sulphur; tars; mineral oils; greases; many mineral salts, such as copper sulphate, copperas, and bichromates; bleaching powder (chloride of lime); photographic "hypo" (sodium thiosulphate), and numerous pigment powders for paint making.

The fine chemicals are those which belong to the class of medicinal chemicals; drugs; photographic developers, such as hydroquinone, metol and pyrogallic acid; salts of rare metals (gold and platinum chlorides, for instance, to say nothing of radioactive compounds); dyes, perfume bases; synthetic flavouring matters; vitamins; plant-growth substances; poisonous alkaloids, like strychnine and atropine; chemical accelerators for rubber vulcanizing processes; anti-knock liquids for petrols; refrigerating compounds, and a host of other chemicals which are far too numerous even to classify.

The chemical industry is anything but static. On the contrary, its expansion during the last quarter of a century has been almost explosive in its magnitude; this fact being due to the enormous advances which chemical science has made in numerous directions during this period, and to the continued and increasing demand for chemical materials and chemically derived preparations of every conceivable variety.

Synthetic Products

Consequently, the great chemical industry, considered collectively, has been an exceptionally flourishing one, an industry which has not known any serious slumps, one which has been singularly free from strikes and lockouts, and one which has been in the van of progress as regards improving the social and general well-being of its numerous employees.

It goes without saying, that the advance of the chemical industry, which proceeds hand in hand with the discoveries of modern chemical science, must result in disturbances of other industries. Such a fact is inevitable.

When synthetic indigo was first discovered, towards the end of the last century, it resulted in an almost complete stagnation of the native indigo-growing industry of India. Most of the Indian indigo growers had to go out of commercial existence, at least so far as their indigo production was concerned; for the

IMPURITIES
REMOVED HERE

DEWAR FLASK
CONTAINING
LIQUID AIR

RADIUM CHEMISTRY IN CAVES

In certain Derbyshire caverns, 280 ft. below the surface, chemical experts deal with radium and its rays. This photograph shows a chemist collecting "emanation" or gas from a store of radium and purifying it by means of liquid air treatment.

synthetic material which was then being produced in the great German chemical factories on the Rhine more than favourably competed, both technically and economically, with the age-old native product.

Take, again, the now almost classical case of natural versus synthetic vanilla.

Vanilla is a highly important flavouring material, entering, as it does, into the production of tobacco, chocolates, and many types of beverages, in addition to confections of all kinds. The odoriferous and flavouring principle of natural vanilla is a chemical substance to which the name "vanillin" has been given.

Natural vanilla is extracted from the beans or seed pods of a species of vine which, although a native of Mexico, is cultivated mostly in the island of Madagascar, off the east coast of Africa.

Synthetic or artificial vanillin first appeared on the market in 1876, but at that time its manufacture was a difficult and an expensive process, so that the natural vanilla pods were well able to withstand the competition of their synthetic rival. Of recent years, however, vanillin manufacture has been enormously cheapened. It is now possible to manufacture it from wood-pulp waste and to retail the synthetic material at a price far below that of the natural product.

Moreover, synthetic vanillin is about five hundred times stronger in flavour than the extract of natural vanilla bean, so that it will not be surprising for the reader to learn that the industrial use of natural

LIME KILNS AT A CARBIDE FACTORY

Two rotary kilns for the continuous production of quicklime from limestone at the South Wales calcium carbide factory of British Industrial Solvents, Ltd. Up to 178 ft. long and 9 ft. in diameter, heated by pulverized coal, they supply quicklime to make 100,000 tons of carbide a year, which is enough for the whole requirements of the United Kingdom.

vanilla bean extract is rapidly disappearing (and, indeed, so far as this country is concerned, has completely vanished since the commencement of the last war).

Citric acid, a very important chemical, was not so long ago produced exclusively from natural fruits of the citrus variety. It can now be manufactured artificially. Thus, with the passing of time, the natural citric acid will become as obsolete as is the naturally derived vanilla.

Synthetics Win

To a large extent, the battle betwixt "synthetic" and natural products is one of price. Sometimes the synthetic or artificial material cannot be produced at the cost of the natural substance. Yet this ruling factor seldom prevails over any lengthy period. In the end, the synthetic or chemically produced material nearly always wins and ousts the natural substance from its former position of supremacy; always, of course, provided that the synthetic product is the equal of the natural material.

Having up to the present concerned ourselves with the more general aspects of the chemical industry, it will be of interest if we now take a more particular survey of some branches of this omnifarious scientific activity and consider a number of its everyday technical aspects.

In general, the chemical industry, in its "fine" and "heavy" branches alike, is an industry of what are termed "unit operations."

This expression may require a little explanation in order to render it clearer to the reader. Let us imagine, therefore, that we are faced with the task of separating, say, a mixture of soda and sand. To do this, the obvious course is to heat up the mixture with water so that the soda will be dissolved and the sand left behind. Then we shall have to filter the resulting soda solution in order to eliminate the sand, and the final operation will be to run out the soda solution (after further evaporation) into shallow tanks to crystallize.

Now during this sequence of work we have to perform three distinct operations, namely, the solution extraction of the soda from the sand, the filtering of the soda solution, and its final crystallization—three "unit operations," in fact, and operations which on a large scale would each call for special consideration as regards plant design and actual performance.

Industrial chemistry, we have said, is an affair of more or less giant-scale "unit operations." It comprises the operations of the laboratory bench transferred (often with many necessary modifications) to the hundreds-of-tons scale. These unit operations are greatly varied in character. They comprise purely physical processes such as extraction and solution, boiling, evaporation, distillation, filtration, heat-exchange processes and such like, in addition to the far more technical "chemical" operations of oxidation, nitration, reduction, acidification, sulphonation, polymerization (or chemical condensation), hydrogenization, heat decomposition and so on.

It is on account of the varied and highly technical nature of its constituent unit operations or processes that the chemical industry, particularly on its "fine" side, is one which so urgently and incessantly demands the highest technical skill for its control and its smooth running.

In the engineering trades, machines can be made for the purpose of turning out complicated metal articles with a very high degree of accuracy, but no machine other than the human brain can watch over the chemical reaction between glycerine and nitrosulphuric acids in the manufacture of nitroglycerine, nor can any purely mechanical or automatic device control the making and testing of the essential purity of an important chemical substance such as chloroform or aspirin.

Indeed, the making of all chemicals must be controlled at nearly every stage by skilled human agency, and, what is more, the entire sequence of operations concerned in the making of a chemical must be arranged so that it is able to proceed perfectly smoothly, economically and with an absolute minimum of danger in respect of fire, poison or explosion.

The fundamental raw materials of the main chemical industry are remarkably few. Indeed, they can be counted up almost wholly on the fingers of one hand alone. Salt, sulphur, limestone, coal, sand, air (for the production of synthetic nitric acid and nitrates), and, in America, petroleum, form the starting points of at least two-thirds of the great chemical industry.

Without this basic minimum of raw materials, the chemical trades, as we know them, would be virtually impotent, for it is this nucleus of common commodities which forms, as it were, the main root of all commercial chemical manufacturing activity throughout the entire world.

Sulphur and Sulphuric Acid

Salt, limestone, coal and, of course, air are abundantly available in Britain, and quite a good deal of necessary sulphur can now be produced from our natural deposits of *gypsum*, which, chemically speaking, is a sulphate of calcium.

This fact is rather fortunate, for, to some extent, it leaves us independent of overseas supplies of sulphur or sulphur-containing minerals for the manufacture of the heavy chemical industry's most important commodity—sulphuric acid, or "oil of vitriol."

Sulphuric acid has been truly described as the "life blood of the world's chemical industry." There is scarcely an important chemical manufacturing or utilizing trade which does not use it either directly or indirectly. So necessary is sulphuric acid in industry generally, that the annual production figures for this particular acid form an admirable and very accurate barometer indicative of the industrial well-being of the nation.

About four million tons of this clear, oily liquid are manufactured annually and are devoted to an innumerable variety of uses, from the refining of petroleum to the

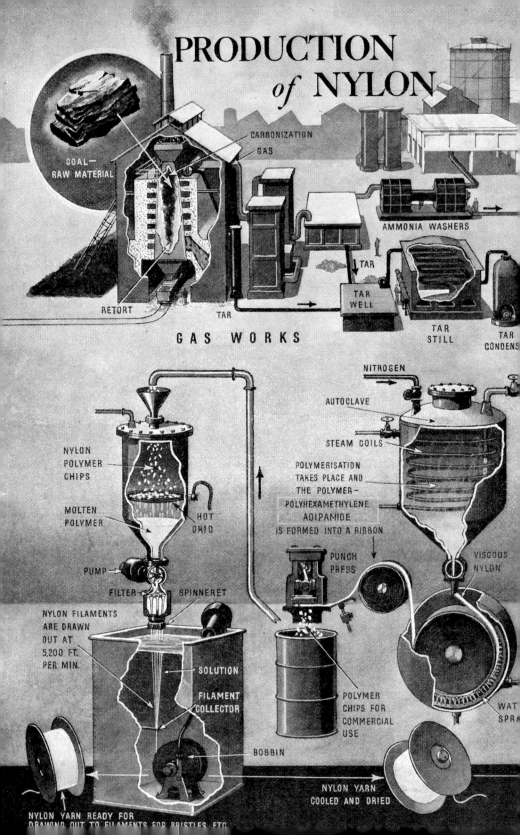

PRODUCTION *of* NYLON

COAL—
RAW MATERIAL

CARBONIZATION

GAS

AMMONIA WASHERS

TAR

RETORT

TAR

TAR
WELL

TAR
STILL

TAR
CONDENS

GAS WORKS

NITROGEN

AUTOCLAVE

STEAM COILS

NYLON
POLYMER
CHIPS

POLYMERISATION
TAKES PLACE AND
THE POLYMER—
POLYHEXAMETHYLENE
ADIPAMIDE
IS FORMED INTO A RIBBON

MOLTEN
POLYMER

HOT
GRID

VISCOUS
NYLON

PUMP

PUNCH
PRESS

FILTER

SPINNERET

NYLON FILAMENTS
ARE DRAWN
OUT AT
5,200 FT.
PER MIN.

SOLUTION

FILAMENT
COLLECTOR

POLYMER
CHIPS FOR
COMMERCIAL
USE

WAT
SPRA

BOBBIN

NYLON YARN
COOLED AND DRIED

NYLON YARN READY FOR
DRAWING OUT TO FILAMENTS FOR BRISTLES ETC.

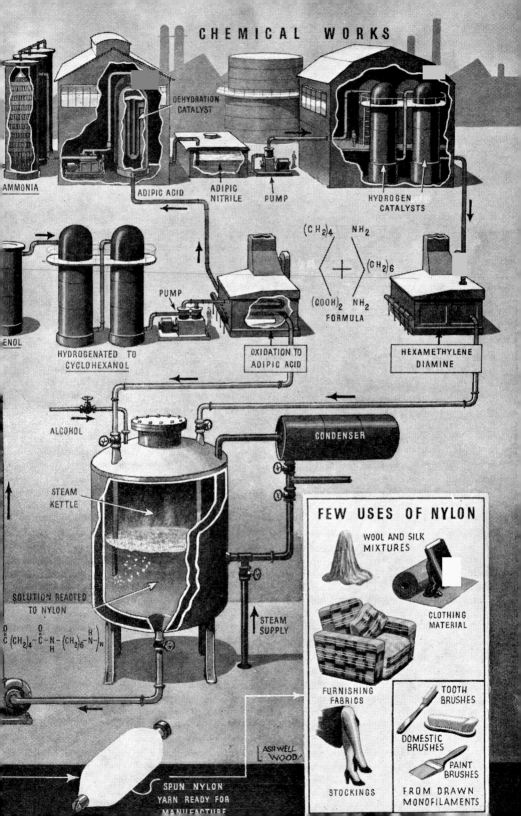

CHEMICAL WORKS

AMMONIA

DEHYDRATION CATALYST

ADIPIC ACID

ADIPIC NITRILE

PUMP

HYDROGEN CATALYSTS

ENOL

PUMP

HYDROGENATED TO CYCLOHEXANOL

OXIDATION TO ADIPIC ACID

$(CH_2)_4$ NH_2

$(CH_2)_6$

$(COOH)_2$ NH_2

FORMULA

HEXAMETHYLENE DIAMINE

ALCOHOL

CONDENSER

STEAM KETTLE

SOLUTION REACTED TO NYLON

STEAM SUPPLY

$$\overset{O}{\underset{}{C}} (CH_2)_4 \overset{O}{\underset{}{C}} - \underset{H}{N} - (CH_2)_6 - \underset{H}{N} -_n$$

FEW USES OF NYLON

WOOL AND SILK MIXTURES

CLOTHING MATERIAL

FURNISHING FABRICS

TOOTH BRUSHES

DOMESTIC BRUSHES

PAINT BRUSHES

STOCKINGS

FROM DRAWN MONOFILAMENTS

ASHWELL WOOD

SPUN NYLON YARN READY FOR MANUFACTURE

manufacture of fertilizers and dyestuffs; from, also, the making of explosives to our own personal utilization of it as the "acid" which activates our car batteries and the accumulators of our radio sets.

Sulphuric acid was first manufactured in the year 1733, but it was known and used in small amounts long before that time. In those days it was made in relatively small glass vessels and it cost anything from ten shillings upwards per pound.

There are two ways of making sulphuric acid. The older one is known as the "Chamber Process." Fundamentally, this process consists in the mutual interaction of two types of gases, to wit, sulphur dioxide (made by burning sulphur or sulphur minerals in air) and certain gaseous oxides of nitrogen. These are mixed together in a large lead-lined enclosed space or "chamber," together with a certain proportion of steam or water spray, the result of their interaction being the formation of sulphuric acid, which collects at the bottom of the chamber.

But this process is gradually becoming obsolete, in consequence of a quicker, cleaner and more economical process which was first developed in Germany just previous to the First World War.

Contact Process

This newer mode of sulphuric acid making is known as the "Contact Process." The basic process has several modifications, but they are all founded on the fact that when a mixture of sulphur dioxide gas and air (or oxygen) is drawn over certain "catalysts," or reaction promoters, such as metallic platinum, vanadium oxide and even some forms of common iron oxide, the sulphur dioxide adds on to itself one more atom of oxygen and so becomes converted into sulphur *tri*oxide. In the language of chemistry, this reaction is conveniently pictured by the following symbols:

$$2SO_2 + O_2 = 2SO_3$$
$$\text{sulphur} + \text{oxygen} = \text{sulphur}$$
$$\textit{di}\text{oxide} \qquad \textit{tri}\text{oxide}$$

The resulting sulphur trioxide, which appears as a white mist, is then absorbed by water (or, in practice, dilute sulphuric

acid), with which it reacts to form sulphuric acid.

In the "contact" process for the manufacture of sulphuric acid, sulphur-containing minerals, notably iron pyrites or a material obtained from gasworks and known as "spent oxide" (in view of its being iron oxide which has absorbed a good deal of sulphur from the crude coal gas), are roasted in long cylindrical furnaces which are provided with adequate ventilating systems. The sulphur in the mineral combines with the air to form sulphur dioxide gas, SO_2.

This gas is led away from the furnace through suitable conduits and it is then most carefully "cleansed" and purified in order to free it from dust, traces of sulphur and, in particular, from arsenic; the latter would completely ruin or "poison" the active platinum or other material over which it has to pass in order to be converted into sulphur trioxide, SO_3.

After purification, the gases from the pyrites furnace or "burners" are completely dried by being made to pass up a coke-filled tower in which they meet a descending stream of strong sulphuric acid; the latter, having a powerful affinity for water, at once absorbs all traces of moisture from the ascending gases.

The purified and completely dried gases are now passed into the "contact chamber," which may take one of several different forms or modifications. In short, however, the contact chamber constitutes an arrangement of heated tubes containing vanadium or iron oxides, and in some instances "platinized asbestos" (i.e. finely divided platinum deposited on asbestos fibre), at a temperature of around 400 deg. C.

Under the energizing action of the vanadium, iron or platinum "catalyst," the sulphur dioxide gas adds on to itself, or "combines with," as the correct expression has it, more oxygen from the air which accompanies it, thereby becoming converted into sulphur trioxide, a solid material which heralds its formation by the appearance of the characteristic white mist.

The gases which pass out of the contact chamber are absorbed in fairly strong sulphuric acid and this, as a result, is

ELECTRO-CHEMICAL TESTS ON METALS

Chemistry of metals and their alloys is nowadays of paramount importance. Above is pictured an analytical chemist making electro-chemical tests on metal solutions in the new laboratories of High Duty Alloys, Ltd., at Slough.

converted into stronger acid. The absorption process is carried out in tall, brick-lined steel towers packed with quartz.

The gases from the contact chamber ascend the tower and, in so doing, the sulphur trioxide content is readily absorbed by the strong sulphuric acid which trickles downwards over the quartz. The resulting "super strength" or "fuming" sulphuric acid (known, technically, as "oleum") is subsequently diluted to form an acid of any required strength.

Turning, now, to an almost equally vital chemical commodity, let us take a glance at the manufacture of an important alkali, common soda, the technical name of which is sodium carbonate.

Ordinary salt, or, rather, its solution, which is known as brine, forms the raw material of soda production.

There is more than one method of soda making, but the most industrially impor-

tant of these is the "Ammonia-Soda" process. This process is really a very simple one. It consists of saturating a strong brine solution with ammonia gas and then with carbon dioxide gas, whereby sodium bicarbonate is precipitated and ammonium chloride (sal ammoniac) remains in solution. The very pure sodium bicarbonate is heated and it is converted into ordinary sodium carbonate or "soda," and the carbon dioxide gas which is evolved during the process is again utilized for the saturation of a further batch of strong brine.

The "Cyclic" Process

Also, the solution from the precipitation of sodium bicarbonate, which, as we have seen, contains ammonium chloride, is warmed with slaked lime, whereby it is chemically split up or decomposed with the evolution of ammonia gas. This gas, like its carbon dioxide ally, is again utilized for the conversion of the brine into sodium bicarbonate.

It is here that the reader's attention may be directed to the above example of what is known in chemical technology as a "cyclic" process, that is, a process which operates continuously, the by-products of the one chemical reaction being economically utilized for the production of a similar and a succeeding reaction.

In this country, the ammonia-soda process has been worked exclusively in the vicinity of the Cheshire salt-bearing areas, where natural brine is plentiful and cheap. It utilizes ammonia from gasworks and carbon dioxide gas which is produced by the heating of limestone.

Chief Industrial Alkali

Sodium carbonate is second only to sulphuric acid in industrial importance. It heads the list of industrial alkalis and it was formerly the one alkali from which most of the others were manufactured. The annual production of this material is about three or four million tons, a figure which, gigantic as it undoubtedly is, still tends yearly to increase.

Another very important alkali is caustic soda, which also is used in enormous quantities throughout technical industry. At one time, caustic soda could only be produced indirectly from sodium carbonate, but now by means of the modern electrolytic process it is made almost exclusively from natural brine.

In the electrolytic process, strong brine flows into a series of cells, each of which is provided with a carbon anode (positive pole), a thin layer of metallic mercury on the floor of each cell comprising the cathode or negative electrode of the cell. On the passage of a current at a potential of about 125 volts through the cells, electrolytic action takes place in each and the solution of brine or common salt (which is, chemically, sodium chloride) is electrically split up into chlorine gas at the carbon poles and metallic sodium at the negative poles.

Since these negative poles comprise ordinary mercury, the liberated metallic sodium dissolves in the mercury and the resulting "amalgam" flows into a water trough in which the sodium is attacked by the water with the formation of a solution of sodium hydroxide or caustic soda. This is afterwards drawn off and heat-evaporated in order to procure the caustic soda as a solid mass.

The chlorine gas, on the other hand, is led off and compressed into cylinders. It is an exceedingly important gas, for it is used not only in the manufacture of bleaching powder, or "chloride of lime," but, also, for the making of chlorates, hypochlorites for bleaching and disinfectant solutions, various solvents of great industrial importance and, also, for the manufacture of some of the "intermediate" compounds used in dyestuff production.

Ammonia is an alkali which everybody knows—and remembers—in view of its intensely pungent and suffocating character. In reality, ammonia is a gas, a compound of one part by volume of nitrogen and three of hydrogen. Chemists symbolize it as NH_3.

The common "household" ammonia, however, is merely a strong solution of this powerfully alkaline gas in water.

Concerning Catalytic Action

Until very recent years, the main commercial sources of ammonia liquor were the various gasworks from whose liquors the ammonia was distilled. Nowadays, however, ammonia is being made on an increasing scale by the direct "burning" or combination of nitrogen and hydrogen at high pressure under the influence of a suitable "catalyst" or reaction promoter.

Here, again, we have another example of the manner in which the still mysterious "catalytic action" is utilized on the mass scale in chemical industry to bring about reactions which would otherwise be impossible, or, at any rate, exceedingly difficult to initiate. This catalytic action is, indeed, a pearl of great price in the manufacturing chemical world.

In the synthetic ammonia process, the catalyst was formerly uranium—the "active" metal of the atomic bomb—but as uranium happens to be fairly expensive,

DEATH TO THE DISEASE GERM

Small-scale preparation of an experimental sulphonamide drug in a modern works laboratory. Popularly known as "M and B's," in allusion to the firm of May and Baker which first produced them, these truly wonder drugs have found startling success.

it has been possible to get common iron oxide to perform the required catalytic or reaction-producing function.

A mixture of three volumes of hydrogen and one volume of nitrogen is compressed to 200-300 atmospheres pressure and passed through "converters," each about 20 ft. high and 2 ft. in diameter. The converters are packed with iron oxide material which is heated to a low red heat.

The gas which issues from the converters contains about 4 per cent of ammonia, the remainder being unchanged nitrogen and hydrogen. These gaseous "conversion products" are strongly cooled, whereby the ammonia is condensed to a liquid, but the nitrogen and the hydrogen pass on and are again returned to the converters.

The necessary nitrogen for the process may be obtained from liquid air or from a gas containing nitrogen, such as "producer gas" (manufactured by passing air over red-hot coke), which contains about 65 per cent of nitrogen mixed with carbon monoxide gas.

Water-gas Method

Hydrogen gas for the ammonia synthesis can be " electrolytic hydrogen," that is to say, hydrogen gas which has been generated by the electrolysis or electrical splitting-up of water, or, as actually happens in practice, of a 20 per cent solution of caustic soda; or, on the other hand, it may be derived by passing water-gas and steam heated to a temperature of about 500 deg. C. over a catalytic substance, such as iron oxide.

Water-gas is made by blowing steam through red-hot coke, in virtue of which the coke (carbon) becomes oxidized to

PURIFYING PENICILLIN

Battery of up-to-date vacuum drying-ovens used in the preparation of penicillin. They are designed to remove the last traces of water from penicillin products and, at the same time, to render them completely sterile or germ-free.

carbon monoxide (obtaining its oxygen from the steam) and thereby liberating the hydrogen of the steam. Thus:

$$C + H_2O = CO + H_2$$
carbon   steam   carbon   hydrogen
monoxide

Water-gas is a Mixture

"Water-gas," we see, is essentially a mixture of hydrogen and carbon monoxide, and when, as previously described, it is mixed with steam and passed over a heated catalyst, the carbon monoxide content of the water-gas reacts with the oxygen of the steam to form carbon *di*oxide and hydrogen in accordance with the following chemical equation:

$$CO + H_2O = CO_2 + H_2$$
carbon   water   carbon   hydrogen
monoxide   dioxide

Ultimately, after passing the gaseous products of this reaction through water under pressure to dissolve out the carbon dioxide,

a gas is obtained which contains about 95 per cent of pure hydrogen, the remainder being a little unchanged carbon monoxide and some nitrogen.

Needless to say, the whole of the synthetic ammonia process is very much more complicated in practical detail than it has been possible for us to describe. Nevertheless, the reader has here the "skeleton" of this nowadays mass-scale industrial process from which he will be in a position to obtain a glimpse at the industrial methods by which ammonia is obtained from such simple materials as coke and steam.

Industrial processes such as we have just considered, that is to say, manufacturing methods which have for their aim the production of mineral acids, alkalis, metal-containing salts and similar compounds, belong to the realm of *inorganic* chemistry, the branch of chemical science which concerns itself mainly with the study of materials other than those containing carbon in anything other than its very simplest forms.

But carbon, as we know, is a very peculiar element. It has the strange and characteristic property of being able to link up with itself, forming long chains and rings of atoms, and it is on this peculiar power of the carbon atom that the whole of Nature's living materials depend. Our very flesh, indeed, is composed of a mixture of exceedingly complex carbon compounds, and it is because these combinations of carbon appear always among life's products that the branch of chemistry which seeks to study them is known as *Organic* Chemistry — the chemistry of organized life.

Carbon Compounds

There are, of course, hosts of carbon compounds which do not appear among any of life's forms. Nevertheless, they must be included among the materials of organic chemistry because they are very definitely substances containing complex linkages of carbon atoms. Many of these materials are of very great commercial importance and, frequently enough, manufacturing processes on truly enormous scales have been devised for their production.

Take, for instance, one of the most modern of our chemical manufacturing activities, the nowadays giant plastics industry. Thirty years ago, synthetic plastics materials were hardly known. Nowadays, these products of an ever-varying nature are being made annually to the tune of tens of thousands of tons.

Let us take one of the better-known processes in the realm of plastics and follow it up from its early stages.

Yes, in this particular instance, let us begin at the test-tube stage and ourselves perform the one simple, fundamental experiment on which the whole of a giant manufacturing industry has been almost miraculously reared.

All we have to do is to place in our diminutive test-tube approximately equal quantities of formalin, a clear liquid with a pungent odour, and carbolic acid, the well-known disinfectant liquid. To our test-

tube, also, we add a small fragment of caustic soda about one-tenth the size of a pea. This acts as a catalytic agent and enables the formalin and the carbolic acid to combine together more readily and easily.

We now heat the test-tube very gently. Almost immediately a commotion seems to take place within the tube. The liquid froths up, becoming darker. It thickens, separates to two layers and eventually would become almost solid. If we were to heat to a higher temperature, water would boil off and the contents of the tube would ultimately become entirely solid.

Now, let us pause to allow the contents of the tube to cool down. After this, we shall see that the test-tube contains a quantity of a sticky, plastic material of anything from a yellow to a dark-brown colour and a watery upper layer. We shall find that this substance is quite unaffected by water, being completely insoluble in that liquid; and, also, more important still, we shall see that if we heat this resinous material it gradually becomes entirely solid and infusible.

In this simple manner we have actually made a synthetic resin, a "plastic," as the term is, of the bakelite type. We have repeated the original experiment out of which the Belgian chemist, Leo Henry Baekeland, in 1909, brought into being the first synthetic resin or "plastics" industry.

What's in a Name?

Baekeland was unable to discover the nature of the plastic material which he had made, but that troubled him little enough. Even at the present time, its exact composition is unknown. All we are aware of is the fact that the carbon atoms in the original ingredients of this plastic resin have combined themselves in some intricate way, or have, as the chemists say, become "polymerized." It is true to say that the chemical name of this synthetic resin, as it appears in the light of modern research, is *polymerized oxybenzyl-methyleneglycol anhydride*.

But life is comparatively short, and not even the chemists refer to it by that appellation. Like everybody else, they just call it

"Bakelite," in honour of its discoverer, Dr. Baekeland.

Now all, or nearly all, of the commercially important synthetic "plastics" are made on this principle of "polymerizing" two or more relatively simple carbon-containing materials together so that a large number of these atom units coalesce to form a large multi-unit compound, which is, of course, the synthetic resin.

On the industrial scale, our simple test-tube is replaced by large metal vessels of iron, copper, nickel or stainless steel, which are heated by means of steam jackets. The vessels are provided with condensers and stirring apparatus and in them the correct formalin-carbolic acid or cresol mixture is heated for a predetermined time, along with a suitable catalytic agent.

After the chemical reaction has got under way, the material within the heating vessel divides into two layers, an upper aqueous layer and a lower layer consisting of the viscid resin. After the upper layer has been distilled off, the lower layer is run off into trays through a bottom valve in the vessel and, after solidification, the material is processed in a variety of ways according to the exact use which is to be made of it.

Synthetic Resin Stages

By varying the conditions of the chemical reaction it is readily possible to obtain resins having different characteristics. In fact, the reaction may be made to proceed in stages, giving, first of all, a jelly-like "liquid" resin, then a resin which, although solid, melts on heating, and, finally, a resin which is practically infusible, this representing the last stage of this chemical "condensation" process.

The use of other materials in place of carbolic acid, or in place of formalin, results in other general types of synthetic resins being obtainable. For instance, if glycerine and a material known as phthalic anhydride (a white, crystalline substance) are heated together, they condense to resins which are almost transparent and which have much use in the lacquer and varnish industries.

It is quite impossible to prophesy the number of different resinous materials of industrial importance which may ultimately become possible by the chemical condensation of various suitable materials. Their names must, indeed, be legion, and as new manufacturing techniques are evolved, so, also, will the character and the variety of such resins extend.

Schoolboy Dye-maker

The making of synthetic dyes represents another great branch of the organic chemical industry, since all these synthetic colouring matters are compounds of the element carbon. Prior to the First World War, Germany held a monopoly of dye-stuffs production, but this was wrested from that country mainly through the activities of British chemists.

The first artificial dye was made as far back as 1856. Its fortunate creator was a schoolboy, William Henry Perkin by name, the son of a builder of Greenford Green, near London. Young Perkin was an enthusiastic chemical experimenter. During his school holidays he tried to find a way of making quinine (an important anti-malarial drug), but instead of quinine he got a good deal of a tarry, black liquid which, when poured into water, gave an intense purple coloration.

In this way, "mauve," the first of the artificial aniline dyestuffs, was brought into being. Perkin and his family set up the following year as dyestuff makers. They made a fortune and, some years afterwards, the younger Perkin was able to retire and to devote the remainder of his long life to pure chemical research.

Artificial dyes have the name "coal-tar" associated with them because, in the majority of instances, they are manufactured from materials which are found in the tarry oil which is one of the products of the distillation of coal for the manufacture of coal gas. Materials such as benzene (from which aniline is prepared), naphthalene and anthracene, form the basis of the synthetic dyestuffs industry.

By treating these basic materials in various ways with nitric acid, sulphuric acid, with strong alkalis, with sulphur compounds and with various other chemicals, there are brought into being sub-

CHLORINATOR
CHARGING HOPPERS

GAS MAINS

MANUFACTURING MAGNESIUM CHLORIDE

Magnesium, one of the lightest of metals, is of rapidly growing importance in modern times. Here is a view of a plant for the manufacture of magnesium chloride from which metallic magnesium is electrolytically produced by the firm of Magnesium Electron, Ltd.

stances which are called "intermediates." These intermediates are colourless themselves, but they are the materials from which the various dyes are directly produced by means of a controlled sequence of chemical operations.

Making the "Intermediates"

A modern dyestuffs factory almost invariably produces its own intermediates. Visit such a factory if you can obtain permission to do so. You will not see therein a mass of intricate machinery. On the contrary, the "plant" will be found to consist of rows and rows of cast-iron pans which often enough operate under considerable pressure and which are mechanically stirred whilst being heated.

These are the "pots," as they are called, in which, let us say, naphthalene (the common white material of moth-balls) is being treated with concentrated sulphuric acid in order to convert it into its various sulphuric acid compounds, which latter, when combined with other suitable sub-

stances, at once produce highly coloured dyestuffs.

Or, perhaps, during our walk round a dyestuffs factory, our eyes may alight upon an assembly of bricked-in boilers from which some stray traces of nitric fumes may proceed. These are the "nitrators," the strong reaction vessels in which one material or other is being "nitrated," i.e. treated with nitric and sulphuric acid in order to turn it into a nitro compound. It is usually the "intermediate" materials which are treated in this manner, for by the introduction of nitric acid complexes into dyestuff materials the whole character and shade of a dye may often be modified profoundly.

We see, also, that the numerous "shops" and "sheds" of our dye factory are filled with a multitude of pipelines of various sizes and shapes. Pipelines great, pipelines small. Pipes made of steel to carry compressed air. Earthenware pipes to carry highly concentrated acids. Copper pipes to convey live steam. Even pipes of transparent glass which clearly reveal their liquid contents.

The design and erection of all these necessary conduits represents a masterpiece of skill on the part of some expert chemical engineer. The hum of machinery may not be very forcibly present. Nevertheless, any chemical works, dyestuff factory or otherwise, is normally a hive of hidden activity, for these pots and pans, these pressure vessels, these curious and sometimes almost uncanny overhead pipelines carrying liquids and gases, necessitate close human control on their functionings, to say nothing of the prompt application of skill and experience if anything should happen to go wrong with them.

But we cannot linger longer on the entrancing subject of synthetic dyestuff manufacture. There are other important chemical materials for us yet to consider.

"Everybody's Drug"

Shall we now take a glimpse at the manufacture of one or two common drugs, aspirin, for example, this nowadays ubiquitous white crystalline material which has become "everybody's medicine"?

Aspirin was first commercially manufactured by the great German chemical industry in 1899, but it has long since become a product of the British chemical trade. It is a very useful drug, not only on account of its efficacy but also in view of its mildness and its general harmlessness.

Oil of wintergreen, a natural product which can now be made synthetically, is well known on account of its anti-rheumatic properties. This oil is a compound of salicylic acid, which latter can be obtained from it. But, fortunately, salicylic acid can also be manufactured synthetically, starting from phenol or carbolic acid, which itself is normally obtained from coal-tar.

The manufacture of aspirin, therefore, commences with phenol, which, by treatment in closed iron pans with caustic soda, is converted into a product known as sodium phenate. The sodium phenate is subsequently processed and obtained in the form of a fine, dry powder. This is charged into an "autoclave," or pressure-reaction vessel, and carbon dioxide gas is forced into the vessel under a considerable pressure. It is absorbed by the sodium phenate, after which the vessel is heated by steam for about three hours to complete the chemical reaction which involves the formation of sodium salicylate.

The contents of the autoclave are now dissolved in water and hydrochloric acid is added to the solution. This precipitates the salicylic acid as a white powder. It is washed and afterwards purified by recrystallization.

The purified salicylic acid is then dissolved in a suitable solvent, such as benzene, and transferred to another reaction vessel in which it is treated with acetic anhydride or acetyl chloride, two liquids which contain the "acetic" group of atoms which is present in ordinary acetic acid, the acid of vinegar. Under these conditions, the acetic group of atoms adds itself on to the salicylic acid grouping, the result being a compound which is chemically known as "acetyl-salicylic acid," or, more popularly and, indeed, universally, as "aspirin."

If, in place of an "acetic" atom grouping, we employ a "methyl" grouping, we obtain methyl salicylate, which is synthetic oil of wintergreen.

Aspirin is, understandably enough, one of the "fine" organic chemicals, for it has to be very carefully made, particular attention being paid to the purity of the ingredients involved in its production.

Sweetness of Saccharin

Another interesting chemical of the "fine" variety is saccharin, the synthetic sweetening agent which is some 550 times sweeter than ordinary sugar. Saccharin was originally discovered by an American chemical worker who happened to go home and sit down for his tea after only very roughly washing his hands. The persistent sweetness of every article of food which he happened to touch led to investigations, and the aforesaid investigations eventually led to the discovery of saccharin. Unfortunately, the full narrative of this discovery is too long to be recounted here.

Anyway, saccharin is made from toluene, the same coal-tar liquid from which we obtain the explosive T.N.T. (trinitro-

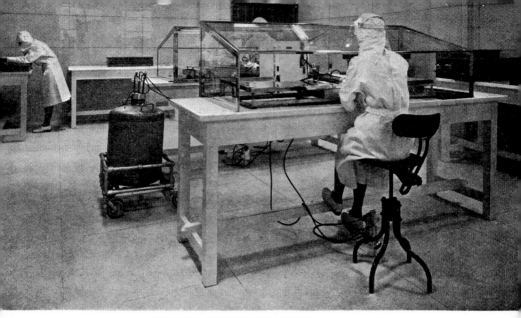

IN A PENICILLIN FACTORY

Pictured above is a corner of a penicillin plant in which penicillin concentrates are undergoing chemical treatment. The workers wear surgical garments and even the room itself is lighted by special ultra-violet ceiling lamps to heighten the sterile conditions.

toluene) and other useful substances. In the modern saccharin process, purified toluene is treated with chlorsulphonic acid, by means of which it is converted into two varieties of toluene-sulphonic chlorides, which are respectively designated *ortho* and *para*.

It is the *ortho* toluene-sulphonic chloride which is needed for saccharin manufacture. This *ortho* compound, being in the nature of an oily liquid, is separated carefully and is then treated with ammonia gas, whereby it becomes converted into a toluene-sulphonimide. This is subsequently oxidized by means of an alkaline solution of potassium permanganate (a well-known oxidizing agent in organic chemistry) and the resulting alkaline solution of the toluene compound is acidified. As a result of the acidification, the reaction product undergoes a re-arrangement of its atoms, becoming converted into *ortho-sulphimidobenzoic anhydride*—which is saccharin.

We have already noted that waste is abhorred in chemical manufacturing processes. Here we find an excellent example of this golden rule. When, for the manufacture of saccharin, toluene is treated with chlorsulphonic acid, two different toluene compounds, *ortho* and *para*, are obtained. The *ortho* compound, we have seen, goes into the production of saccharin, but the *para* compound is useless for this purpose.

This, however, is carefully processed up, first with ammonia and afterwards with bleaching powder, and it ultimately is converted into a material having the rather formidable name of para-toluenesulphono-chloramide, the sodium salt of which compound is sold as a powerful disinfectant under the name of "Chloramine T."

In this way, from one single parent substance—toluene—the chemical industry obtains two closely related compounds, one of which becomes saccharin and the other ends up as a disinfectant, Chloramine T.

It may be of interest to realize that saccharin is not the sweetest thing known, as it is commonly supposed to be. By treating saccharin with an ammonium salt, we obtain a substance to which the name of "sucramine" has been applied. This is many times sweeter than even saccharin.

Chloroform is a compound which is known, at least by repute, by all. The manufacture of this typically organic liquid is a comparatively simple procedure. It may be made by treating alcohol or

LEARNING THE ART OF ANALYSIS

Students at the Imperial College of Science and Technology, South Kensington, London, carrying out an intricate piece of chemical analysis in one of the college laboratories.

acetone with bleaching powder. Normally, acetone is used nowadays for this important process, the bleaching powder (which is a chlorine-containing compound) being mixed with the purified acetone in the requisite proportions and the mixture being subsequently heated in an electric still. A chemical interaction results, as a consequence of which chloroform is generated and distils over.

The chloroform, however, still contains traces of impurities from which, if it is to be used for anæsthetic purposes, it must be rigorously freed. This is done by oxidizing away these impurities with chromic acid solution, after which the chloroform is separated, dried and finally very carefully distilled.

It is a truism to state that the organic chemical industry as it has evolved in our country and in Germany, to say nothing of other Continental countries, has been and still is largely based on the utilization of coal-tar products, which, up to the present time, have usually been forthcoming in adequate abundance.

But there is now rising a new chemical industry, one which takes not coal-tar as its basic material, but, instead of this, *crude petroleum*. Naturally enough, such a branch of manufacturing activity is of American origin and growth. It is one with which we in Britain cannot always adequately compete, for we have only small natural supplies of petroleum.

Nevertheless, it is to liquid petroleum crudes and their associated gases that many industrial research chemists are turning their attentions in their efforts towards the discovery and utilization of still newer materials.

There is growing up in America a giant chemical industry, based on petroleum, which will surely rival even the big German chemical monopolies of past years. The organic chemistry of the future, some authorities tell us, is not the chemistry of the coal-tar derivatives. It is the chemistry of the petroleum products.

And, indeed, the economic trend of chemical manufacturing matters does seem to be in the direction of petroleum, a material which is available in such enormous quantities.

Yet, for many a long year, coal-tar, or, at least, its important constituents, will still be sought after for the making of the world's chemicals. For within the black, treacly, highly-odoriferous coal-tar distillates we have potentially the first beginnings of countless drugs, colours, perfumes, flavours, to say nothing of innumerable materials of a miscellaneous nature, all of which are yearly becoming more and more completely indispensable to modern industry and to modern civilization in general.

Petroleum, indeed, may yet turn out to be the chemical abode of many synthetic materials as yet unknown. Nevertheless, its possibilities seem to be in an altogether different direction from those of coal-tar. The ideal of our future researchers, therefore, must be to combine the utilitarian capabilities of the two products, to unite the synthetical aspects of petroleum residues with those of our native coal-tar distillates.

The technical promise of this ideal is great. Only civil, political and economic disagreement between the great nations can hinder or prevent the ultimate fructification of this surely praiseworthy and far-seeing aim of modern chemical science.

Test Yourself

1. We make contact with the products of chemical manufacturing activities during almost every hour of our daily lives.
   Can you mention off-hand, and in less than a minute, a round dozen of these products?

2. Explain the essential difference between a chemical-producing industry and a chemical-converting industry.

3. "Heavy" and "fine" chemicals represent the two great divisions of the chemical manufacturing world. Assign the following chemicals to these two classes:
   Radium barium bromide, saltpetre, common soda, synthetic musk, sulphuric acid, aspirin, chloroform, superphosphate fertilizer, synthetic vitamins, metol (photographic developer), synthetic vanilla (vanillin), caustic soda, saccharin, hydrochloric acid, bleaching powder, gold chloride, strychnine, ammonia.

4. What is a "unit operation" in the chemical industry?

5. What is the function of the "catalyst" in the contact process of sulphuric acid manufacture? Name three different catalysts which may be applied for this purpose.

6. How is soda made from salt (or brine)?

7. What is the principle of the synthetic ammonia process?

8. What is the fundamental peculiarity of the element carbon on which the entire science of organic chemistry rests?

9. With what experiment did modern plastics manufacture begin?

10. What are dyestuff "intermediates"?

11. How is aspirin made on the manufacturing scale?

12. From what prime substances are the following important chemicals made? (a) Saccharin; (b) chloramine T; (c) bleaching powder; (d) synthetic oil of wintergreen; (e) chloroform; (f) aniline; (g) chlorine gas; (h) bicarbonate of soda.

Answers will be found at the end of the book.

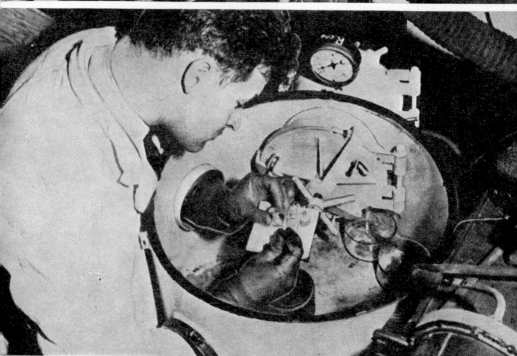

ATOMIC RESEARCH FOR PEACEFUL ENDS

Research into the secrets of nuclear fission was stimulated by war needs, but is already result-ing in great advantages to all peoples of the world. Above are shown scientists of the University of Chicago Metallurgical Laboratory at work. (Top) Machining uranium on a lathe. (Bottom) A physicist at work in a laboratory dedicated to atomic research.

CHAPTER XV

SCIENCE IN PEACE AND WAR

SCIENCE is the card-indexing of the knowledge of nature and the use of that index. It is because man is the only live being who is able to do this by intelligence, and not merely by instincts, such as a dog uses in his way about the world, that he has arisen from the ape man.

Some prehistoric genius once seized a burning brand from a forest fire and maintained, continually, a fire outside his cave, which kept him warm in winter. Perhaps, after a forest fire, he found an animal roasted; he liked its taste and found cooked flesh kept longer than raw.

Primitive Fire-making

His intelligence enabled him to connect fire and roasting and to imitate the process in his own fire, possibly by wrapping his joint in clay. Then, rubbing a piece of wood to a point, for a weapon, he discovered it got hot. His ability to think rationally connected heat and fire, so that methods for generating his own fire, when and where he wanted it, by rubbing two sticks together, made him independent of waiting for another forest fire when his cave fire went out.

It is difficult to say what have been man's greatest discoveries since he obtained, gradually, mastery over Nature, collecting her knowledge, indexing it and discerning the relationship between apparently unrelated facts. The pot, the wheel, and the needle are indispensable. It took tens of thousands of years for them to be discovered and developed, and not until Charlemagne's time, in the eighth century, was the modern horse collar, which places the weight on the horse's shoulder, instead of his neck, invented. The horse was no longer in danger of being strangled, so loaded wagons, ten times heavier, could be drawn.

Today man has fashioned Nature's laws and phenomena to a myriad uses, to conquer her attacks on man's welfare, to harness her great forces and to wrest, faster and faster, many more secrets from her.

Yet. . . .

It was about eight thousand years ago that man began to grow his own food and rear his domestic animals, instead of gathering wild fruits and hunting wild animals. He began to study, with a little system, the materials he used and really to master his environment. He had become a scientist, admittedly a very primitive and elementary one, but, all the same, a scientist.

Man also being capable of reasoning and expressing his thoughts, first by talking and later with the added aid of writing, developed politics, governments, wars, trade, art, literature and the other activities covered by that all-embracing word, "civilization." To win in trade or war you must be stronger and cleverer than your competitor or opponent, and so —despite the traditional conservatism of military commanders, ministers and merchants—new materials, ships, manufactures and weapons had to be encouraged and developed.

For four thousand years the metalworker supplied the needs of peace and war by his rule-of-thumb methods and the traditional knowledge handed down from generation to generation. He carried out experiments which told him that if the copper-tin alloy, bronze, contained more than 12 per cent of tin ·it became too brittle and, if less, then too soft.

Metal Working

He discovered how to work and forge small pieces of brittle cast iron into sharp, hard, tough swords and spearheads. He worked gold and silver into ornaments and coins. He made pots and pans. Today he is the "metallurgist" who, with microscopes, testing machines, X-rays and chemicals, tests and develops more new alloys in a month than the old metal-worker discovered in a century.

The development in agricultural methods was scarcely noticeable until the last few hundred years; but shipbuilding and civil engineering made vast strides from burnt-out tree trunk canoes to the Roman galleys two thousand years ago, and the Armada's proud Spanish galleons. The larger the ship the more goods it could carry and, after the discovery of gunpowder, the more guns it could defend itself with.

Chariots and carts enabled people to carry goods more quickly from villages and towns. They had to cross streams and rivers, so bridges had to built. Great cities developed because traders and merchants, growing prosperous, found it easier to establish markets for visiting customers than to travel with their wares.

Civilization's Progress

Great walls and fortresses guarded the cities against invaders, sewage schemes and water conduits had to be invented to keep the masses of people healthy. Soldiers and statesmen, philosophers and farmers, poets and mathematicians, engineers and scientists abounded in the greatness of Greece and Rome. Scientific thought was confined almost entirely to the Greeks, who when conquered by the Romans provided them with the scientific knowledge which the Romans used for medicine, agriculture, architecture and engineering.

The Greek and Roman civilizations relied on slaves to mine, quarry, grind corn and carry loads. Therefore, though the Greeks realized that for man to master Nature he must obey Nature's laws, they did not develop machines after experimenting with steam and compressed air. They relied on slaves to do the work now done by machines.

Science was used for both peace and war; but the scale on which it was applied was not great.

When the barbarians destroyed the decaying Roman civilization, they cleared the ground for future rebuilding; but for several hundred years Europe was engulfed in the gloom of the Dark Ages. Learning left Europe and settled in the Byzantine Imperial Court at Constantinople.

The needs of war, agriculture and medicine kept a little scientific knowledge alive. But it was only here and there that tiny plants of knowledge struggled to get to the light.

Then came the thirteenth century, with its great change in outlook. The Arabic-speaking races and the Jews had developed a real interest in science through their translations of Greek authors and by their own experiments. Through contact with the Near East and the Moors, Europe passed to a more rationalistic mind, particularly through the rediscovery of Aristotle between 1200 and 1225. Saint Thomas Aquinas created "the priceless habit of looking for an exact point and of sticking to it when found," which has ever remained with scientists, though Saint Thomas's philosophy has long been repudiated.

It was the studious Franciscan friar, Roger Bacon (1214-94), who founded British science and scientific outlook by being the only man in the European Middle Ages to understand clearly that experimental methods alone give certainty in science. The scientific revolution had begun. Every statement of supposed fact should be capable of verification. He invented, among other things, the reading-glass and discovered gunpowder in Europe. The English first used it at the Battle of Crecy. A chronicler said: "The English remained still and let off some bombards they had, to frighten the Genoese."

Privileges for Scientists

Gunpowder made war more expensive. It stimulated the chemist into action, the heavy metal industry to produce great cast cannon, and the mathematician's brain into working out the problems of aiming. The scientist found he could gain privileges, money and the freedom for his apparently useless researches by devoting some of his time to war research. He was partly able to free himself from the stranglehold of religious dogma, and from persecution as a wizard, or agent of the devil.

In Italy, the great Leonardo da Vinci, regarded, until modern times, largely as a

EXTERIOR OF A HIGH-SPEED WIND TUNNEL

Scientific research and discovery proceed unabated in times of both peace and war. For example, now that aeroplanes are flying at speeds approaching that of sound, precise information on such factors as air resistance, lift and stability have become of increasing importance. Wind tunnels supply many of the answers to aircraft designers' problems, and the testing of components, and even of complete aircraft before mass production, is an essential process in the development of efficient and safe designs of new prototypes.

painter and sculptor, because he did not publish his work, did an immense amount of scientific work. He left five thousand pages of notes in mirror writing, which reads from right to left, since he was left-handed. From 1483 until 1519 he invented, among many other things, the lifebelt, diving-suit, many-sided fortresses, dredgers, chimney cowls, and rope-making, silk-winding and wool-spinning machines, and metal-rolling presses.

Before His Time

He attempted to apply power from water mills and horse-driven winches to the textile machinery. He designed machine tools, the anti-friction roller bearing, screw-cutting machines, an hydraulic press, the parachute, the helicopter and left much useful data on flight. Unfortunately, much remained locked up in his notes and the century which followed his death became anti-scientific.

Progress in England

While the Continent persecuted Galileo and other scientists, England, now free from the edicts of the Roman Church, was broadening her outlook. Gilbert made discoveries in magnetism, Harvey discovered the circulation of the blood and thus turned all eyes to the future. He founded the science of physiology, making modern medicine and surgery possible.

James I's Lord Chancellor, Francis Bacon, well known for his essays, wrote his great book on science, *Novum Organum*, emphasizing the importance of experiment

THREE-BLADED
NON-FERROUS
ROTOR

GRAVITY-FEED
PETROL TANK

TORQUE-COUNTERING
JET ORIFICE

TWO-SEAT
COCKPIT

SHOCK-ABSORBING
LEGS

FUSELAGE OF
ALUMINIUM ALLOY

JET PRINCIPLE APPLIED TO HELICOPTER

*From one side of the tail of this hovering Cierva helicopter, a jet of exhaust gases escapes
in order to cancel out the natural tendency of the aircraft's fuselage to rotate in the direction
opposite to that in which the rotor is spinning.*

and the application of science to industry.
He was the first to understand the relationship between science and society.
"Knowledge," he said, "that tendeth but
to satisfaction, is but a courtesan," and its
proper use is for "the benefit and relief of
the state and society of man."

Research in Industry

It was during Bacon's lifetime that
Queen Elizabeth and Cecil had fostered
metal-mining, brass-founding, wire-draw-
ing, glass, paper, starch and soap industries
and, through making people eat fish three
days per week, obtained a large number of
skilled sailors to man the warships. Agriculture was developed to provide well-fed
soldiers. Skilled workers came from a
Europe dominated by the Spaniards.
Holland made great technical strides,
whereby for a century she led world trade.
And Bacon, seeing all this, advocated the
modern principle of "Research in Industry."

Industry and commerce had made
demands for knowledge, received it and
then settled down. This was partly due to
the aim of self-preservation in time of

war and partly to the desire to maintain
the prosperity of the country. But further
improvements were made by scientists,
which was natural, because once a scientist
gets interested in a development, he continues his experiments after the manufacturer's initial needs have been satisfied.
The now prosperous industry was slow in
adopting the new improvements, because
it saw no need for the extra expense of
new or modified plant. And so science
continued to be starved by industries and
governments.

The seventeenth century saw a great
interest in scientific investigation by traders
and leisured people during their working
and leisured hours. These people liked to
get together to discuss their work, with
the result that, in 1662, the Royal Society
was founded.

Among its members was the Hon.
Robert Boyle, whose work on the expansion
of gases laid the basis for modern
pneumatic tools and air compressors. The
mixture of merchants and scholars was
furthering Francis Bacon's ideal of co-
operation between science and society; for,

during the seventeenth and eighteenth century, the Society was much concerned with using scientific knowledge and experiment, as, for example, in improving building materials and the design of roofs, chimneys and drains to obtain a fireproof and healthy London after the Great Plague and Fire.

Age of Reason

The eighteenth century, "The Age of Reason," saw the foundation of nineteenth-century industrialism. The steam engine was invented, coal used instead of wood for smelting iron, crucible steel was made, the coke oven invented. There was so much iron that Britain now exported it, instead of importing it.

The plentiful supply of iron and steel in the nineteenth century made it possible to develop the power loom and power-driven machinery. The cottage industry had given way to the factory. The profitable, well-established industry of this country, without a competitor in the world, was soon going at full steam.

While industry had developed, so had war. The problems of war in the nineteenth century had some effect in the establishment of new industries by scientific research. The percussion cap, discovered in 1814, ignited gunpowder, without using the cumbersome flint and steel. Bigger guns, requiring more accurate firing, were essential.

Henry Bessemer invented a cannon with a rifled bore, which twirled a shell, instead of a cannon ball, so that it went straight in the line aimed, instead of deviating like the ball. Cast-iron cannon cracked and burst with the charge's explosion. Steel could be made only in relatively small quantities. Bessemer set to work and produced his converter, which reduced steel production costs to one-fifth per ton and enabled fifteen to twenty tons of steel to be produced in minutes instead of hours.

New industries arose through the scientific invention of individuals, except for Edison, who organized an industrial research team in his laboratory long before the new industries were compelled, by their very nature, to follow suit. Oil

technology, the aeroplane, wireless, dynamite for quarrying and mining, the generator, electrical engineering, and the work on the electron and atom, were products of the nineteenth and early twentieth centuries, whose significance was not fully appreciated by the military authorities.

It was not until well on in the 1914-18 war that the British Government realized that science's great advance during the previous fifty years had provided the means for war on a scale never before imagined. Thereafter science was accused of being the cause of war.

The reason for the isolation of science was that during the greater part of the nineteenth century the Royal Society and many leading scientists lost their understanding of science's position in the life of the community. No longer was Britain's population less than ten million; it was nearly forty. The scientists went into their ivory towers, and most of them rarely, if ever, came down to earth again.

Theory and Practice

Faraday, Lord Rayleigh, Clerk-Maxwell, Sir J. J. Thomson, discoverers of the dynamo, theory of flight, wireless-wave theory and the electron, respectively, were, for example, content to publish their work in scientific journals and leave it at that. There were exceptions, such as Lord Kelvin, who applied his theoretical work to practical inventions; Swan, who invented the electric lamp; Pasteur, who saved France's vineyards and cured rabies, and Lister, the great protagonist of antiseptic surgery. But they were the few among many. Science had become divided into "pure" science the aristocrat, and "applied" science the handmaid.

The efforts of all those pioneers, from Roger Bacon in the thirteenth century to Sir Humphry Davy in the nineteenth, to introduce science to and then maintain its close relationship with the life and needs of the community, were being frustrated in Britain.

But there were great changes ahead.

Foreign manufacturers were beginning to use scientists in all branches of their work. Germany developed its great chemical industry. The British manufacturer and merchant, secure in a century's prosperity, supplied plant and raw materials. He did not realize that by using scientific knowledge and scientists in well-organized teams, the foreign competitors were making up for their hundred years' industrial leeway with alarming rapidity.

The 1914-18 war created a new situation. Industry's small unco-ordinated laboratories, excellent in their own way, proved insufficient for war. It was a new kind of war waged with instruments, tanks, motors and wireless, besides guns and rifles. Poison gas or chemical warfare quickly appeared. Science was being used as never before by one side attempting to exterminate the other.

Not Responsible for Wars

Science did not cause either the First World War or the Second. Both were started by the greed of rulers and governments. They prostituted scientific discovery to their own ends; but, strange though it may seem, in both wars the German Military Staff was hesitant in applying new scientific development and discovery to its war needs. Britain, having learnt much from 1914-18, set to work with a will, creating radar and the Mulberry Harbour. A scientific revolution had occurred in Britain.

That revolution had its beginnings in 1917, when the Department of Scientific and Industrial Research came into being. The D.S.I.R., as it is universally known, set out to establish its own industrial laboratories, researching on such as Building, Roads, Food, Fuel, etc., and, during the between-war years, encouraged thirty industries to form co-operative Research Associations with their own laboratories. These are usually financed equally by the State and the industry. The drive for scientific research was for peaceful use, though the Government spend an almost equal amount on defence research.

But modern wars are not matters of gunpowder and cannon. Every type of industrial and scientific activity, from buttons to bombs, pencils to planes, tinfoil to tanks, dish-cloths to dreadnoughts, are essential to modern warfare. The soldier cannot do without the scientist. Even the very atoms themselves have become explosive with the atomic bomb.

Importance of Research

Vast has been the progress, yet both wars have delayed fundamental scientific progress. The wireless valve depends on a very abstruse mathematical paper by O. W. Richardson on what happens to electrons thrown off by a red-hot wire. It looks quite useless, but without it Fleming could not have invented the wireless valve. Sir J. J. Thomson's work on cathode rays in magnetic and electric fields made radar and television possible. But fundamental work, done in the quiet of universities, requires time and patience and a very select team of brilliant research students, such as Rutherford and Thomson gathered together at the famous Cavendish Laboratory, Cambridge.

War disperses such teams. Their members are needed to work on urgent, immediate problems. The 1914-18 war delayed the apparently "useless" work on atomic research by Rutherford's team for some years. The 1939-45 war has delayed work in mathematics, geology, astronomy, biology and the social sciences. War only accelerates the developments of existing knowledge for definite ends, wasting materials to produce materials to waste more material. There is no regard for cost. Physics, Chemistry and Engineering advance at the expense of the other branches of science. Scientific knowledge should advance evenly on all fronts.

Servant or Master?

Though, since the dawn of history, the scientist has been responsible for the improvements in man's standard of life, for without his developments of materials and techniques there would be no material progress, he is still the handmaid of politicians, governments, and industrialists. He has made the discoveries; but he has had little or no say regarding their use. Whether they be used to benefit the community or exterminate it is not, in the

GREAT DISCOVERY OF INESTIMABLE VALUE TO MANKIND

In any attempt to assess the relative values of great scientific discoveries, X-rays stand pre-eminent for their contribution to progress in medicine and industry. Above is just one of their applications: the examination of an aeroplane wing by an American mobile unit.

minds of the non-scientific, a matter of any concern to the scientists.

The scientists have been frustrated too long and now they have come down from their ivory towers. The Royal Society has, since 1938, become increasingly concerned with the effect of science on the community. The scientists' trade union, the Association of Scientific Workers, is much concerned with the place of the scientist in the modern world. It has even been advocated that statesmen should be scientists; that scientific discovery be administered by scientists only. But that view is an extreme one and, in due course, a stage will be reached providing a compromise between those regarding the scientist as a servant and those who think he should be master.

Though the powerful Royal Society and many scientific institutions and societies have been living in ivory towers, the British Association for the Advancement of Science, membership of which is open to anyone interested in the advancement of science, has, despite its comparatively meagre resources, been doing much, through its famous annual week-long meetings, to interest the public in science and the scientists in the public.

Achievement in Sight

The "British Ass," as it is affectionately called, has been working for well over a hundred years. Its aims are, at last, being achieved.

The perennial question, "Is Science Good or Evil?" is one asked only by unthinking people. The horrors of war are always being used to show its evil influence; but as we have seen, wars are not caused by science. The great wars of history: the Hundred Years War, the War of Austrian

AN OUTSTANDING SCIENTIFIC ACHIEVEMENT OF THE CENTURY
Above is seen a mobile radar-controlled searchlight for detecting enemy aircraft. But radar is equally of service in peacetime, for as a navigational aid it is making the airways and seaways many times safer than before, by providing "vision" through darkness and fog.

Succession, the Napoleonic Wars, the Wars of the Roses, were certainly not caused by science. In any case, Great Plagues, the Black Death of the Middle Ages, famines, influenza epidemics have caused many more and often more painful deaths than have been caused by war. Science has abolished the terror of the plague in Britain. It can now, at last, defeat malaria, which causes millions of deaths per year in India alone.

Science is, most definitely, the handmaid of progress. Its broadest definition is

simply: man's effort to subordinate his environment to his own welfare, which leads to "Knowledge based upon accurate observation of facts and the relation of them to general principles or laws."

Today, uncreasable cotton, unshrinkable wool, nylon stockings, Perspex (the non-splintering transparent plastic), polythene (for insulating very high-voltage cables and wires carrying extremely rapidly alternating currents), make our life pleasanter. They are the results of scientific work during the past few years. Today, no child, if immunized, need dread diphtheria undefended; the M and B kills dangerous germs in the bloodstream. The average person lives much longer, childbirth is far less dangerous and infantile mortality much less than even fifty years ago. This list of blessings could be expanded almost indefinitely.

Who today would care to live in the small, low houses of Elizabeth's time with their stench and primitive sanitary arrangements? No gas, coal, electricity, running water, anæsthetics for operations, newspapers, cheap books, universal education, decent roads, railways or radio!

Wide Scope for Science

A modest suburban house is a more luxuriously comfortable palace than ever Queen Elizabeth knew. It has all happened because man, the scientist, once regarded as an odd being, is coming more and more into every section of human activity. The psychiatrist mends your mind; the chemist makes your clothes and food; the biologist studies your body's actual working; the physicist gives you radio and television; the biochemist and plant physiologist make bigger and better wheat yields per acre; the engineer makes your train, bus and car; the marine zoologist studies your fish; the bacteriologist kills harmful germs and makes others do work producing flax; the medical scientist finds the causes of diseases and their prevention; the metallurgist's efforts made possible the machinery to produce this book at a reasonable price. When man uses science for sane purposes he betters the world.

Science for Good or Evil?

It is man alone who is responsible for making science a good or evil thing. Atomic power can be used to blast us to extinction or it can be developed to give us cheap energy in the future. Wisely, governments are controlling research themselves through committees on which there are laymen and scientists. This is now "The Age of Science."

Governments, now and in the future, will have to realize that the scientist's work affects the very core of our existence and well-being, that decisions and new schemes require the scientist from their start. A new town, trading estate, factory or main road depends, from the start, on the geologist, so that the first three may receive adequate water supplies and the latter does not sink on hidden bogs. Factories are known to have been erected miles from water and where their wastes have to be expensively treated to avoid pollution.

The scientist was not called in.

Overcoming Fatigue

The social scientist, studying our habits and comfort at home and at work, has not yet come into his own. If we want fewer hours of work without decreasing output we must work with greater efficiency. Much work was done during the war by the social scientist studying conditions and methods of working. People did more, yet were less tired. Needless exertion was eliminated.

One of the most important fields for study is the housewife's domain. Good, well-designed, healthy homes, bright, clean factories and reduced hours depend largely on the combined work of many scientists. Their efforts should not be frustrated through ignorance and prejudice.

Results by Reasoning

It is a far cry from the Ancient Greeks with their human slaves to the present with its mechanical slaves. The machine is rapidly becoming the unskilled labourer, the hewer of wood and drawer of water. The educational schemes of the future will create ever-increasing numbers of scientists and technicians. A new outlook is developing. Problems may be regarded from a scientific attitude. There may be less tendency to be dogmatic; evidence and opinions may be properly considered as the scientist looks at his results before he derives a theory from them.

Science has made the globe small through the aeroplane, telephone, wireless and television. The scientist has usually been internationally minded, because knowledge knows no territorial limits. Therefore, as time goes on, scientifically minded nations should become freely

CAMERA
ELECTRON GUN
CONTROL PANELS

CAMERA
CABLE
COUPLERS

PULSE DELAY
CIRCUITS

CAMERA
CABLES

AN INVENTION WITH GREAT EDUCATIONAL POSSIBILITIES

Television has great educational possibilities in addition to its entertainment value, and is one more example of the direction of scientific effort to purely peaceful purposes. Above is a view of some of the apparatus at the B.B.C.'s London television studio.

co-operative, politically and economically, and expressing opinions freely without causing bad feeling.

By that time the scientist will have won the struggle against the non- and often anti-scientific outlook of many government administrators. The practical scientist often upsets the treasured theories of non-scientific people. The scientist is still too much in their hands and tied by secrecy restrictions imposed by vested interests, be they in Government departments or industry. The scientist should be a member of the highest councils of the nations so that his advice may have full effect when necessary. No sane man would go to a butcher for an operation.

Stupendous Energy

And so the Fifth Age of Man has been born: the Age of Science, heralded by the atomic bomb. The academic discoveries of the Curies, Sir J. J. Thomson and Lord Rutherford, of mathematicians such as Einstein, Dirac and Louis de Broglie, have revealed the world's master secrets. Wilful nature has answered one of man's cleverest probings into her inner secrets by giving him the key to unlock, at will, the floodgates keeping in stupendous energy.

The problem of harnessing that energy, so as to keep it under control, and of keeping the key in trusted hands, so that the world is not overwhelmed has created the greatest international question of all time

Whether the energy of a score of bombs, each 20,000 times more powerful than any known explosive, shall open wide the gates and destroy, in a few minutes, a city such as London, or whether, in properly controlled plants, the energy will flow smoothly and continuously, doing useful work, depends on international, human goodwill. It has linked the scientist and the layman inextricably together. Both must learn to co-operate properly.

At Grips with Nature

War showed how large-scale, planned, teams of research workers can advance swiftly in the application of the work of university research. Now fundamental research is begun again in those universities. Discovery is ever becoming swifter and so the lessons of large-scale wartime industrial development must be observed and allow man a greater hold on nature. In time, atomic energy will make cheap power, enabling man to produce and live more fruitfully.

But man does not live on atomic energy alone. There are other great discoveries, which may greatly change our lives. Scientists have found how to manufacture, artificially, some of those growth-controlling substances called hormones. Methoxone kills certain weeds by entering them and causing such confusion that they grow in odd ways, eventually strangling themselves. Perhaps, in time, man will control his own growth and a cabbage may become a politician, or, perhaps better, vice versa!

Radar and echo-sounding instruments make sea and air navigation ten times safer than a few years ago. Cholera, typhoid, diphtheria, malaria and tuberculosis are conquered or are being conquered. Foods once the luxuries of a few will become available to all. Psychology applied to man and his personality will prevent many square pegs being put in round holes.

What Lies Ahead?

The importance of the fission of the atom lies not in its explosive power, but in its possible use for providing man with the boundless energy to be distributed through an enormous network to enable him to live a higher, pleasanter, healthier, richer life than he has ever done before.

Man, that is, you and I, can now, despite himself, live peacefully and fruitfully through the coming centuries.

But it will not be the fault of science if he does not do so. Unfortunately, too many of the nations of the world look upon the many problems with a most passionate, partisan, nationalistic outlook, whilst others seek to enchain by the creation of one form of international totalitarianism or another. Only a few are capable of applying the reasonable outlook of science to the lives of the nations. Let us see that our nation is endowed with this power.

GUIDE TO FURTHER STUDY

THERE is great and lasting pleasure to be obtained from science as a hobby. Many of the famous scientists of the past did all their scientific work in their spare time. Gilbert, the man who discovered that the earth is a magnet, was a doctor. Lavoisier, who showed that matter is not destroyed by burning, was concerned with tax collection in his daily life.

Logarithms were discovered by Napier in his spare time, while Priestley, the discoverer of oxygen, was a clergyman. Experiments in kite-flying in a thunderstorm enabled Franklin to demonstrate the similarity between electricity and lightning, and led him to invent the lightning-conductor. He was a self-educated man whose main work was diplomatic.

Probably the most notable success story in scientific work is that of Faraday, the father of electrical engineering. At the age of twelve he became a bookseller's errand boy, and later apprenticed to bookbinding, and he was thus able to educate himself by reading the books he had to bind. His great chance came when a customer, who knew of his studious habits, presented him with tickets for some lectures by Davy. Faraday wrote notes of these lectures and sent them to Davy with his observations and a request for a job. He got the job and, in due course, he became Davy's successor. Davy himself, to whom credit is due for recognizing Faraday's budding genius, used to say that his greatest discovery was Michael Faraday.

While few can aspire to such heights as were reached by Faraday, useful work may still be done by amateur scientists who are prepared to take their work seriously. In our own times, we have the example of the discovery of the value of short waves in radio. These high frequencies were allotted to amateurs in the belief that they were useless for commercial purposes, but the amateurs showed that the very reverse was the case.

It must, however, be recognized that the chances of making a great contribution to science are smaller than they were in the days of the pioneers. Whereas, in the old days, a single individual could know all that was to be known about several sciences, it is now hardly possible for a man to be expert in all branches of any one science. Moreover, and this relates particularly to applied sciences, such as engineering, the present tendency is for discoveries to be made by teams of research workers with considerable financial backing, rather than by lone workers using home-made apparatus.

Although the possibility of a great discovery cannot be ruled out, that possibility should not be regarded as a reason for taking up a scientific hobby. Rather let the hobby be chosen for its interest and for the pursuit of knowledge for its own sake, even if it is second-hand, and let the discoveries be incidental.

Applying Scientific Methods

In following a scientific hobby, a person learns much more of value than the facts he accumulates. He learns to appreciate and to apply scientific methods of thought and experiment, and can hardly fail to benefit from the application of these methods to the problems of everyday life. Provided that he does not expect science to know all the answers, and realizes that there are things in life to which the scientific method cannot properly be applied, he will enjoy a richer and fuller life.

The choice of the particular branch of science to be embraced as a hobby must depend both on individual inclination and on the amount of money which can be devoted to it.

Astronomy may be studied without the expenditure of much money, though a telescope will greatly enlarge both the interest and the field of study.

Chemistry, physics, electricity and magnetism, and radio are all popular choices, though they tend to be more expensive because of the need for professionally-made apparatus. Measuring devices cannot usually be made at home, but people with clever fingers can spend many happy hours in making apparatus for some projected experiment. In this way they not only save money but satisfy their creative instincts.

The various chapters of this book give details of many interesting scientific experiments. Not all can easily be carried out in the home, but there are many which demand only simple apparatus and easily-obtained materials.

Necessary Equipment

A few chemicals, some test tubes, and the part-time services of a gas stove or other heating agent, are sufficient to open the way to the study of a wide range of experiments in inorganic chemistry. Much that is of fundamental importance may be learned from the behaviour of metals, acids, alkalis and salts in various combinations, while very little more equipment is needed for chemical analysis of a qualitative nature.

Many of the fundamental laws of optics may be checked with no more complicated apparatus than a source of light, such as an electric lamp in a punctured tin, a mirror or two and some lenses, together with a few pins and a piece of wood in which to stick them. Even in such simple experiments as these, there is much to be learned which is incidental to their main purpose.

The principles of levers and pulleys may be verified with the most elementary apparatus, and billiard balls may be used to demonstrate some of the laws of dynamics.

Magnetic experiments require only relatively simple equipment. Magnetic fields may be studied with the aid of one or two magnets and some iron filings, while permanent records of the results may be kept if waxed paper is used. If a simple magnetometer is constructed, the earth provides a test magnetic field at no cost to the user.

In electrical work, much may be done with the aid of a battery, a home-made galvanometer, a supply of wire, and a few other odd pieces of gear.

The construction of wireless apparatus can be pursued as a profitable hobby from which much knowledge of the subject can be gained. In almost every town there are shops where surplus military radio components can be purchased. For a few shillings it is often possible to secure a useful collection of valves, capacitors and other pieces of apparatus. Second-hand electrical apparatus, too, is frequently obtainable at extremely reasonable prices.

In the assembly of a wireless receiving apparatus and the installation of simple bell and telephone circuits for use in the home, more can be learned about the principles of the subjects concerned than can be gained from books alone.

Science and art may be combined in one pursuit such as photography. Apart from the artistic interest, this hobby gives scope for study and experiment in both optics and chemistry.

The foregoing does not purport to be an exhaustive list, but it should at least provide, in conjunction with the earlier chapters, enough food for thought to enable each individual to choose the hobby which is best suited to his or her purse, tastes, and inclinations.

Joining a Practical Group

Practical knowledge can be extended by joining a local wireless or scientific society. There are many in existence, both as local organizations and in connexion with factories. Such societies are usually eminently practical in their activities. Members demonstrate their own apparatus and exchange experiences, and authorities attend to give lectures.

Students should also watch local newspapers for announcements of lectures by scientists and engineers at the public libraries and other institutions which make a practice of encouraging the pursuit of knowledge. For the more ambitious, courses of evening lectures are frequently arranged by and in co-operation with technical colleges.

In the following pages it is assumed that the reader intends to work without the benefit of a course of lessons, either personally or by correspondence, and that he desires guidance in his reading to follow up and extend what he has learned from this book.

At the outset, it must be realized that books on science fall broadly into two classes. There are popular works, which are intended to be read straight through from cover to cover, and in which the more difficult matters are either side-stepped or cleverly glossed over. At the other end of the scale there are very dry and learned textbooks and works of reference. Nobody would think of reading such works from beginning to end. They are, and should be, used as sources of information in somewhat the same way as a dictionary is used.

Choosing One's Books

Between these two extremes there are numerous books, varying widely in difficulty and in depth and width of treatment, according to the type of reader to whom they are addressed. These books could again be subdivided into those which are intended as an adjunct to live teaching and those suitable for a student working on his own, though some, of course, fall into both classes.

In starting to read a new subject it is advisable to begin with the popular type of book which surveys the whole field of study without going deeply into any part of it. When one or two books of this kind have been read, the student will have gained a good idea of the nature of his subject, of the relative importance of various aspects of it, and of the way in which they depend on one another. He will also perceive how the subject is related to his everyday life and work, and he should be helped to avoid the narrow specialization which produces the uneducated technician.

The next stage is to tackle an elementary textbook. In reading a textbook the student is required to make a conscious effort, if his reading is to be any use. He must understand each chapter before proceeding to the next, and must learn such facts or formulæ as are of sufficient importance. These will usually be printed in heavy type or distinguished in some similar manner. No argument or proof should be left until it is thoroughly understood and can be reproduced at the time of reading.

If the author assumes that a piece of information or an algebraic process is common knowledge, and the student is not familiar with it, then he must break off his reading and fill in this gap in his background. This is most important, because scientific knowledge is built up brick by brick, and a weakness in the foundations will cause cracks in the whole structure. It is surprising how often a thing which is not properly understood keeps appearing in later work, and how easy it is to understand when a real effort is made to get to the bottom of it.

When a subject lends itself to numerical problems, it is essential to practise their solution. If, on reaching the end of a chapter, the student finds that he cannot easily solve the numerical exercises given, then he may be certain that he has not properly understood the matter and should attack the chapter again from the beginning. In this kind of self-testing it is legitimate to refer to the text for formulæ which may be needed, but not to look for a worked example and to try and follow it step by step.

The purpose of worked examples is to illustrate the application of general methods and to indicate mathematical tricks which produce neat solutions. The lone student is advised to avoid textbooks which omit the answers to their numerical problems. To him, such questions are merely a cause of exasperation.

Problems and Answers

It is often possible to find a little book containing problems and their answers, with, at most, a few hints on the methods of attack. Such a book is of very great value to anyone working on his own and it should be brought into use at the end of each chapter, or section of reading, in the textbook.

Some discretion must be exercised in the selection of the problems to be tackled. Failing guidance, the best method is to select those which appear most like the exercises in the textbook, but not to be dismayed if they cannot be solved. There may be, in an apparently simple problem, some new principle which has not yet been encountered, and only an experienced teacher can tell, by reading a question, whether this is the case. It is for this reason that undirected students are best served by problems embodied in textbooks, for the author knows just what he expects the student to have learned at each stage.

Interpreting Symbol Meanings

Unnecessary difficulties are sometimes caused by the appearance of Greek letters in mathematical formulæ. Although few people move their lips when reading, most experience an awkward sense of discontinuity when they encounter a symbol with which they cannot associate a sound. It is, therefore, well worth while to learn the names and sounds of the few Greek letters in common use. The added facility in reading will more than compensate for the slight trouble involved, and if a new letter is met, it can always be called "squiggle" for the time being.

Whatever the subject to be studied, many of the methods of learning are the same. These methods, and much other useful information, are set out in an interesting manner in the *Student's Guide*, by Adams. This is available in a cheap edition and forms a valuable addition to the library of any student, whether he works alone or under the direction of a skilled teacher.

In studying the heavens, no great progress can be made without the aid of a good star atlas. An atlas of this kind, which is very suitable for readers of this book, is *A Beginner's Star Atlas and Reference Handbook*, by Aitken. This work not only contains excellent star charts but much other valuable information as well. *Whitaker's Almanack* may usefully be employed in conjunction with the star atlas. It contains a great deal of astronomical information, including the positions of the sun, the moon, and the planets.

The beginner will also require a book which deals with astronomy in a simple way. He may well make his choice from two books by Reed, *A Guide to the Sky* and *Elementary Astronomy*, and two others,

First Steps in Astronomy, by Burns, and *The Revolving Heavens*, by Waterfield.

For general reading, the following are recommended: *The Stars in Their Courses*, by Jeans, *Worlds Without End*, by Spencer Jones, *Astronomy*, by Smart, and *Life on Other Worlds*, by Spencer Jones. Once the above works have been mastered, the student may proceed to more advanced books, such as *The Universe Around Us*, by Jeans. Others will doubtless suggest themselves in the course of earlier reading.

Readers who wish to follow up the chapter on "Matter and Motion" are advised to begin their studies by reading a general elementary book, which shows how scientific laws and facts are met in everyday life. A good book of this type is *Everyday Science*, by Parsons.

It would then be interesting to take an excursion into history and to read about the state of the knowledge of mechanics in medieval times, as exemplified in *The Mechanical Investigations of Leonardo da Vinci*, by Hart. The comparison between the old and the new will be further emphasized by reading another good modern book, such as *Science for the Citizen*, by Hogben, which gives a very comprehensive account of present-day scientific knowledge and contains many practical examples.

The student may then feel disposed to tackle a textbook such as *University Physics*, Vol. 1, by Champion. This book will take him to a standard, in the subject, represented by a second-year course at a university, but it should be noted that a knowledge of the calculus is required to obtain the fullest benefit from this and similar textbooks.

Atomic Theory

A final suggestion is *Atoms*, by Perrin. This book was originally written in French, but an English translation is available. It deals with the atomic theory of matter and is illustrated by a variety of experiments, many of which were first performed by the author and his co-workers.

The mention of atomic theory leads naturally to the subject of Chapter V, "Within the Atom." For the effective study of this branch of physics a working knowledge of the calculus is desirable, but a good general picture may be obtained without that equipment if the reader is prepared to take as read certain portions of the works mentioned here.

A good starting point is *Ions, Electrons, and Ionizing Radiations*, by J. A. Crowther, a book which gives an account of the little world within the atom. This might be followed by *Structure of the Atom*, by Andrade, which gives a comprehensive account of the way in which both the whole atom and its nucleus are built up. Another book, which emphasizes the connexion between matter and waves, is *New Conceptions of Matter*, by C. G. Darwin.

Disintegrating the Atom

The atomic bomb has stimulated widespread interest in atom splitting and the way in which the effect is brought about.

A great deal of information is given in *Science News*, Vol. 2, edited by Peierls and Enogat. This book deals with the underlying theory as well as practical aspects of the atomic bomb.

For the further study of the subject of heat, the reader is recommended to select a book dealing with general physics, for example, *Everyday Physics*, by Hadley, and to read the section devoted to heat. The particular book mentioned contains many excellent illustrations of the application of the principles of heat to matters met in everyday life. Moreover, the other sections of the book are readily available for reference when relevant material is encountered in the heat section.

This book, or a similar one, may be followed by one such as *Textbook of Heat*, by Stewart and Satterly, which covers the ground up to intermediate standard, or *Textbook of Heat*, by Allen and Marshall, which goes somewhat further.

A book which is interesting and easy to read is *Heat and Its Workings*, by Mott-Smith. Those who are specially interested in the phenomena of refrigeration will find much of value in *Modern Electric and Gas Refrigerating*, by Althouse and Turnquist. This is an American book, but it should be available in many libraries in this country.

The applications of science covered by the expression "Power" may best be followed by reading a survey of the whole field, for example, *One Hundred Years of Engineering*, by Cressy, together with a textbook such as *Engineering Science—A Second-Year Course*, by Ward. When this ground has been covered, the reader will have decided what are his particular interests. He may also discover gaps in his knowledge. These gaps should be filled by reading some of the works mentioned in connexion with heat, and electricity and magnetism, together with a good book on mechanics, because these sciences are fundamental in the study of power. Moreover, a serious student will need to equip himself with a working knowledge of each of them. For general reference, the six volumes of *Modern Mechanical Engineering* will prove to be very useful.

Those who are especially interested in prime movers may read *Engines*, by Andrade, followed by *Primer of the Internal Combustion Engine*, by Wimperis, while the application of prime movers to electric power generation is covered in *Electric Power Stations*, by Carr.

Study of Sound

There are a number of books on sound which may profitably be read as a sequel to Chapter VIII of this book, but the order in which they are read is not of much consequence. A good starting point would be *The World of Sound*, by Bragg, which is based on a series of six Royal Institution lectures and contains illustrations of many experiments. Among the chapter headings are "Sounds of the Town, of the Country, and of the Sea." The nuisance aspect of sound is emphasized in *Noise*, by McLachlan. The author deals with the causes of noise and its measurement, and gives examples of many everyday sounds. A valuable feature of the work is a bibliography containing nearly one hundred and fifty references to other writings on the same subject.

Sound in the wrong place, or at the wrong time, is labelled noise and is said by doctors to cause nervous strain. On the other hand, musical sounds are considered to be soothing, and it is this aspect of the general subject which is presented in *Science and Music*, by Jeans, and in *Science of Musical Sounds*, by Miller.

The first-named book presents to the non-technical reader such scientific facts as are relevant to the study of music, in a manner which assumes no previous knowledge of mathematics or science. It contains pictorial representations of the sounds made by a variety of musical instruments. The second book is based on a course of lectures dealing with the characteristics of various musical instruments, including the human voice, and some experiments are described in the text. The treatment is non-mathematical, so that the work is eminently readable.

The sounds of war are, unfortunately, all too familiar. Nevertheless, some readers will be interested to read about them in *Sound Waves—their Shape and Speed*, by Miller. The first part of this book is of general interest because it is devoted to an account of the ways in which sound waves may be recorded. Particular attention is given to a machine called a "Phonodeik," which photographs sounds. Sample records are included in the book. Part 2 deals entirely with sounds made during the proving of guns on an American range.

As a result of recent research, it is now possible to design buildings with some knowledge of their probable acoustic characteristics. Those whose interests lie in this direction will find much data of value in *Practical Acoustics for the Constructor*, by Glover.

Turning now to another branch of physics, namely, the study of light, a book which immediately springs to mind is *Universe of Light*, by Bragg. As in the case of the book on Sound by the same author, this work is based on a course of Royal Institution lectures. It is non-mathematical in treatment and, of course, it is well illustrated by experiments.

One of the advantages of the study of light is that many of the experiments can be carried out with the aid of very simple apparatus. Standard experiments are described in all the textbooks and the reader is advised to obtain one of the many excellent works available. Among them are *Light*, by Champion, *Light*, by Saunders, and *Light and Heat*, by Noakes. The first of these covers the requirements of first- and second-year courses at a university, while the second covers the work normally done in schools. It starts at the beginning and contains numerical examples with answers. Edser's book is rather more ambitious in its scope than either of the others and it covers a wider field. It, too, contains a selection of numerical questions with answers.

A particular aspect of the study of light forms the subject of *Light and Colour*, by Houstoun. The book is written primarily for amateurs, yet it contains much to interest the serious student. The treatment is non-mathematical throughout.

Books on Electricity

Electricity and magnetism as a pure science may best be studied in a good school textbook, for example, *Electricity and Magnetism*, by Duncan and Starling, while for those who wish to go further in the same direction, *Electricity and Magnetism*, by Starling, may confidently be recommended, with the warning that a fair mathematical equipment is needed to follow it properly.

Most readers will probably want to study the subject from the electrical technology approach. In this case, they may refer to a pure science book, or not, as they please, when some awkward theoretical point arises. It is well to begin with a general book of a popular nature, such as *Principles of Electricity Illustrated*, or *Romance of Electricity*, by Randell.

Those who can manage more mathematics may then tackle a textbook such as *Electrical Technology*, by Cotton, *Naval Electrical Manual*, by Fortescue, or *Electrical Technology*, by Davidge and Hutchinson. Although a knowledge of the calculus is necessary to get the most out of these books, those who are without it will find them interesting and useful if some of the mathematics is skipped.

When the chosen textbook has been mastered, there is the choice of a wide variety of specialist books, each dealing with one aspect of electrical engineering. Some of these can be read without first reading a textbook, but others are hardly suitable in that case.

The generation of electric power has already been mentioned in connexion with Chapter VII. Transmission, distribution, and control are well covered in *Electrical Power*, by Starr, and in *Transmission and Distribution of Electrical Energy*, by Cotton, or, if a smaller work is desired, *Distribution and Utilization*, by Taylor.

Practical Works

Utilization of power in a general way suggests *Utilization of Electric Energy*, by Taylor, while separate uses each have their own literature. It is impossible to list all these books, but one or two examples may be quoted. The application of electricity to railways is covered in *Electric Traction*, by Dover, and in *Electric Trains*, by Agnew, while, at the other extreme, illumination is dealt with in such works as *A Symposium on Illumination, Theory and Design of Illuminating Engineering Equipment*, by Jolley, Waldram, and Wilson, and *Modern Industrial Illumination*, by Hughes.

The design and construction of rotating machinery may be studied in *Electric Motors and Generators*, while *Design of Alternating Current Machines*, by Say and Pink, and *Design of Direct Current Machines*, by Clayton, will be found very useful for reference. Transformers are covered in *The J and P Transformer Book*, by Stigant and Lacey, and in *Transformers*, by Monk.

For switchgear, the reader may refer to *The Switchgear Handbook*, by Coates and Pearce, or *Electric Switch and Controlling Gear*, by Garrard, while the associated subject of protective gear and its applications are covered in the *Protective Gear Handbook*, by Kaufmann. Measuring instruments and methods are described in *Electrical Measurements and Measuring Instruments*, by Golding, while *Electrical Instruments*, by Drysdale and Jolley, is a standard work of reference.

Most of the books mentioned above require a fair standard of mathematical knowledge if they are to be used to the greatest advantage. Where a more easily readable book is wanted, something suitable may be found in the "Electrical Engineer" series, edited by Molloy. Among the titles in this series are *Installation and Maintenance of Electric Motors*, *Power Rectifiers*, *Physics for Engineers*, and *Elementary Mathematics for Engineers*.

A wide range of numerical problems is to be found in *Problems in Electrical Engineering*, by Smith, or, if hints on solution are wanted, there are two volumes entitled *Classified Examples in Electrical Engineering*, by Monk. For reference *Electrical Engineering Practice*, by Meares and Neale, in four volumes, contains a mass of useful information on all electrical topics, while there is a variety of handbooks which serve a similar purpose on a less ambitious scale.

The communications side of electrical work has an extensive literature of its own, though in many books a working knowledge of electrical theory, especially alternating current theory, is assumed. A useful book on which to make a start is *Foundations of Wireless*, by Scroggie, another, which is more expensive, is *Basic Radio*, by Hoag, while television receivers are covered in detail in *Television Receiving Equipment*, by Cocking.

Radio Circuits

For detailed studies of radio circuits the reader is advised to consult *Classified Radio Receiver Diagrams*, by Squire, and *Radio Circuits*, by Miller. Those who intend to pursue their radio interests practically as well as by reading will find a great deal of helpful information in *Radio Laboratory Handbook*, by Scroggie. This book not only gives advice on the equipment of an amateur laboratory and describes how certain items may be constructed, but contains valuable hints on experimental methods appropriate to high-frequency work. A book containing an immense amount of reference information is *Radio Designer's Handbook*, by Langford-Smith.

The study of chemistry may well begin with an historical approach. With this idea in mind, the reader may try *The Lure and Romance of Alchemy*, by Thompson,

Discoveries in Chemistry, by Gibson, and *Prelude to Chemistry*, by Read. The last-named work is notable for its illustrations, many of which are reproductions from old books and manuscripts.

The next step might be the reading of two or three works of a popular nature, such as *The Romance of Chemistry*, by Philip, *Modern Chemistry*, by Prescott, *Chemistry in Daily Life*, by Glasstone, and *Chemistry in the Service of Man*, by Findlay. These books are of interest to the general reader and will give a foundation on which a more detailed knowledge can be built.

One of the works mentioned, *Chemistry in Daily Life*, has an unusual feature which is likely to be of special value to readers of this book. At the end of each chapter there are to be found lists of questions, subjects for discussion, suggestions for further reading, and lists of experiments connected with the subject of the chapter. Yet another book on the same general lines is *Chemistry Today*, by Allcott and Bolton. Most of its chapters deal with chemistry as applied to some specific matter.

After the preparation outlined above, an elementary textbook may be tackled with confidence. Such a book is *Everyday Chemistry*, by Partington, which aims at a standard a little beyond that of matriculation, while covering a rather wider range of topics than that examination demands. Among other books which are suitable for reading at this point are *Chemistry*, by Adlam, and *A General Chemistry*, by Morris. Thereafter the reader may safely be left to make his own choice.

The intensely interesting field of organic chemistry, which touches everyday life at so many points, is of importance to all who are keen on science. Among the general books which are suitable for beginning the study of this subject are *Elementary Organic Chemistry*, by Kemp, and two books with the same title, *An Introduction to Organic Chemistry;* one of these is by Read and the other by Baker.

Two other volumes which may usefully be read at this stage are *Chemistry, Life, and Civilization*, by Britton, and *The Stuff We're Made Of*, by Kermack and Eggleton. For those whose tastes run in that direction

there is *Explosives*, by Read, while the growing use of plastics makes *Plastics*, by Yarsley and Couzens, a book of value to all.

The literature on industrial chemistry is not very extensive, and not all of it is sufficiently attractive for the average non-technical reader. The books mentioned below are suitable for general reading.

In beginning his studies, the reader might choose either *Industrial Chemistry*, by Read, or *Industrial Chemistry—an Elementary Treatise for Student and General Reader*, by Riegel. Either of these books will give him a general acquaintance with the problems of industrial chemistry without going deeply into the details of particular processes. Somewhat similar ground is covered in *Introduction to Industrial Chemistry*, by Levy, and *Outlines of Industrial Chemistry*, by Thorpe, but both of these books treat the matter from a technical standpoint.

Industrial Use of Chemistry

Two other general works which might be read at this stage are *Creative Chemistry*, by Slosson, and *What Industry Owes to Chemical Science*, by Pilcher. The first of these is written in a light and picturesque style and covers a great deal of ground, while the second is highly informative in a general way. Another book, which shows the industrial application of chemical principles, is *Chemistry from an Industrial Standpoint*, by Thorne.

Among textbooks, in which more detailed information on specific products and processes may be found, are the two volumes of *Industrial Chemistry*, by Rogers, *Chemical of Commerce*, by Shell and Shell, and *Chemicals and Industrial Materials with their Commercial Uses*, by Argles.

Those to whom the historical approach appeals will like to read *Origins and Development of Applied Chemistry*, by Partington, while the practical man will find much to interest him in *Chemical Works—their Design, Erection, and Equipment*, by Dyson and Clarkson.

In addition to general books, such as those mentioned here, there is a wide range of technological works which deal with specific departments and branches of the subject of industrial chemistry.

The history of science makes interesting reading because it throws light on the way in which present-day theories have developed. It shows how various alternatives have been tried and found wanting as a result of fresh discoveries, and how the whole body of knowledge has been built up, step by step. Some of the accepted theories of their day now seem fantastic in the light of modern knowledge, yet they were held to be correct in their time.

An insight into this historical aspect of science may be obtained by reading *A Short History of Science in the Nineteenth Century*, by Singer, and *A History of Science*, by Dampier. Other works which may be read with advantage are *The World of Science*, *A Short History of Science*, and *The Century of Science*, all by Taylor. The history of medicine is covered by *A Hundred Years of Medicine*, by Lloyd, while *The Evolution of Physics*, by Einstein and Infeld, performs a like service for physical science. Among the cheaper books there are *Greek Science*, by Farrington, *What Happened in History*, by Childe, and two volumes entitled *British Scientists of the Nineteenth Century*, by J. G. Crowther.

Another facet of this subject is revealed by reading older books, written by some of those whose names shine in the history of science. The following are examples of works of this type: *The Sceptical Chemist*, by Boyle, *The Origin of Species*, by Charles Darwin, *Circulation of the Blood*, by Harvey, *Experimental Researches in Electricity*, by Faraday, and *Inquiries into Human Faculties*, by Galton.

The impact of science on life is a problem which is much discussed at the present time. Some scientists consider that their responsibility ends when their discoveries are presented to the public, while others feel a moral obligation to see that their work is used for the benefit of mankind and not for its destruction. In this connexion, *The Social Function of Science*, by Bernal, and *The Social Relations of Science*, by Crowther, may well be read.

Research is another topic which is now often in the news. The condition of research at the present time is thoroughly surveyed in *Industrial Research and Development in the United Kingdom*, by Heath and Hetherington.

Some books of a more general nature, which are well worth their place in a reading list, are *Modern Science*, by Levy, *The Nature of the Physical World*, by Eddington, *Britain's Heritage of Science*, by Schuster and Shipley, *An Outline of the Universe*, in two volumes, by Crowther, *The Scientific Attitude*, by Waddington, and *Science and the Modern World*, by Whitehead.

Biography is represented by *Famous American Men of Science*, by Crowther, and *Rutherford of Nelson*, by Evans, while those who prefer essays may like to read *Science and Everyday Life* and *The Inequality of Man*, both by J. B. S. Haldane. *Essays of a Biologist*, by Julian Huxley, is a book which should be read by all.

A very readable book on mathematics is *Mathematician's Delight*, by Sawyer, while geological studies are the subject of *Geology in the Service of Man*, by Fearnsides and Bulman. In the same connexion, *Minerals in Industry*, by Jones, may be mentioned.

Value of an Encyclopedia

Whatever the branch of science to be pursued, it is useful to have available a good encyclopedia for general reference, especially when matters relating to another subject are encountered. A typical example is the four volumes of *Technical and Scientific Encyclopedia*.

The lists of books given in the foregoing pages do not purport to be exhaustive. They represent merely a personal selection, made mainly by the authors of the earlier chapters, from the very large number of excellent books available for readers and students of all kinds, at all levels. The omission of any particular book must not, therefore, be taken to imply any criticism of it or any slur upon it. It is hoped that the suggestions made here will start the reader upon a course of reading and study which will fill his leisure with an absorbing interest for the remainder of his life. If they succeed the authors will be amply repaid.

ANSWERS TO "TEST YOURSELF"

THE purpose of most of the questions is to enable you to discover for yourself how closely you are following the text of the book. Few persons can assimilate all the main facts at a single reading, and there is no cause for discouragement if your answers show you that you have forgotten many of them. What is worth remembering is worth a second and, if necessary, a third or even a fourth reading.

CHAPTER II

1. (a) The diurnal motion of the stars across the sky, including the motion round the pole of the circumpolar stars, and the rising, towards the east, and setting, towards the west, of stars further from the pole.

(b) A gradual change in the aspect of the sky throughout the year.

2. Planets, comets, meteors, satellites of planets, asteroids (minor planets), stars, gaseous nebulæ, dark nebulæ, extragalactic nebulæ (island universes).

3. A star is self-luminous, a planet is not. Stars are more massive than planets, and have a much higher temperature. Stars (with the exception of a small class of dwarf stars) are larger than planets and have a lower density.

4. A small movement round the centre of gravity of the earth and moon; movement of revolution round the sun; it is carried with the sun through space relative to neighbouring stars; it is carried with the sun and neighbouring stars in the rotation of the galaxy and in its motion through space relative to other galaxies.

5. Yes; there is a greater range in size and weight.

6. It consists of a great number of stars which are so remote that they are individually invisible to the naked eye, but the collective light is sufficient to be perceived.

7. Eclipses of the sun are caused by the moon coming in the direct line between the sun and the earth. Eclipses of the moon are caused by the moon entering the shadow of the earth thrown by the sun.

8. That its period of axial rotation is equal to the period of its orbital revolution round the earth.

CHAPTER III

1. 7 hr., 38 min., 44 sec.

2. (a) Correction for equation of time to reduce from local true solar time to local mean solar time; (b) correction for longitude of Penzance west of Greenwich to reduce from local mean time to G.M.T.

3. The meridian of longitude 180 deg. east or west of Greenwich, slightly modified to avoid differences in date reckoning in closely adjacent territories. The date is changed when crossing the date line in order to keep a correct date reckoning.

4. The interval of time between two consecutive transits of the sun across the meridian (the solar day) is longer than the true period of rotation of the earth (the sidereal day) because of the orbital revolution of the earth; $366\frac{1}{4}$ sidereal days equal $365\frac{1}{4}$ mean solar days; hence the difference in length is about 3 min., 56 sec.

5. The longitude can be determined by determining the sidereal time by observation, converting to local mean time, and comparing with G.M.T. by means of radio time signals. The latitude can be obtained by observing the altitude of the Pole star, or the meridian altitude of the sun or of a star.

6. The observation of the altitude of a celestial body fixes the position as on a certain circle (the position circle). The observation of the altitude of a second body determines another position circle. The two circles intersect in two points; one of these points will be far away from the position of the ship or aircraft, which must, therefore, be at the other point of intersection.

CHAPTER IV

1. Zero.

2. Both together.

3. The stone is subject to the external force of gravity. With vertical projection, the downward force is in the same straight line as the projecting force and hence the body is undeviated. At any other angle of projection, the downward force produces a continual deviation from the direction of projection and hence the curved path.

4. Light in electric lamps; heat in electric fires and furnaces; mechanical energy in electric motors attached to sewing machines, electric clocks, etc.; chemical energy in electro-plating; sound energy in radio.

5. The motion would simply become irregular and the machine would eventually stop with the heavier weights in the lower half of the wheel.

6. 12 lb.; 8.

7. Centrifugal force outwards must be balanced by an equal tension inwards, the so-called centripetal force, for the stone to move only circumferentially.

8. 4 ft.-tons; 4 ft.-tons. No difference numerically, but physically in the first case motion occurs and 4 ft.-tons represents the energy change, whereas in the second case the lever could be held fixed and the couple would be static, producing no change in energy.

9. 4000 ft.-sec.; due west.

10. 10 ft.-sec., for the angular momentum stays constant and, the radius having been halved, the velocity is automatically doubled.

11. If the force is applied slowly, the large inertia of the object will have time to respond and the top string then has to carry both the pull and the weight of the object, whereas the lower string experiences the pull only. Hence the top string snaps first. If the pull is sudden, the inertia of the object prevents it from responding immediately and nearly the whole pull is experienced for the moment by the lower string which consequently snaps first.

12. Action and reaction being equal and opposite in all cases, the two trucks are pulled together by equal and opposite forces. The only difference is that they meet more rapidly the greater the pull.

13. If the fly has settled, its normal weight will be registered. If it flies horizon-ally its normal weight will again be registered, since it has to be supported by the air which transmits the pressure on to the bottom of the bottle. If it flies upwards its weight will appear greater, for its wings must press down on the air to give the fly its upward acceleration and the reaction of the pressure on the floor will be larger. If it falls freely its weight will vanish, for it has nothing to sustain and hence no pressure is transmitted to the floor.

14. For his centre of gravity to descend, the reaction upwards must be less than the weight downwards. Hence the machine which registers the reaction on the floor will temporarily show an apparent decrease in weight.

15. In the horizontal posture the centre of gravity has to be raised a smaller distance for the body to clear the bar.

16. All the angular momentum is imparted at the instant the diver leaves the diving platform. The number of somersaults then depends on how much he can reduce his moment of inertia by doubling his body and drawing in his extremities and on the distance between the diving platform and the water. If the "dive" is made initially upwards, more somersaults are possible, for time of flight is gained. Several factors are thus involved and there is no precise critical moment.

CHAPTER V

1. Collision of an α-particle with a nucleus without and with disintegration, respectively. Balance of kinetic energy reappears as a net change in mass of the system.

2. By electrical discharge, X-rays, heating, solution, artificial disintegration and nuclear fission, a positive ion and one or more electrons.

3. Centrifugal force.

4. By the dropping down of the outermost electron from an excited orbit of large size to a smaller orbit for that electron. The energy of the emitted light photon is equal to the difference of the mechanical energies of the electron in the two orbits.

5. The empty space is permeated by electrical forces; these cause two portions

of matter to repel each other sufficiently to prevent superposition.

6. Neutron, proton, negative and positive electron; electrons; protons and neutrons.

7. By bombardment with α-particles, neutrons or positive ions. Ejection of protons, neutrons, or α-particles.

8. Condensation of fog tracks. Test of conservation of momentum and energy in atomic collisions; photographs of nuclear disintegrations.

9. Neutral nuclear particles with no electric charge and a mass almost equal to that of the proton. As they are not repelled by the nuclear charge, the slowest neutrons can penetrate the heaviest nuclei.

10. Photo-electric effect. No; bundles of electromagnetic energy.

11. States that radiation consists of localized bundles of electromagnetic energy.

12. (1) Electron orbits, like planetary orbits, are produced owing to balancing of centripetal and centrifugal forces; (2) momentum and energy conserved in non-disintegrating particle collisions; (3) only certain electronic orbits possible contrasted with planetary orbits of any size; (4) mass and energy only additatively conserved in nuclear disintegrations.

13. From mass and energy balance in nuclear disintegration processes; creation and destruction of positive and negative electron pairs.

14. By impact of nuclear particles; the cyclotron.

CHAPTER VI

2. −459·6 deg. F., −297·4 deg. F., −55 deg. C., −17·8 deg. C., 15·6 deg. C., 1300 deg. F., over 5400 deg. F.

3. 4·8 ft.—but the structure allows for 6ft.

4. Very nearly $\frac{11}{12}$ths of the heat is lost through the windows—and that's why curtains matter!

5. $\frac{27}{32}$nds therm, or 170 cu.ft.

6. 80·5 cals. per gram.

7. 532 cals. per gram.

CHAPTER VII

3. 0·20 deg. F., or 0·11 deg. C.

4. 85 h.p.

5. 480 h.p.

6. (a) 28,600 ft.-lb.; (b) 52 h.p.

7. 2·07 h.p.

8. 23·5 per cent.

CHAPTER VIII

1. (i) The insect vibrates its wings at a musical frequency; (ii) the sound is conducted by the metal of the pipe and any material in it.

2. All surfaces and objects reflect the sound and the reflected sound reaches the ears some time after the direct. In a large room this causes a prolongation of each word, which may last until the next word is issued or even longer. In the open air very little sound is reflected back so that ordinary speech is weaker than in a room.

3. The violinist is effectively increasing and decreasing the length of the vibrating string, and so lowering and raising the pitch. Resin allows the bow to grip the string.

4. The sheet of paper or blade of grass becomes a vibrating body due to its tension and mass.

5. Speaking tubes and ear-trumpets effectively confine the sound received at their large openings to the small opening of the ear. Electrical hearing aids make the sound louder by amplification.

6. A megaphone confines the sound produced by the mouth to the direction of its horn. Thus, sound which would otherwise go in an unwanted direction is not wasted. Loudspeakers on railway stations have the same effect as would be produced by a number of announcers placed at the various locations.

7. Because sound travels much more slowly than light. Other examples are: firing of a gun a distance away, a woodcutter chopping trees in the distance, a train whistling as it is leaving a station.

CHAPTER IX

1. The glass reflects light from the room which may be much brighter than the light coming from outside.

2. First part explained in text. Bi-focal lenses use weaker lens for distant vision and strong lens for near objects.

3. Our eyes are adjusted for contact

with air. When they are in contact with water of a higher refractive index than air, they act as though they have a strong concave lens pressed against them and blurred images are produced behind the retina. A diver has a plane glass window which does not produce this effect.

4. The dust particles scatter the light in all directions and so reveal themselves. Glass ornaments produce dispersion.

5. Such glass, while transmitting almost as much light as clear glass, scatters it in all directions and so the incandescent interior does not dazzle the eye.

6. First part explained in text. A spray is made of tiny droplets.

7. By examining the spectrum of the light emitted by them.

8. Coloured objects appear so owing to the various colours they reflect. Thus, a red object which reflects no blue light will appear black in a blue stage lighting. Various stage lights are used which are not single spectrum colours, so that, for example, a yellow dress may appear green under one lighting and orange under another.

9. When one of the lens surfaces forms a concave or convex mirror of correct focal length to produce an image on the retina, objects will be seen behind the wearer.

10. The small holes act as pin-hole cameras and the circular images on the ground are really images of the sun.

CHAPTER X

1. (a) Deficiency; (b) surplus of electrons.

2. The pressure driving an electric current.

4. Current is a flow of electrons. Direct current flows from negative terminal of battery or generator to positive.

5. $E = I \times R$.

10. Attract.

12. 1:5 step-up transformer.

13. By using the 200-volt D.C. to drive a motor coupled to a generator or alternator.

14. *Primary battery:* chemical action non-reversible; battery useless when run down. *Secondary battery:* chemical action reversible; can be recharged when run down.

16. $\frac{1}{1000}$th ampere. 1,000,000 ohms. 1000 cycles. $\frac{1}{1,000,000}$ volt.

CHAPTER XI

3. Because the power expended in overcoming resistance $= I^2 R$.

5. Electric train, tramcar, radiogram, electric fan, hair-drier, food-mixer, vacuum cleaner, electric coffee-grinder, electric clock, electric screen-wiper, electric polisher, etc.

CHAPTER XII

1. When heated, the cathode of a diode emits negatively charged particles, or electrons, some of which are attracted to the anode when this is positively charged. If the anode voltage is increased, the number of electrons also increases, until a condition is reached when the anode attracts all the electrons emitted. This condition is called "saturation".

2. Frequency corresponding to 150 metres $= \frac{3 \times 10^{10} \text{ cms/sec.}}{150 \times 10^2 \text{ cms}} = \frac{300}{150} \times 10^6$ c/s $= 2$ Mc/s.

3. The purpose of the rectifying valve in a radio receiver is to convert the alternating current supply to unidirectional current or direct current to feed the high-potential electrodes of the other valves. In a half-wave rectifier, current passes during only alternate half-cycles, but in a full-wave rectifier both half-cycles are utilized.

4. A tuned-anode amplifier is one in which the anode load is a tuned circuit which resonates at the frequency of the incoming signal. It is used in radio-frequency and intermediate-frequency amplifiers.

5. Demodulation is the process by which a signal is reproduced having the characteristics of the original modulating signal. The three common methods of demodulation are diode, cumulative grid and anode-bend detection.

6. A multiple valve contains in one envelope two or more groups of electrodes associated with independent streams of electrons: one or more of these electrodes may be common to the respective groups. Examples of such valves are double-diodes,

double-triodes, diode-triodes, triode-pentodes, double-diode-triodes, double-diode-pentodes, triode-hexodes and triode-heptodes.

7. The ribbon microphone consists of a permanent magnet between the poles of which is supported a thin corrugated strip or ribbon of aluminium, the ends of which are connected to a suitable transformer. Sound waves striking the ribbon cause it to vibrate between the poles of the magnet, so producing an audio-frequency voltage in the winding of the transformer.

8. The action of a frequency-changer is to combine the incoming radio-frequency signal with that of a local or beat oscillator, in order to produce a modulated signal the frequency of which is the difference of those of the incoming and local signals: this frequency is called the intermediate frequency. The advantage is that a higher and more stable amplification is obtained than would otherwise be possible.

9. Practically all modern loudspeakers are of the moving-coil type. This consists of a speech- or voice-coil wound on a former attached to the narrow end of a conical diaphragm. The coil is free to move axially to and fro in the annular air-gap of a strong magnet. The output current from the last stage of a radio receiver flows through the speech-coil, causing it to vibrate and set in motion a column of air in front of the speaker diaphragm: this reproduces the original sound.

10. Fading is due to interference between one ray, which may be direct or reflected, and a reflected ray. The phase and amplitude of the latter vary with the height and intensity of the ionized layers, causing fluctuations of the resultant signal. The effect on the receiver may be minimized by the employment of automatic gain control: this is a device, actuated by the received signal, which varies the amplification of the receiver in order to maintain an approximately constant output.

11. The fluorescent spot is deflected towards the top right-hand portion of the screen, along a line inclined at 45 deg. to the horizontal.

12. At the television transmitter, a synchronizing signal is sent out at the end of each horizontal line and another at the end of each vertical frame scan. These signals are used at the receiver to "trigger" the line-scanning generator and the frame-scanning generator respectively, so that the scanning of the picture is exactly synchronized with that at the transmitter.

13. In colour television, the object to be televised is scanned successively in the component colours, i.e. in red, green and blue in the three-colour system, or blue-green and red-orange successively in the two-colour system. The signals so produced are arranged to form at the receiver correspondingly coloured images which are superimposed to reproduce a picture in its natural colours.

14. A beam station is constructed for the purpose of communication with an area which lies in one direction with respect to the transmitter: a broadcasting station radiates in all directions. A beam station differs from the latter mainly in regard to the aerial, which consists of an array or combination of arrays of equally-spaced radiators so arranged that transmission takes place in the form of a unidirectional beam.

CHAPTER XIII

1. An element may be either a single substance or a mixture of isotopes, each of which has the same atomic number but a different atomic weight. Some of the heavier elements disintegrate into other elements, whereas some elements may be artificially disrupted into atoms of lighter elements. Hence the matter constituting the various elements is interrelated.

2. Its atomic number.

3. (*a*) An atom is the smallest particle of an element that can exist in a compound.

(*b*) A molecule is the smallest particle of an element or chemical compound that is capable of a separate existence.

4. From the relationship:
   (i) Vapour density

$$= \frac{\text{Molecular weight}}{2 \cdot 016}.$$

   (ii) Molecular weight
   = Number of atoms in a molecule × Atomic weight.

(iii) Atomic weight
   = Equivalent weight × Valency.

5. (i) Vapour density and, therefore, Molecular weight.
   (ii) Percentage analysis of the compound by weight and the atomic weights of the elements.

6. From the Law of Multiple Proportions it can be deduced that an element may have more than one equivalent weight. The atomic theory, however, shows that these equivalent weights are related to the atomic weight thus:

Equivalent weight × Valency
   = Atomic weight.

7. Valency $= \dfrac{\text{Atomic weight}}{\text{Equivalent weight}}$.

8. Protons and neutrons.

9. An electron is a particle of mass equal to $\frac{1}{1800}$th part of that of an ordinary hydrogen atom, and carries a unit charge of negative electricity.

A proton is a particle, equal in weight to a hydrogen atom, and carries a unit charge of positive electricity.

A neutron is an uncharged particle of mass equal to that of a proton. It may be regarded as resulting from the coalescence of a proton and an electron.

The nucleus of the helium atom is the alpha-particle, which consists of 2 neutrons and 2 protons. Together they supply a mass of 4 and the two protons provide a nuclear charge of 2, this being the atomic number.

10. The 11 electrons of sodium are arranged thus: K2, L8, M1; whilst those of the chlorine are arranged thus: K2, L8, M7.

In forming sodium chloride, sodium gives its single electron from its M-shell to the chlorine atom, the M-shell of which is thereby raised to 8, i.e. to a "stable octet." In a molecule of sodium chloride the electronic configuration of the sodium atom is that of the stable neon atom, and that of the chlorine atom becomes the same as that of the stable argon atom. The sodium atom has one more positive charge in its nucleus than it has electrons surrounding it. It is, therefore, a positively charged ion (kation), whereas the reverse is true of the chlorine, which is, therefore, a negatively charged ion (anion). Hence the valency involved is one of electrovalence.

11. Analysis by weight, coupled with the atomic weights of hydrogen and oxygen, lead to the formula $(H_2O)_x$. The value of x may be determined by finding the vapour density of steam when compared with that of hydrogen, and calculating the molecular weight of water. Then:

$$x = \frac{\text{Molecular weight}}{\text{Molecular weight indicated by the simplest formula, viz., } 18(H_2O)}.$$

12. (a) by two covalent linkages;
    (b) by one covalent linkage becoming an electrovalent linkage.

13. An isotope of an element has the same distinguishing atomic number as the other members of the mixture of which an element consists. These isotopes have different atomic weights.

Thus, deuterium is the heavy isotope of hydrogen. Like ordinary hydrogen, its atomic number is *one*, but its atom is twice as heavy as the predominating light isotope of hydrogen. Similarly, the atomic number of uranium is 92, but the atomic weight of one isotope is 235, whereas that of the more abundant is 238.

As the result of either radioactive or artificial disintegration of elements, atoms are produced that may be isotopic with certain elements although such isotopes do not form part of the ordinary mixtures of isotopes that are regarded as elements and found in nature.

14. Electromagnetic methods as in the text; different rates of (a) diffusion of uranium fluorides; (b) production of hydrogen isotopes by electrolysis.

15. Radioactivity, as shown by certain heavy metals, e.g. radium, thorium, uranium, is produced by the emission of either positively charged particles (alpha-particles) or negatively charged particles (beta-particles) associated with gamma rays, which are similar to X-rays. These particles are spontaneously shot off from the atomic nuclei, which, in case of the emission of alpha-particles, lose 4 units of mass and 2 units of positive electricity. When beta-particles are lost, the atomic nucleus loses a negligible amount of mass but increases in positive electricity by one *unit*.

These changes are known as *radioactive disintegration.*

It is probable that the nuclei of the heavy elements are radioactive because the electrical energy stored within them is too great for their mass and size.

16. Artificial or induced radioactivity, which are synonymous terms, refers to the radioactivity of unstable isotopes that are first formed by artificial means such as by the bombardment of atomic nuclei with suitable missiles. It sometimes happens that one of the products of the disruption of an atom may be an *unstable* isotope of an element, which is not found in nature, and it, therefore, transforms itself into the *stable* isotope of another element, the change being made possible by the radioactive emission of positive or negative electrons.

17. "Nuclear fission" is the term applied to the artificial disruption of atoms in which the resulting two or more fragments, and, therefore, new atoms, are comparatively large. See pp. 283-285.

18. Dalton: First modern atomic theory.
Avogadro: Modified atomic theory as now generally accepted. Introduced concept of atoms and molecules.

19. Principle: Periodic arrangement in the sequence of increasing atomic numbers—short periods and then long periods, in middle of latter the transition elements appear.

20. Very unstable: spontaneously fissionable.

21. Atmospheric nitrogen is "fixed" when it is made to combine with other elements or compounds, e.g.:

(i) *Oxygen*, by passing air through an electric arc followed by rapid cooling. Some nitric oxide is thereby formed which by reacting with more oxygen and then with water can be converted into nitric acid.

(ii) *Hydrogen.* When nitrogen is mixed with hydrogen under pressure and passed over a catalyst at a moderately high temperature some ammonia is formed.

(iii) *Calcium carbide.* Under suitable conditions of temperature and pressure, nitrogen reacts to form calcium cyanamide—a valuable fertilizer.

22. Nitrogen is the essential constituent of the body-builders, the proteins.

It is also the essential constituent of all explosives, except those depending on atomic fission.

23. Air is a mixture.

24. An acid is a compound which by neutralizing an alkali forms a salt, in which an hydrogen atom or atoms of the acid have been replaced by an equivalent amount of metal originally present in the alkali or base.

Hydrogen ions.

25. (i) Neutralization is the term given to the reaction between an acid and alkali.
(ii) A salt is the product resulting from neutralization.

26. Water dissolves carbon dioxide from the air, particularly water in contact with calcium carbonate, i.e. chalk, limestone.

27. (*a*) Each carbon atom holds three hydrogen atoms and the other carbon atom.

(*b*) As each carbon atom holds only two hydrogen atoms it is supposed to be attached to the other carbon atom by *two* bonds or a *double bond.*

(*c*) The two C-atoms are joined together by means of a *triple bond.*

28. A hydrocarbon is a compound of hydrogen and carbon only, whereas a carbohydrate is a compound of carbon. hydrogen and oxygen.

29. In "saturated" hydrocarbons, the atoms of carbon and hydrogen are held together by means of simple valency bonds: $C_{25}H_{52}$.

30.
$$CH_3—CH_2—CH_2—CH_3$$
$$CH_3—CH—CH_3$$
$$|$$
$$CH_3$$

31. Enzymes.

32. Aldehydes contain the characteristic grouping $>CHO$, e.g., $RCHO$, where R may be H or any organic group consisting of C and H and other atoms.

Ketones contain the grouping $>CO$, e.g. $\frac{R}{R'}>CO$, where R and R' may be either the same or *different* groups of atoms of C and H. Derived by oxidation of primary and secondary alcohols respectively.

33. CH_3OH CH_2OH CH_2OH

CH_2OH $CHOH$

CH_2OH

Because each compound has an -OH group.

34. (i) CH_3

CO

CH_3

(ii) Fermentation of carbohydrates.

(iii) One of the products of the "dry" distillation of wood.

(iv) Heating calcium acetate.

35. A *salt* results from the reaction between a *base* and an *acid* with the elimination of water. Likewise, an *ester* results from the reaction between an *alcohol* and an *acid*, with the elimination of water—the alcohol behaving as if it were a base.

CHAPTER XIV

1. Soap, soda, aspirin, paint, petrol, face cream, vitamins, health salts, ink, brilliantine, photographic film, plastic mouldings.

2. Chemical-*producing* industries actually manufacture basic chemicals required for a multitude of purposes; chemical-*converting* industries mix, blend or otherwise modify basic chemical substances for the production of directly usable goods.

3. "Heavy" chemicals: saltpetre, common soda, sulphuric acid, superphosphate fertilizer, caustic soda, hydrochloric acid, bleaching powder, ammonia. "Fine" chemicals: radium barium bromide, synthetic musk, aspirin, chloroform, synthetic vitamins, metol, synthetic vanilla, saccharin, gold chloride, strychnine.

4. In practice, a "unit operation" means the doing of one thing at a time. Filtration, solution, evaporation, crystallization, nitration, hydrogenization are all conveniently known in the chemical industry as "unit operations."

5. The catalyst acts in a mysterious way as a "reaction promoter" or a "reaction energizer," causing a chemical reaction to take place between two or more substances which would not otherwise readily react together. In the contact process of sulphuric acid manufacture, the heated catalyst effects the combination of sulphur dioxide gas and oxygen, forming sulphur trioxide which subsequently combines with water to produce sulphuric acid. Metallic platinum (finely divided), vanadium oxide, iron oxide are typical catalysts for the sulphuric acid contact process and for other chemical manufacturing processes.

6. By the "ammonia-soda" process. This consists in saturating brine with ammonia gas and then with carbon dioxide gas, whereby sodium bicarbonate is precipitated from the liquor. The sodium bicarbonate is then heated in order to convert it into ordinary or "common" soda, which, chemically, is sodium carbonate.

7. A mixture of 3 volumes of hydrogen and 1 volume of nitrogen is passed (under a pressure of 300-400 atmospheres) over heated iron oxide which acts as a catalyst and causes a partial combination of these gases into ammonia — NH_3.

8. The ability of the carbon atom to link itself to other carbon atoms, forming long chains and rings to which atoms of other elements (notably hydrogen and oxygen) may become attached.

9. The heating together of formalin and phenol (carbolic acid) in the presence of a little caustic soda.

10. Chemicals of complex composition which, although colourless themselves, can be converted directly into highly coloured dyes.

11. Phenol (carbolic acid) is treated with caustic soda to form sodium phenate. This is then reacted with carbon dioxide gas in an "autoclave," or pressure vessel, sodium salicylate being thereby produced. This is purified and then converted into salicylic acid. The salicylic acid is treated with acetic anhydride and is thus converted with "acetyl-salicylic acid," otherwise "aspirin."

12. (*a*) Toluene; (*b*) toluene; (*c*) lime and chlorine gas; (*d*) salicylic acid and methyl alcohol; (*e*) bleaching powder and acetone; (*f*) benzene; (*g*) common salt (brine); and (*h*) common salt (brine).

INDEX

(Page references printed in italics indicate illustrations)

381